Test Bank

UNDERSTANDING ABNORMAL BEHAVIOR

Test Bank

Revised by
Anita Rosenfield

Written by
Arthur G. Olguin
Santa Barbara City College

UNDERSTANDING ABNORMAL BEHAVIOR

Seventh Edition

David Sue
Western Washington University

Derald Sue
Teachers College, Columbia University

Stanley Sue
University of California, Davis

HOUGHTON MIFFLIN COMPANY   BOSTON   NEW YORK

Publisher: Charles Hartford
Senior Sponsoring Editor: Kerry Baruth
Senior Development Editor: Sharon Geary
Senior Manufacturing Coordinator: Jane Spelman
Senior Marketing Manager: Katherine Greig

CONTENTS

TO THE INSTRUCTOR

This *Test Bank,* containing 100 multiple-choice and three essay questions with sample answers per chapter, is designed to help instructors evaluate their students' mastery of material presented in the Seventh Edition of *Understanding Abnormal Behavior* by Sue/Sue/Sue.

In the *Test Bank,* multiple-choice questions have been broken down into three types—conceptual questions (C) ask the student to formulate an answer based on his or her understanding of a concept, factual questions (F) ask the student to recall information from the text, and applied questions (A) introduce a real-life scenario and ask the student to apply his or her acquired knowledge to make a choice. The sequence of questions follows the order in which the information appears in the text. The format of the items follows basic principles of test construction, and the level of difficulty is purposely varied.

In the margin beside each multiple-choice item in the *Test Bank* lies a notation like the following:

Ans: b
Page: 289
Obj: 11
Type: C

The first entry designates the correct answer. The second entry specifies the page number in the main textbook where the information is located. The third entry indicates the number of the learning objective that the item addresses. A list of learning objectives begins each chapter of the *Test Bank* as well as the *Study Guide* and the *Instructors Manual*. The final entry identifies the type of question provided, as explained above.

The information provided in the key can be used in several ways. By systematically choosing items according to the learning objectives, an instructor can ensure that a test assesses the breadth of students' understanding of the course material. By varying the proportion of items that are conceptual, factual, or applied, the instructor can manipulate the extent to which a test assesses the depth of students' understanding of the material.

Adopters of *Understanding Abnormal Behavior* can obtain the test items in a computerized version, which is available for use with IBM, Macintosh, and Windows formats. The program allows instructors to add, edit, and scramble questions and prepare answer keys, along with a variety of other useful features. For further information, please contact your local Houghton Mifflin sales representative, or call our Faculty Services Center at 1-800-733-1717.

I hope that you find the *Test Bank* useful and welcome your suggestions for improving it in future editions.

Art Olguin, Ph.D.
Santa Barbara City College

CHAPTER 1
Abnormal Behavior

LEARNING OBJECTIVES

1. Describe the primary objectives of abnormal psychology, including description, explanation, prediction, and control of abnormal behavior. (pp. 3–5)

2. Identify and distinguish between the various kinds of mental health professionals. (pp. 5-6)

3. Identify four definitions psychologists use to define abnormal behavior and their assumptions, strengths, and limitations. (pp. 5–13)

4. Describe the multicultural perspectives in defining abnormal behavior including definitions of the terms *cultural universality* and *cultural relativism*. (pp. 9–10)

5. Distinguish between Szasz's views on mental illness and Wakefield's (1992) views of abnormal behavior, the textbook authors' definition of *abnormal behavior*, and that of the DSM-IV. (pp. 12–13)

6. Discuss how researchers determine the scope of mental disorders in the United States. (pp. 13–17)

7. Describe the most prevalent disorders and how mental disorders are influenced by age and gender. (pp. 14–16)

8. Discuss common myths concerning the mentally disturbed and the facts that refute them. (pp. 17–18)

9. Summarize the various explanations of abnormal behavior from prehistoric times through the Middle Ages. (pp. 18–20)

10. Describe the changes that occurred in the conceptualization and treatment of abnormal behavior after the era of witchcraft, including the rise of humanism and the reform movement of the eighteenth and nineteenth centuries until the present. (pp. 20–23)

11. Discuss the main assumptions of the biological and psychological viewpoints on perceptions of abnormal behavior. (pp. 23–25)

12. Discuss the contributions of mesmerism and hypnosis to the psychodynamic viewpoint. (pp. 24–25)

13. Describe the impact of the drug revolution and managed care on the mental health profession. (pp. 25–28; Mental Health & Society)

14. Discuss the rise of *multicultural psychology*, and explain how social conditioning, cultural values, and sociopolitical influences may account for apparent differences in abnormality in minority groups. (pp. 29–31)

15. Explain the term *biopsychosocial approach* and its use in conceptualizing the multiple factors underlying abnormal behavior. (p. 31)

MULTIPLE–CHOICE QUESTIONS

Ans: a
Page: 4
Obj: 1
Type: F

1. Which statement about abnormal psychology is *accurate*?
    a. Abnormal psychology seeks to describe, explain, predict, and control unusual behaviors.
    b. Although abnormal psychology has made several gains in the past 20 years it is not yet a scientific field of study.
    c. The subject matter of abnormal psychology is restricted to extremely bizarre behavior.
    d. The subject matter of abnormal psychology is restricted to common behaviors that cause people mild distress.

Ans: c
Page: 4
Obj: 1
Type: F

2. In conducting a psychodiagnosis, psychologists _____ abnormal behavior.
    a. eliminate
    b. control
    c. describe
    d. predict

Ans: d
Page: 4
Obj: 1
Type: A

3. Dr. Thompson collects information in order to describe and draw inferences about an individual's psychological disorder. Dr. Thompson is engaged in
    a. therapy.
    b. predicting dangerousness.
    c. research.
    d. psychodiagnosis.

Ans: b
Page: 4
Obj: 1
Type: C

4. The fact that different psychologists have different theoretical orientations most directly affects how they _____ abnormality.
    a. classify
    b. explain
    c. define
    d. describe

Ans: c
Page: 4
Obj: 1
Type: A

5. A psychologist says, "Juan's abnormal behavior is likely due to a combination of biology and inadequate interpersonal skills." The psychologist is
    a. predicting the future symptoms of Juan.
    b. giving Juan a psychodiagnosis.
    c. offering an explanation for Juan's problem.
    d. describing how to control Juan's symptoms.

Ans: a
Page: 4
Obj: 1
Type: C

6. Which statement regarding the prediction of abnormal behavior is *accurate*?
    a. Even experienced professionals find it hard to accurately predict how an individual will behave.
    b. Psychologists are not interested in predicting clients' future behavior.
    c. Prediction is unrelated to understanding the cause of abnormality.
    d. Psychologists tend to underpredict the violent behavior of clients.

Ans: c
Page: 4
Obj: 1
Type: F

7. Therapy is *most* closely related to which of the four objectives of abnormal psychology?
    a. Explanation
    b. Prediction
    c. Control
    d. Definition

Ans: d
Page: 4
Obj: 1
Type: C

8. When psychologists talk about the control of abnormal behavior, they mean that they
   a. seek to understand the underlying cause of that behavior.
   b. restrict the freedom of dangerous clients.
   c. try to anticipate the future behaviors of clients.
   d. use therapy to alter client behavior.

Ans: a
Page: 4
Obj: 1
Type: F

9. Which of the following defines *therapy* most accurately?
   a. A program of systematic intervention designed to alter behavior, emotion, or thought
   b. The scientific study of abnormal behavior
   c. A system of observing abnormal behavior in an attempt to classify it
   d. The application of a theoretical model to explain the cause of abnormal behavior

Ans: b
Page: 4
Obj: 1
Type: A

10. A psychologist develops several activities for clients aimed at helping them become more self-disciplined and feel more confident about trying new behaviors. This example illustrates
    a. how epidemiological work is done in the field.
    b. how therapy may be seen as an attempt to control behavior.
    c. the function of providing an explanation for abnormal behavior.
    d. the essential need for accurate psychodiagnosis.

Ans: c
Page: 6
Obj: 2
Type: F

11. Clinical psychologists usually have _____ degrees, unlike psychiatrists, who have _____ degrees.
    a. bachelor's (B.S.); medical (M.D.)
    b. medical (M.D.); Ph.D.
    c. doctorate (Ph.D. or Psy.D); medical (M.D.)
    d. master's (M.S.); doctorate (Ph.D.)

Ans: b
Page: 6
Obj: 2
Type: A

12. Harold is a mental health professional who has a medical degree and prescribes antidepressants and antipsychotic medication. He completed a three-year residency in order to complete his training. We can guess that Harold is a
    a. social worker.
    b. psychiatrist.
    c. clinical psychologist.
    d. psychoanalyst.

Ans: c
Page: 6
Obj: 2
Type: A

13. Linda, Jayne, and Sheryl all are called "doctor." All are mental health professionals. However, Linda has a Psy.D., Jayne has an M.D., and Sheryl has a D.S.W. We can predict that
    a. Sheryl is a psychiatrist.
    b. Linda is a social worker.
    c. Linda is a clinical psychologist.
    d. Jayne is a clinical psychologist.

Ans: d
Page: 6
Obj: 2
Type: F

14. Psychiatrists must have an M.D.; clinical psychologists must have a Ph.D. or Psy.D. Psychoanalysts must have
    a. a master's (M.S.) degree.
    b. an M.D.
    c. only a bachelor's (B.S.) degree.
    d. an intensive personal analysis as part of psychoanalytic training.

Ans: a
Page: 6
Obj: 2
Type: A

15. Johanna is an M.D. who received intensive training in the ideas of Sigmund Freud. She also went through psychotherapy herself as part of this training. We can guess that Johanna is
   a. a psychoanalyst.
   b. a marriage and family counselor.
   c. a psychiatric social worker.
   d. a behaviorally oriented counseling psychologist.

Ans: b
Page: 7
Obj: 3
Type: C

16. When it comes to defining *abnormal,* which terms are accurately paired?
   a. Cultural universality—deviation from ideal mental health
   b. Infrequent—statistical deviation
   c. Personal discomfort—multicultural perspective
   d. Cultural relativity—deviation from ideal mental health

Ans: a
Page: 7
Obj: 3
Type: C

17. One strength in using the statistical criterion is that it
   a. uses an objective method of defining abnormal behavior.
   b. stresses the attainment of realistic goals.
   c. examines how the individual views his or her own behavior.
   d. accounts for the complexity of behavior observed in people from different cultures.

Ans: d
Page: 7
Obj: 3
Type: C

18. A psychologist defined mental retardation solely on the basis of how far from "normal" an individual's IQ score is. The criterion used is
   a. deviation from ideal mental health.
   b. cultural relativism.
   c. cultural universality.
   d. statistical deviation.

Ans: c
Page: 7
Obj: 3
Type: C

19. "There are at least two problems with it: First, it does not distinguish desirable from undesirable behavior; second, it means that anyone who is original or nonconforming is likely to be defined as abnormal." What criterion for defining abnormality is being discussed?
   a. Subjective discomfort
   b. Deviation from ideal mental health
   c. Statistical deviation
   d   DSM-IV definition

Ans: a
Page: 8
Obj: 3
Type: F

20. The ideal mental health, statistical, and multicultural perspectives are
   a. illustrative of the problems mental health professionals have in trying to define abnormality.
   b. used by all therapists to guide their treatment of clients.
   c. ways of conceptualizing abnormal behavior that stem from biological science.
   d. given equal acceptance by psychologists, irrespective of their theoretical orientation.

Ans: b
Page: 9
Obj: 4
Type: A

21. "You must understand the values and expectations of the society in which behavior occurs before you decide that abnormality exists." This quote *best* reflects the _____ view of abnormality.
   a. traditional
   b. cultural relativist
   c. epidemiological
   d. cultural universality

Ans: a
Page: 9
Obj: 4
Type: A

22. Jamie says, "If a woman refuses to marry and have children, it is a definite sign of abnormality." How does cultural relativism respond to such a statement?
   a. It rejects it.
   b. It takes no stand on such statements.
   c. It supports only the point about sex differences.
   d. It supports it.

Ans: d
Page: 9
Obj: 4
Type: F

23. The most fruitful approach to using multicultural criteria is to rely on
   a. neither cultural universality nor cultural relativism.
   b. the cultural relativism approach.
   c. the cultural universality approach.
   d. some combination of cultural relativism and cultural universality.

Ans: b
Page: 10
Obj: 5
Type: F

24. Practical definitions of abnormality emphasize the observation of
   a. cultural universals.
   b. discomfort, deviance, and dysfunction.
   c. categories listed in the DSM–IV-TR
   d. deviations from an ideal form of behavior.

Ans: c
Page: 10
Obj: 3
Type: A

25. Juanita visits a mental health center complaining of fatigue, anxiety, and an inability to sleep. If her symptoms are considered a form of abnormal behavior, it is because she is showing
   a. delusions and hallucinations.
   b. severe dysfunction.
   c. personal discomfort.
   d. statistically rare behavior patterns.

Ans: b
Page: 10
Obj: 3
Type: F

26. Headache is to _____ as delusions are to _____.
   a. dysfunction; deviance
   b. discomfort; deviance
   c. deviance; dysfunction
   d. discomfort; dysfunction

Ans: d
Page: 11
Obj: 3
Type: F

27. Sensory misperceptions, which may include hearing voices   others do not hear or seeing things other do not see, are called
   a. dysfunctions.
   b. disorientations.
   c. delusions.
   d. hallucinations.

Ans: a
Page: 11
Obj: 3
Type: A

28. Mel has the mistaken belief that his father has stolen his identity and that his mother is trying to poison him. Mel's mistaken beliefs illustrate
   a. delusions.
   b. disorientation.
   c. underachievement.
   d. hallucinations.

Ans: c
Page: 11
Obj: 3
Type: A

29. Although no one else can hear them, Jack says that he hears voices accusing him of terrible crimes. He also reports that insects are crawling under his skin. Jack is suffering from
    a. delusions.
    b. extreme dysfunction.
    c. hallucinations.
    d. disorientation.

Ans: a
Page: 11
Obj: 3
Type: A

30. During a diagnostic interview, a psychiatrist asks the client if he or she knows what day it is, what his or her name is, and where he or she is. These questions are designed to assess
    a. disorientation.
    b. discomfort.
    c. subjective distress.
    d. dysfunction.

Ans: d
Page: 11
Obj: 3
Type: F

31. Dysfunction is assessed in terms of the discrepancy between
    a. thoughts and feelings.
    b. expectations and attitudes.
    c. cultural norms and actual behavior.
    d. personal potential and actual performance.

Ans: c
Page: 11
Obj: 3
Type: A

32. Teresa, normally an energetic mother of three small children, is suddenly unable to go shopping, prepare meals, or even dress her children. Teresa's behavior illustrates the practical definition of abnormality called
    a. disorientation.
    b. discomfort.
    c. dysfunction.
    d. deviance.

Ans: a
Page: 12
Obj: 5
Type: C

33. Thomas Szasz believes that
    a. mental illness is best seen as a form of social control a society uses to reduce deviant behavior.
    b. the causes for most mental disorders will ultimately be found in brain pathology.
    c. individuals who are suffering from mental illnesses have biological diseases.
    d. medication is far superior than psychotherapy in reducing the suffering of individuals with mental disorders.

Ans: c
Page: 12
Obj: 5
Type: A

34. A psychologist determines abnormality on the basis of how the behavior is seen by society, the individual performing it, and the psychologist herself. This psychologist is using a definition of abnormality that is
    a. psychogenic.
    b. based on cultural universality.
    c. integrated.
    d. based on statistical rarity.

Ans: d
Page: 12
Obj: 5
Type: F

35. Strupp and Hadley proposed a three-part means of judging mental health. The three vantage points they suggested using are
   a. the individual, the family, and the mental health professional.
   b. society, the mental health professional, and biological dysfunctions.
   c. the individual, the family, and biological dysfunctions.
   d. the individual, the society, and the mental health professional.

Ans: b
Page: 12
Obj: 5
Type: C

36. Wakefield (1992) argued that mental disorder is a "harmful dysfunction." What does he mean by this?
   a. People with mental disorders are biologically functional but mentally dysfunctional.
   b. People with mental disorders have biological dysfunctions that cause socially defined harm.
   c. People with mental disorders do harm to their own bodies when they do not seek treatment.
   d. People with mental disorders typically interfere with society's ability to function.

Ans: a
Page: 12
Obj: 5
Type: F

37. Abnormal behavior may be defined as behavior that
   a. departs from cultural norms and harms the individual or others.
   b. is deviant in every culture.
   c. departs from cultural norms.
   d. represents severe mental illness.

Ans: d
Page: 13
Obj: 5
Type: A

38. Jerry's behavior is quite unusual, but neither he nor anyone he comes in contact with feels it is detrimental. According to the text,
   a. Jerry is not abnormal because his behavior does not deviate from an ideal mental health state.
   b. Jerry is abnormal because his behavior is statistically rare.
   c. Jerry is abnormal because his behavior deviates from the norm.
   d. Jerry is not abnormal because his behavior does not cause harm.

Ans: b
Page: 13
Obj: 5
Type: F

39. "A behavior pattern in an individual that is associated with distress, disability, or increased risk of death, pain, or loss of freedom" is the definition of abnormal behavior according to
   a. humanistic psychologists.
   b. the *Diagnostic and Statistical Manual of Mental Disorders*.
   c. cultural relativists.
   d. the National Institute of Mental Health.

Ans: c
Page: 13
Obj: 6
Type: C

40. Epidemiological studies are useful for providing
   a. clear criteria allowing mental health professionals to distinguish people who are normal from those who are abnormal.
   b. specific criteria concerning the etiology of various disorders.
   c. information about large numbers of people who represent various segments of the population.
   d. experimental data on cause-and-effect relationships.

Ans: a
Page: 13
Obj: 6
Type: C

41. Suppose you were graphing the percentage of Americans showing serious mental disorders. You had two data points, both taken from surveys of New Yorkers, one in 1950 and the other in the 1970s. The graph would show
    a. a horizontal line showing 25 percent of the population with severe impairment at both times.
    b. a diagonal line going down from 15 percent in 1950 to less than 1 percent in 1975.
    c. a horizontal line showing 1 percent of the population with severe impairment at both times.
    d. a diagonal line going up steeply from 15 percent in 1950 to 50 percent in 1975.

Ans: d
Page: 13
Obj: 6
Type: C

42. Research evidence shows that the rate of mental disturbance in the United States has _____ since 1950, when research showed that 25 percent of those interviewed showed severe impairment.
    a. gone up and then gone down
    b. dropped significantly
    c. increased significantly
    d. stayed about the same

Ans: c
Page: 14
Obj: 7
Type: F

43. Which statement about psychiatric disorder in the United States is *accurate*?
    a. Depression and anxiety are more common in men than in women.
    b. Compared to adults, a larger percentage of children have serious mental disorders.
    c. Psychiatric disorder is present in about one-third of Americans.
    d. Phobias are more common in the elderly than in the young.

Ans: d
Page: 14
Obj: 7
Type: F

44. Research shows that in the United States, women are more likely than men to have problems with
    a. hallucinations.
    b. schizophrenia.
    c. alcohol.
    d. depression.

Ans: a
Page: 14
Obj: 6
Type: C

45. Both the Midtown Manhattan Study in the 1950s and the National Institute of Mental Health epidemiological study in the 1980s found that
    a. a large minority of Americans experience impaired mental health.
    b. very few Americans suffer from serious mental disorders.
    c. half of Americans show severe mental impairment.
    d. mentally ill people frequently engage in violent criminal behavior.

Ans: a
Page: 16
Obj: 13
Type: F

46. According to the Surgeon General's Report on Mental Health (1999), mental illness is:
    a. more debilitating than malignant diseases such as cancer.
    b. equally as debilitating as malignant diseases such as cancer.
    c. almost as debilitating as malignant diseases such as cancer.
    d. less debilitating than malignant diseases such as cancer, but more debilitating than chronic disorders such as arthritis.

Ans: b
Page: 14
Obj: 7
Type: A

47. Chris has been feeling very stressed at work lately. Chris copes with that stress by using drugs and alcohol. Chris
    a. should wait to see if the stress symptoms go away on their own.
    b. displays symptoms frequently seen in men in general.
    c. should be hospitalized immediately.
    d. suffers from primary gender socialization disorder.

Ans: d
Page: 14
Obj: 7
Type: F

48. Research shows that in the United States women are *more* likely than men to have problems with
    a. schizophrenia.
    b. phobias (irrational fears).
    c. alcohol.
    d. depression.

Ans: c
Page: 14
Obj: 7
Type: A

49. Suppose that in one region of the country we had two fast-growing populations: those over the age of sixty-five, and men in their late teens and early twenties. We could predict increasing rates of which disorders?
    a. Schizophrenia and anxiety
    b. Depression and phobias
    c. Cognitive impairments and drug dependence
    d. Schizophrenia and depression

Ans: d
Page: 16
Obj: 6
Type: F

50. Approximately what percentage of people in a large American city would we expect to be receiving mental health services?
    a. 90 percent
    b. 75 percent
    c. 50 percent
    d. 33 percent or fewer

Ans: a
Page: 17
Obj: 8
Type: A

51. Jason says, "Abnormal behavior is a function of the context in which the behavior occurs and what the observer thinks is abnormal." Jason's remarks
    a. contradict the myth that mentally disturbed people can always be recognized.
    b. support the myth that mentally disturbed people can use willpower to recover.
    c. support the myth that mentally disturbed people can always be recognized.
    d. contradict the myth that mentally disturbed people cannot be cured.

Ans: d
Page: 17
Obj: 8
Type: F

52. Which of the following statements regarding the causes of mental disorders is *accurate*?
    a. In most disorders, heredity and the environment play almost equal roles.
    b. In most disorders, environmental factors have little influence; heredity is the predominant cause.
    c. Heredity has little influence on disorders such as schizophrenia and mental retardation.
    d. In some disorders, heredity plays a causal role, but in all disorders, the environment is extremely important.

Ans: b
Page: 17
Obj: 8
Type: F

53. Abraham Lincoln, William James, and former Senator Thomas Eagleton are all examples of
   a. mentally disordered people who were dangerous to others.
   b. famous people who recovered from mental disorders.
   c. mentally disturbed people who made creative contributions because of their disorders.
   d. people who were denied treatment for a mental disorder.

Ans: c
Page: 17
Obj: 8
Type: A

54. A respected doctor in a small rural village stated, "Individuals who have mental illnesses cannot be cured and probably cannot hold down a job." This statement
   a. gives the impression that people with mental disorders can cure themselves only with willpower.
   b. assumes that we can easily identify people with mental disorders.
   c. suggests that people who suffer from psychological problems cannot make meaningful contributions to society.
   d. assumes that mental disorders are caused predominantly by environmental factors.

Ans: d
Page: 17
Obj: 8
Type: C

55. Many psychological problems stem from situations that are not under an individual's control. This fact counters the myth that
   a. mental illness is incurable.
   b. mental patients are usually dangerous.
   c. most mental disorders are caused by inherited biological defects, although the specific nature of the deficiency is unknown.
   d. mental illness is caused by weak personal willpower.

Ans: b
Page: 18
Obj: 8
Type: A

56. Morgan is a highly respected teacher and poet whose works have been published in three languages. He also suffers from bipolar disorder and has never been successfully treated. This case
   a. supports the claim that mental disorders are usually the result of bad parenting and past traumatic experiences.
   b. contradicts the claim that people with mental disorders cannot contribute until they are cured.
   c. contradicts the claim that mentally disturbed people are recognizable.
   d. supports the idea that mentally disturbed people can never function normally or hold down jobs.

Ans: c
Page: 18
Obj: 8
Type: A

57. Dr. Chu reports, "Mental patients are no more dangerous than other people." What does research say about the doctor's statement?
   a. No such research has been done.
   b. Research shows that patients are considerably more dangerous when the disorder is genetic.
   c. Research shows that individuals with dial diagnosis are slight more dangerous than other patients.
   d. Research tends to support his idea.

Ans: a
Page: 18
Obj: 9
Type: C

58. Throughout history, most popular ideas about abnormal behavior have been
   a. rooted in the beliefs of a given time period and society.
   b. based on religious dogma of the day.
   c. unrelated to the beliefs of previous generations.
   d. based on scientific evidence.

Ans: d
Page: 18
Obj: 9
Type: F

59. It is generally believed that prehistoric people considered the major cause of serious abnormal behavior to be
     a. biological disequilibrium.
     b. genetic inheritance.
     c. childhood mistreatment.
     d. demonology.

Ans: b
Page: 18
Obj: 9
Type: C

60. In some non-Western societies today, headaches, depression, and seizures are all believed to be caused by offended ancestral spirits or by evil forces that possess the sufferer. This type of explanation is called
     a. naturalism.
     b. demonology.
     c. trephining.
     d. exorcism.

Ans: d
Page: 19
Obj: 9
Type: F

61. Trephining refers to the process of
     a. putting leaches on the body to remove bad blood.
     b. making a person chant and pray to drive out evil spirits.
     c. changing one's diet to improve one's physical and mental health.
     d. boring a hole in the skull to let demons escape.

Ans: a
Page: 19
Obj: 9
Type: A

62. Dr. Frank finds a human skull that dates from 5500 B.C. It has many fractures in it and a clearly carved hole. From its shape, we can tell it was a man's skull. Dr. Frank assumes that the hole got there because someone used trephining to rid the man of his mental disorder. What alternative explanation is there?
     a. Blood clots resulting from a blow to the head had been removed through surgery.
     b. The man had been tortured because church officials considered him a witch.
     c. Hippocrates had treated the man for melancholia.
     d. The man was a victim of an exorcism.

Ans: c
Page: 19
Obj: 9
Type: F

63. Exorcism involves
     a. increasing one's activity level so that, by becoming fit, a person's body can recover from a physical or mental illness.
     b. chipping a hole in the skull of a person believed to be possessed by demons.
     c. praying and chanting over or flogging and starving a person to cast evil spirits out of the body.
     d. examining the brains of people who have severe mental disorders.

Ans: c
Page: 19
Obj: 9
Type: F

64. The first biogenic approach to abnormal behavior can be traced to
     a. the rise of the Christian Church during the Dark Ages.
     b. Philippe Pinel in eighteenth-century Paris.
     c. Hippocrates in ancient Greece.
     d. Galen in ancient Rome.

Ans: b
Page: 19
Obj: 9
Type: A

65. Suppose an archaeologist unearthed an ancient Greek document that contained instructions for the treatment of mental disorders such as melancholia and mania. What would the writing probably say?
    a. "Hypnotize the person and encourage the person to express his or her negative emotions."
    b. "Have the family treat the person with rest, good diet, and moderate exercise."
    c. "Treat the person as you would a witch."
    d. "Take a sharp stone and cut a hole in the person's skull to let out the evil demons."

Ans: c
Page: 19
Obj: 9
Type: A

66. "Your sadness is what I call melancholia. It is a problem with your brain, the cure for which is abstinence from sex, rest, and, if necessary, the removal of some of your bad blood." During what era would this advice *most* likely have been given?
    a. Sixteenth-century Paris, France
    b. Prehistoric times
    c. Ancient Greece
    d. The Dark Ages

Ans: d
Page: 19
Obj: 9
Type: F

67. He practiced in Rome and related mental illness to the brain and central nervous system. His greatest contribution may have been compiling all medical knowledge from Hippocrates' time to his own. Who was he?
    a. Pinel
    b. Mesmer
    c. Weyer
    d. Galen

Ans: d
Page: 20
Obj: 9
Type: F

68. During the Middle Ages, treatment of mentally disordered people tended to be
    a. based on a disease model.
    b. caring and humane.
    c. based on scientific principles.
    d. cruel.

Ans: b
Page: 20
Obj: 9
Type: F

69. The early Christian Church believed that
    a. demons could be released through the cathartic method.
    b. many behaviors we call mental disorders were the result of supernatural forces.
    c. science was the most effective way to understand abnormal human behavior.
    d. abnormal behavior was primarily the result of biological abnormality.

Ans: a
Page: 24
Obj: 9
Type: A

70. Imagine that half the clerical employees in one building of a school begin to have headaches, feel agitated, scratch themselves furiously, feel numbness in their fingers, and faint. There is no biological explanation. This incident would *most* likely be seen by psychologists as an example of
    a. mass hysteria.
    b. exorcism.
    c. hypnotic susceptibility.
    d. mesmerism.

71. Imagine that you could use a time machine to travel back to the thirteenth century. You see groups of people in a village jumping, dancing, and having convulsions in the town square. All over Europe, you find similar groups of raving people. You would have witnessed

Ans: b
Page: 21
Obj: 9
Type: A

    a. the phenomenon called trephining.
    b. the mass hysteria called St. Vitus's Dance.
    c. the phenomenon called lycanthropy.
    d. the mass hysteria called mesmerism.

72. What was the *Malleus Maleficarum*?

Ans: d
Page: 21
Obj: 9
Type: F

    a. A compilation of all medical knowledge regarding abnormal behavior from the Greeks and Romans
    b. A description of how to treat madness in the Dark Ages
    c. A guide to building hospitals for the mentally ill that were more humane
    d. A guidebook for identifying and exterminating witches

73. Which statement below concerning witchcraft is *accurate*?

Ans: b
Page: 21
Obj: 9
Type: F

    a. At first, the church made no distinctions between types of demonic possession.
    b. Witchcraft became a way of explaining peculiar behavior when the church was under attack.
    c. The church tried to stop people from accusing deviant people of being witches.
    d. The treatment for witchcraft typically involved prayers, gentle persuasion, and sympathy.

74. Recent analysis of historical documents during the age of witchcraft shows that

Ans: a
Page: 21
Obj: 9
Type: F

    a. while some witches may have been mentally disordered, most were not.
    b. few people were ever accused of being witches and almost none were killed.
    c. many witches were actually mentally retarded, not mentally disordered.
    d. almost all witches were mentally disordered.

75. Humanism is

Ans: b
Page: 22
Obj: 10
Type: F

    a. the scientific study of behavior.
    b. the philosophical movement that emphasized human welfare and individual uniqueness.
    c. the biological theory of abnormal behavior first used by the ancient Greeks.
    d. the name the Catholic Church gave to the practice of identifying and executing individuals they believed were witches.

76. The humanistic movement of the Renaissance

Ans: c
Page: 22
Obj: 10
Type: F

    a. emphasized the value of the cathartic method.
    b. presented the first biogenic theory of abnormal behavior in recorded history.
    c. strongly criticized the idea of witchcraft.
    d. led directly to deinstitutionalization of mentally disordered individuals.

77. "I reject the idea of witchcraft. Disturbed people are sick people who deserve our sympathy, not torture and death." Who would have been *most* likely to say these words?
    a. Pope Innocent VIII, head of the Catholic Church in 1484
    b. Benjamin Rush, a psychiatrist in colonial America
    c. Hippocrates, a physician in ancient Greece
    d. Johann Weyer, a physician who lived in the 1500s

78. Who ordered the chains to be removed from inmates at a mental asylum and is considered a founder of the moral treatment movement?
    a. Clifford Beers
    b. Johann Weyer
    c. Philippe Pinel
    d. Dorothea Dix

79. "Although I lived in a different country than Philippe Pinel, I also worked to establish moral treatment for mental patients." Who might have said this?
    a. William Tuke
    b. Galen
    c. Jean-Martin Charcot
    d. Friedrich Anton Mesmer

80. What kind of techniques were used by moral therapists?
    a. antipsychotic medications
    b. controls such as chains, starvation, restraints, and hot baths
    c. mesmerism
    d. prayer, work, and kindness

81. Imagine that we travel back in time and meet two Americans. The first says, "I am sometimes called the father of U.S. psychiatry. I used bloodletting to treat my mental patients, but I insisted they be treated with respect." The second says, "Although I was only a schoolteacher, when I saw the deplorable conditions under which mental patients were living, I devoted my life to establishing suitable mental hospitals." The first person was _____; the second was _____.
    a. Benjamin Rush; Dorothea Dix
    b. William Tuke; Clifford Beers
    c. Clifford Beers; Dorothea Dix
    d. Benjamin Rush; Friedrich Anton Mesmer

82. A history book states, "Benjamin Rush introduced humane policies into American mental hospitals, but it took Dorothea Dix to make significant positive reforms in mental hospital care. After her work, inhumane treatment was eliminated in the United States." What, if anything, is *incorrect* in this statement?
    a. No portion of the statement is incorrect.
    b. It is incorrect to say that Dix made significant positive reforms.
    c. It is incorrect to say that inhumane treatment was eliminated by Dix.
    d. It is incorrect to say that Rush introduced humane policies.

Ans: b
Page: 22
Obj: 10
Type: C

83. Frenchman Philippe Pinel and American Benjamin Rush were both concerned with
    a. the development of private "madhouses" because they were highly profitable.
    b. the moral treatment of patients in hospitals.
    c. helping patients gain easy access to medications.
    d. instituting the use of shamans in the modern treatment of mentally disturbed individuals in an attempt to be culturally sensitive.

Ans: c
Page: 22
Obj: 10
Type: F

84. Each of the following people contributed substantially to the moral therapy movement *except*
    a. Philippe Pinel.
    b. Benjamin Rush.
    c. Friedrich Anton Mesmer.
    d. William Tuke.

Ans: d
Page: 23
Obj: 10
Type: A

85. Imagine that we could go back to the late 1800s and hear Emil Kraepelin, the great psychiatrist, talk about the nature of abnormality. Which statement would he have been *most* likely to make?
    a. "Whenever behavior prevents people from performing the tasks they are expected to perform, it is a sign of abnormality."
    b. "Abnormality is a deviation from ideal personality traits such as competence, self-actualization, and creativity."
    c. "Every culture has its own unique set of symptoms and disorders."
    d. "Categories of mental disorders in one culture are nearly identical to disorders elsewhere."

Ans: a
Page: 23
Obj: 11
Type: A

86. Dr. Juarez discovers that certain symptoms of behavior reliably occur in clusters. Her discovery would be seen as
    a. evidence of a syndrome.
    b. support for a psychological viewpoint.
    c. an illustration of epidemiology.
    d. support for a biological viewpoint.

Ans: b
Page: 23
Obj: 11
Type: F

87. Mental disorders seen in terms of symptom clusters that have their own cause, course, and outcome are considered _____ in origin.
    a. socio-cultural
    b. biological
    c. psychological
    d. culturally universal

Ans: d
Page: 24
Obj: 11
Type: A

88. A psychologist says, "There are certain emotional disorders for which we can find no evidence of brain pathology." This psychologist's statement reflects a(n) _____ viewpoint.
    a. organic
    b. biogenic
    c. humanistic
    d. psychological

Ans: c
Page: 24
Obj: 12
Type: F

89. Mesmer's lasting contribution to psychology is his
   a. research showing the relationship between syphilis and the mental deterioration seen in general paresis.
   b. development of a textbook for psychiatry that described the major disorders.
   c. demonstration that psychological factors like suggestion can cure mental problems.
   d. demonstration that the masses can fall for a false set of beliefs.

Ans: b
Page: 24
Obj: 12
Type: A

90. Imagine that you are in Paris in 1775. People tell you their physical and mental health is remarkably improved when they experience a strange sleeplike trance. Later you hear that the man who performed these remarkable cures was investigated and forced to leave Paris. What forerunner of hypnosis were the people of Paris talking about?
   a. Catharsis
   b. Mesmerism
   c. Exorcism
   d. Trephining

Ans: a
Page: 25
Obj: 12
Type: F

91. When Charcot and the physicians of the Nancy school used hypnosis, it was to
   a. research and treat the disorder called hysteria.
   b. uncover the unconscious motives of their clients.
   c. investigate the causes of general paresis.
   d. understand the meaning and purpose of dreams.

Ans: d
Page: 25
Obj: 12
Type: F

92. Which historic figure is correctly matched with his contribution?
   a. Griesinger—the linking of hypnosis to hysteria
   b. Mesmer—founder of the Nancy school
   c. Charcot—authored *Textbook of Psychiatry*
   d. Breuer—developed the cathartic method

Ans: b
Page: 25
Obj: 12
Type: F

93. Catharsis assumes that
   a. abnormal behavior is affected primarily by cultural norms.
   b. reliving forgotten emotions reduces suffering.
   c. astrology and planetary movements affect human emotions.
   d. drug treatment, coupled with social skills training, improves mental functioning.

Ans: c
Page: 25
Obj: 13
Type: F

94. What was a significant effect of the drug revolution on mental health care?
   a. It greatly increased the number of people dependent on illegal drugs.
   b. It showed that troublesome psychiatric symptoms are caused primarily by biological factors.
   c. It helped reduce the number of patients in mental institutions.
   d. It led directly to the managed care movement.

Ans: a
Page: 25
Obj: 13
Type: F

95. Which statement concerning prescription privileges for psychologists is most likely to come from a physician, rather than from a psychologist?
   a. Granting such privileges could endanger the public.
   b. Pharmacology interventions may supplant psychological ones.
   c. Rather than compete with medicine, psychologists should use their unique skills to deal with broader societal needs.
   d. Prescription privileges would increase the length of education and burden training programs.

Ans: a
Page: 27
Obj: 13
Type: A

96. Dr. Shah says, "It is the industrialization of health care, where large organizations determine what type and duration of treatment clients can have." What is Dr. Shah describing?
    a. Managed health care
    b. Multicultural psychology
    c. Moral therapy
    d. The drug revolution

Ans: d
Page: 28
Obj: 13
Type: F

97. As a follow-up to Rosenhan's (1973) study, Scribner (2001) asked seven chronic schizophrenics with acute symptoms to present themselves for care at mental health agencies. What did these patients experience?
    a. All were treated on an out-patient basis.
    b. All were institutionalized.
    c. All were refused treatment.
    d. All were initially refused treatment, but one was admitted after stating he might harm himself or others.

Ans: c
Page: 29
Obj: 14
Type: A

98. A psychologist says, "Because they have higher birthrates, racial and ethnic minorities in the United States are already a numerical majority. This increase in diversity has led to the field called multicultural psychology, which is interested in increasing the cultural sensitivity of mental health professionals." What portion of this statement is *incorrect*?
    a. It is incorrect to say that multicultural psychology is interested in increasing cultural sensitivity.
    b. It is incorrect to say that racial minorities have higher birthrates.
    c. It is incorrect to say that minorities are currently the majority.
    d. It is incorrect to say that diversity has led to multicultural psychology.

Ans: a
Page: 29
Obj: 14
Type: F

99. Social conditioning, sociopolitical influences, and bias in diagnosis are factors that help explain
    a. sex and gender differences in mental health.
    b. the reason managed health care developed.
    c. the success of hypnosis and catharsis in changing an individual's behavior.
    d. the increase in the number of mental health professionals in the United States.

Ans: d
Page: 29
Obj: 14
Type: A

100. At one mental health center, 75 percent of patients treated for depression and anxiety are women. Which comment illustrates the explanation of social conditioning?
    a. Women are biologically vulnerable to feelings of sadness and anxiety.
    b. Having been discriminated against for centuries, women are sad and fearful.
    c. Most therapists are males and they misunderstand women's concerns.
    d. Women are raised to be emotional and fragile.

Ans: b
Page: 31
Obj: 15
Type: F

101. A person who subscribes to the biopsychosocial approach to mental disorder would probably agree that
    a. behaviorism was much more influential in the treatment of mental disorders than drug treatment or psychoanalysis.
    b. biological factors are only a part of the picture for explaining and treating mental disorders.
    c. biological factors are the most important causes of most mental disorders.
    d. research has little place in contemporary abnormal psychology.

Ans: c
Page: 31
Obj: 15
Type: C

102. If, after reading about four different disorders, you believe you have all of them, you are probably
    a. suffering from obsessive-compulsive disorder.
    b. experiencing catharsis.
    c. experiencing medical student syndrome.
    d. severely mentally disordered.

ESSAY QUESTIONS

1. List three of the criteria used to define abnormal behavior. Discuss the strengths and weaknesses of each criterion.

2. Chart the major ideas and historical figures in the history of treating the mentally ill from the era of witchcraft until the present.

3. Briefly discuss the changing views of mental disorders throughout history. Be sure to include in your discussion a comparison and contrast of views across cultures and across time periods.

SAMPLE ANSWERS

1. The statistical deviation definition argues that abnormal behavior is rare behavior. Clearly, the origin of the word *abnormal* has this idea in mind, and the concept of deviance connotes rare events. However, the statistical deviation view equates commonplace with healthy. It fails to look at the types of rare behavior and whether all rare behavior is in need of treatment or change. Exceptional creativity is not what most people consider abnormal behavior.

   The deviation from ideal mental health makes the important point that mental health should not be the mere absence of pathology, that we should strive for highly valued capacities such as competence or integration. However, a pluralistic culture finds it hard to agree on a single prized value. Furthermore, so many people are likely to be deficient that such a definition would label large portions of the population abnormal.

   Cultural definitions of abnormality either emphasize universality—that certain behaviors are abnormal regardless of culture—or relativism—that abnormality is completely defined by the norms of specific cultures. Most psychologists find a middle ground between these extreme positions.

   Finally, practical definitions of abnormality emphasize the effects of behavior on the individual or those around him or her. Behaviors that cause one discomfort (physical or emotional) can be said to be abnormal. Discomfort may also occur in family members and friends of the individual. The danger here is that unconventional behavior that makes people feel uncomfortable will be labeled pathological. Another component of a practical definition is deviance, behaviors that are bizarre. Most cultures agree that seeing or hearing things others do not (hallucinations) is a sign of abnormality. False beliefs unchanged by evidence (delusions) are also characteristics of deviant behavior. Finally, cultures have expectations for individuals in society; those who fall well short of expected performance of roles might be seen as dysfunctional.

   No matter what definition is used, subjective judgments abound. In practice, abnormality is defined when several signs of it are present.

2. During the fifteenth and sixteenth centuries in Europe, when the Roman Catholic Church was under attack, witchcraft became a common explanation for deviant behavior. At one time, treatment was relatively mild for people who were seen as being involuntarily possessed by the devil. Exorcisms involving incantations, purges, fasting, and other rituals were used to restore people to sanity. Harsher treatments were reserved for those voluntarily in league with the devil. Eventually, the distinction blurred. In 1484, the pope called for the identification and extermination

of witches. More than 100,000 people were executed. Earlier historians asserted that many were actually mentally ill; more recent work suggests that only a small minority were.

The Renaissance marked a time of increased rationality and concern about human welfare and dignity called humanism. Johann Weyer, a German physician, courageously challenged church teachings on witchcraft and argued that these people suffered from physical or social problems. Treatment of mentally ill people continued to be cruel throughout the 1600s and 1700s. At the beginning of the 1800s in France (Philippe Pinel), England (William Tuke), and the United States (Benjamin Rush), a new viewpoint called moral treatment came about. It argued that people who were treated humanely could be restored to sanity. Later, Dorothea Dix campaigned for reforms in mental hospitals and established hospitals for the poor in the United States. The treatment of mental patients has often been exposed as inadequate or heartless. Still, most people would agree that conditions are better today than at any time in the past.

3.   Two influential themes came from Greek and Roman cultures (700 B.C. to fifth century A.D.): the relationship between mental disorder and psychological conflict and mental disorder as a physical illness with biological causes. After the fifth century, mental disorders in many cultures were viewed as the result of possession by evil spirits. In the Chinese culture, for example, mental illness often was viewed as caused by the spirits of ancestors, an angry or restless soul, or other superhuman beings. In addition, the Chinese viewed mental illness as the result of an imbalance of the yin and yang—dual forces within the universe representing polar entities (negative and positive, good and bad). The Middle Eastern cultures also viewed mental disorders as being the result of evil spirits. Traditional African societies also attributed mental disorders to malicious spirits, including the spirits of offended ancestors.

In the late 1700s the emphasis on evil spirits, demons, and witchcraft gave way to the moral movement, with reformists advocating for more humane treatment of people with mental disorders. Specifically, reformists advocated treating patients kindly and respectfully, offering guidance and support, and encouraging fresh air and activity. In addition to changes in the treatment of the mentally ill, the scientific study of mental disorders was emphasized. People came to realize that psychological disorders were caused by physical factors or personal and social conditions. Along with this realization came the tradition of scientific observation and exploration leading to developments such as the diagnostic classification system of Emile Kraepelin and Freud's theory of personality. In the twentieth century, there is a strong emphasis on exploring the biological bases of psychological disorders (including brain functioning, genetic transmission of disorder, and neurochemical factors), as well as on social behaviors acquired through learning.

CHAPTER 2
Models of Abnormal Behavior

LEARNING OBJECTIVES

1. Define *psychopathology* and describe what a model is. Discuss how models are used in describing psychopathology and how a clinician's choice of a model influences thought and action toward abnormal behavior. (pp. 35–37)

2. Describe the biological models, including the major structures of the human brain, neurons, and the role of neurotransmitters, and how knowledge of biochemistry can be used in the treatment of mental disorders. (pp. 37–41; Table 2.1)

3. Discuss the relationship between genetics and psychopathology, including the differences between genotype and phenotype, and explain how the Human Genome Project is revolutionizing our understanding of the impact that genes have on human life. (pp. 40–43)

4. List the criticisms of the biological model and describe how the diathesis-stress approach has tried to address some of these criticisms. (p. 43)

5. Describe the basic concepts of psychodynamic theory, including the components of personality structure, the concepts of psychosexual stages and defense mechanisms, and the role anxiety plays in the development of psychopathology. (pp. 43–46)

6. Briefly describe psychoanalytic therapy and how the psychoanalysis of the neo-Freudians differed from traditional Freudian psychoanalysts. (pp. 46–48; Tables 2.2 & 2.3))

7. Discuss the criticisms of the psychodynamic model. (pp. 46-47)

8. Discuss the concerns of the behavioral models of psychopathology. Describe the components of the classical conditioning model and relate those components to psychopathology. (pp. 48–50)

9. Discuss how operant conditioning can be applied to understanding psychopathology. Specify the assumptions of the operant conditioning model and compare them with classical conditioning. (pp. 50–52)

10. Describe the observational learning model and its relevance to psychopathology. Evaluate the behavioral models. (pp. 52–53)

11. Describe the assumptions of the cognitive models and how unproductive schemas, irrational and maladaptive thoughts, and distortions of thought processes contribute to psychopathology. Describe the elements of cognitive therapy. (pp. 53–54; Table 2.4)

12. Evaluate the cognitive models. (pp. 54–56)

13. Describe the contributions of the humanistic and existential approaches including the notions of the concept of the self and the actualizing tendency. Discuss the development of abnormal behavior and its treatment according to Carl Rogers. (pp. 56–58)

14. Discuss the criticisms of the humanistic and existential approaches. (pp. 58-59)

15. Identify the three distinct assumptions of the family systems approach, including the development of personality and identity within the family, the relationship between family dynamics and psychopathology, and treatment approaches. (pp. 59–60)

16. Evaluate the strengths and limitations of the family systems model. (p. 60)

17. Discuss the assumptions of the multicultural models of psychopathology, including the inferiority and deprivations/deficit models, and relate these ideas to psychopathology. Evaluate the strengths and limitations of the multicultural model. (pp. 60–64; Mental Health & Society)

18. Using Table 2.5, compare and contrast the biological, psychodynamic, humanistic/existential, behavioral, cognitive, family systems, and multicultural models of psychopathology. Discuss the utility of integrating models into an eclectic approach such as that found in the "tripartite framework." (pp. 64–69; Table 2.5)

19. Discuss the case of Steven V. from various etiological models and how each model would treat Steven V. (pp. 36-37; 65–67)

MULTIPLE–CHOICE QUESTIONS

Ans: b
Page: 35
Obj: 1
Type: F

1. Psychopathology is *best* defined as
   a. damage to the brain.
   b. the study of abnormal behavior.
   c. social rejection of deviant people.
   d. a category of criminal behavior involving antisocial acts.

Ans: d
Page: 36
Obj: 1
Type: C

2. A psychologist who uses the words *patient, mental illness,* and *cure* when discussing disorders is using the _____ model.
   a. psychodynamic
   b. psychogenic
   c. statistical
   d. medical

Ans: a
Page: 35
Obj: 1
Type: C

3. Models do all of the following *except*
   a. provide a clear and definitive explanation for phenomena.
   b. describe a theoretical approach.
   c. provide an analogy for a phenomenon.
   d. apply terms from other fields to describe a phenomenon.

Ans: c
Page: 37
Obj: 2
Type: C

4. A psychologist who believes that changes in thoughts or emotions are associated with changes in the activity or structure of the brain agrees with the _____ model of psychopathology.
   a. humanistic
   b. psychodynamic
   c. biological
   d. cognitive

Ans: b
Page: 37
Obj: 2
Type: F

5. The biological model of psychopathology emphasizes the explanatory power of
   a. family interactions.
   b. dysfunctions of the brain.
   c. irrational beliefs.
   d. behaviors learned in the environment.

Ans: d
Page: 38
Obj: 2
Type: A

6. Peter survived a stroke that damaged much of the tissue in the left hemisphere of his brain. We can expect that Peter will
    a. have trouble controlling his emotional behavior.
    b. be unable to sense touch on the left side of his body.
    c. experience impaired visual-spatial abilities.
    d. experience paralysis on the right side of his body.

Ans: c
Page: 38
Obj: 2
Type: F

7. Forebrain is to _____ as hindbrain is to _____.
    a. sleeping and dreaming; language and consciousness
    b. schizophrenia; substance abuse
    c. higher mental functions; vegetative functions like sleep
    d. sight and hearing; smell and taste

Ans: a
Page: 39
Obj: 2
Type: A

8. Dr. Bach says, "Neurons are nerve cells that have different functions. The dendrite of the neuron is a thin extension that releases neurotransmitters into the space between neurons called the synapse." Which part of Dr. Bach's statement is *incorrect*?
    a. It is incorrect to say that the dendrite is a thin extension that releases neurotransmitters.
    b. It is incorrect to say that neurons are nerve cells.
    c. It is incorrect to say that neurons have different functions.
    d. It is incorrect to say that the synapse is a space between neurons.

Ans: b
Page: 40
Obj: 2
Type: C

9. Which statement about neurotransmitters is *accurate*?
    a. Neurotransmitters are released by the dendrites into the axon.
    b. Drugs that block or facilitate neurotransmitter activity can alleviate symptoms of mental disorders.
    c. Neurotransmitters consistently have an excitatory effect on the human nervous system.
    d. Only a few neurotransmitters have been identified by scientists.

Ans: b
Page: 40
Obj: 2
Type: F

10. Dopamine is related to several mental disorders. Insufficient dopamine is a possible cause of _____, while having receptors that are oversensitive to dopamine may be related to the disorder called _____.
    a. Parkinson's disease; bipolar disorder
    b. Parkinson's disease; schizophrenia
    c. schizophrenia; Parkinson's disease
    d. schizophrenia; depression

Ans: a
Page: 40
Obj: 2
Type: A

11. Dr. Colletti is thinking about two patients: "How ironic that Mrs. A has Parkinson's disease because she has too little of it and her daughter, Joan, suffers from schizophrenia because she has too much." What is the "it" the doctor is thinking about?
    a. Dopamine
    b. Axon terminals
    c. GABA
    d. The neurotransmitter lithium

Ans: c
Page: 40
Obj: 3
Type: F

12. Autonomic nervous system reactivity in humans and "nervousness" in animals appear to be
    a. learned.
    b. psychogenic.
    c. inherited.
    d. related to dopamine activity.

Ans: d
Page: 41
Obj: 3
Type: F

13. A person's observable physical or behavioral characteristics are the
   a. same thing as their genotype.
   b. result of inheritance only.
   c. result of environmental factors only.
   d. same thing as their phenotype.

Ans: b
Page: 42
Obj: 4
Type: F

14. Which of the following is true about the current findings of the Human Genome Project, which is developing a "manual" for the basic blueprint of the entire genetic material found in each cell of the body?
   a. Scientists are now able to read and understand the human genome.
   b. Scientists have discovered the genes associated with the occurrence of certain hereditary diseases, such as Huntington's chorea, cystic fibrosis, and muscular dystrophy.
   c. Scientists have developed drugs and other interventions to cure some genetically inherited diseases.
   d. Most diseases have been found to be caused by a single gene.

Ans: a
Page: 43
Obj: 4
Type: A

15. Which statement about the biological model is *accurate*?
   a. It has helped find effective drugs for treating disorders.
   b. It has shown that the phenotypes of most disorders result from similar genotypes.
   c. It has shown that genotype and phenotype are identical for most disorders.
   d. It has proved that inheritance is the direct cause of most disorders.

Ans: c
Page: 43
Obj: 4
Type: C

16. Which of the following is an *accurate* criticism of the biological model?
   a. It deemphasizes scientific investigation.
   b. It has failed to identify specific neurotransmitters related to specific disorders.
   c. It cannot tell whether disorders cause biochemical changes or biochemical changes cause disorders.
   d. It burdens patients with the feeling that they are responsible for their disorders.

Ans: d
Page: 43
Obj: 4
Type: C

17. Faith says that she agrees with the diathesis-stress view of psychopathology that
   a. biochemical changes influence the structure of the brain to produce most disorders.
   b. the environment plays little if any role in the development of disorders.
   c. genetics are unimportant in the explanation of disorders.
   d. both genetics and environmental factors interact to cause disorders.

Ans: b
Page: 43
Obj: 4
Type: F

18. In the diathesis-stress theory, the diathesis is
   a. the amount of stressful life changes that activates a disorder.
   b. the individual's predisposition to develop illness.
   c. an individual's neurotransmitter imbalance.
   d. a faulty schema the individual uses to understand the world.

Ans: a
Page: 43
Obj: 5
Type: C

19. The two main distinguishing ideas in the psychodynamic model are
   a. childhood experiences explain adult personality; anxiety results from unconscious conflicts.
   b. the causes of disorders are largely conscious; culture determines the expression of symptoms of disorder.
   c. diathesis and stress.
   d. parents teach children abnormality; symptoms start with biology.

Ans: d
Page: 44
Obj: 5
Type: F

20. Freud's form of therapy is called
    a. cognitive therapy.
    b. regression therapy.
    c. object-relations therapy.
    d. psychoanalysis.

Ans: c
Page: 44
Obj: 5
Type: C

21. Suppose Steven V. feels an overwhelming need for sex and a complete inability to delay his desires. According to a psychoanalytic thinker, at that moment Steven's personality is dominated by the
    a. superego.
    b. reality principle.
    c. id.
    d. ego.

Ans: a
Page: 44
Obj: 5
Type: A

22. Two characters on the "Star Trek" television series, Mr. Spock and Commander Data, are completely logical. They make their decisions on the basis of realistic considerations, not emotions or moral judgment. From a psychodynamic perspective, they
    a. are all ego.
    b. are all id.
    c. are all superego.
    d. completely lack an ego.

Ans: b
Page: 44
Obj: 5
Type: A

23. Thuy is faced with a dilemma: She lives in a war-torn country in which for years the economy has been severely disrupted. In order to feed herself and her children, she steals food, but she feels a great sense of guilt when she does. According to Freud, the two personality structures involved in this dilemma are the
    a. defenses and the ego.
    b. ego and the superego.
    c. id and the superego.
    d. object-relations and the collective unconscious.

Ans: a
Page: 44
Obj: 5
Type: A

24. Jason exploits other people and never feels guilty about it. He rarely helps other people and feels no pride when he does. According to psychodynamic thinking, Jason has
    a. an underdeveloped superego.
    b. an underdeveloped ego.
    c. too much ego ideal.
    d. no id.

Ans: c
Page: 44
Obj: 5
Type: F

25. According to Freud, the two *most* important instincts in people are
    a. pleasure and reality.
    b. responsibility and irresponsibility.
    c. sex and aggression.
    d. fear and happiness.

Ans: d
Page: 45
Obj: 5
Type: A

26. Dr. Young says, "My client faced such severe traumas in her first two years of life that her emotional development was arrested in that period. The result is that although she is twenty-nine years old, she is passive and feels helpless." Dr. Young is describing the psychodynamic concept of
    a. realistic anxiety.
    b. defense mechanism.
    c. ego ideal.
    d. fixation.

Ans: a
Page: 45
Obj: 5
Type: C

27. The central concept that represents the core of Freud's theory of psychopathology is
    a. anxiety caused by unconscious conflicts.
    b. irrational thinking.
    c. imitation of faulty role models.
    d. disturbed family interactions.

Ans: b
Page: 45
Obj: 5
Type: C

28. Which of the following sources of anxiety is *correctly* matched with its psychoanalytic term?
    a. External dangers—moralistic anxiety
    b. Unethical conduct—moralistic anxiety
    c. Uncontrolled id impulses—realistic anxiety
    d. Conflict between ego ideal and one's actual behavior—realistic anxiety

Ans: b
Page: 46
Obj: 5
Type: C

29. Defense mechanisms are used to protect
    a. unconscious material from being exposed to the id.
    b. the ego from anxiety and guilt caused by unacceptable impulses.
    c. the id from being deceived by the superego.
    d. the ego from an unrealistic perception of reality.

Ans: d
Page: 47
Obj: 5
Type: A

30. Molly felt humiliated by and was angry at her boss. She had worked very hard, including some overtime hours, to prepare an important presentation. Yet this morning, in front of her co-workers, Molly's boss threw the presentation on her desk and loudly told Molly that she was incompetent. Molly did not say anything, but when she got home, she yelled at her children for not having their homework done and their rooms picked up. Molly's anger at her children illustrates the concept of
    a. projection.
    b. repression.
    c. reaction formation.
    d. displacement.

Ans: a
Page: 47
Obj: 5
Type: A

31. Vera goes to a party where she says almost nothing to anyone. She leaves the party thinking, "Everyone there was so cold and unfriendly. They are all so afraid of making new friends. They really have sick minds." Vera's defensive reaction best illustrates
    a. projection.
    b. rationalization.
    c. reaction formation.
    d. regression.

Ans: c
Page: 46
Obj: 5
Type: C

32. Defense mechanisms have all the following characteristics *except*
    a. they operate unconsciously.
    b. they protect individuals from anxiety.
    c. they are used only by neurotic people.
    d. they distort reality.

Ans: b
Page: 46
Obj: 6
Type: A

33. Jill is seeing a psychologist who shows her ambiguous pictures and inkblots to better understand her unconscious. Word association tests and hypnosis are also used. What kind of therapy is Jill probably experiencing?
    a. Multimodal therapy
    b. Psychoanalysis
    c. Cognitive therapy
    d. Person-centered therapy

Ans: a
Page: 47
Obj: 6
Type: C

34. Unlike traditional psychoanalysts, neo-Freudians tend to
    a. deemphasize sexual motivation as the cause of behavior.
    b. view all behavior as originating predominantly from conscious thought.
    c. deemphasize the importance of personal choice and future goals.
    d. feel that talking in therapy is a waste of time.

Ans: d
Page: 48
Obj: 6
Type: F

35. Erik Erikson, Carl Jung, and Alfred Adler had what in common?
    a. They supported Freud's idea of the collective unconscious.
    b. They rejected Freud's idea of unconscious motivation.
    c. They rejected the importance of human self-actualizing tendencies.
    d. They were neo-Freudians.

Ans: c
Page: 48
Obj: 6
Type: C

36. Which statement about object relations therapy is *accurate*?
    a. It rejects the importance of childhood experience as a cause of adult disorder.
    b. It is a cognitive approach used to understand family dynamics.
    c. It is a neo-Freudian idea involving exploration of past interpersonal relationships.
    d. It employs a humanistic-existential set of concepts.

Ans: c
Page: 47
Obj: 6
Type: A

37. Which client would be *most* likely to benefit from psychoanalysis?
    a. A poor person with limited verbal skills
    b. An older woman in immediate crisis
    c. A well-educated anxious man
    d. A psychotic older man

Ans: b
Page: 47
Obj: 7
Type: A

38. Dr. O'Brien says, "Psychodynamic theory has had little impact on psychology because it is based largely on observations in uncontrolled conditions. Further, the theory does not apply to women, and the therapy is ineffective with many kinds of disorders." Which part of Dr. O'Brien's statement is *incorrect*?
    a. It is incorrect to say that its therapy is ineffective with many disorders.
    b. It is incorrect to say that psychoanalysis has had little impact on psychology.
    c. It is incorrect to say that it is based on observations in uncontrolled conditions.
    d. It is incorrect to say that the theory does not apply to women.

Ans: d
Page: 47
Obj: 7
Type: C

39. Which of the following is an *accurate* statement about psychodynamic theory?
    a. Freud's conclusions about male-female differences have been supported by many research studies.
    b. The theory is quite precise in its terminology, which makes it reliable in predicting future events.
    c. It is too general and unspecific to explain very many disorders.
    d. Freud's observations about human personality are difficult to evaluate.

Ans: c
Page: 49
Obj: 8
Type: C

40. A psychologist who sees a client's problems as caused by a lack of useful, productive behaviors and lack of consequences following inappropriate actions probably supports the _____ model of psychopathology.
   a. existential
   b. psychodynamic
   c. behavioral
   d. humanistic

Ans: a
Page: 49
Obj: 8
Type: A

41. Dr. White says, "All behavior—both normal and abnormal—is learned through interaction between the person and the environment." Dr. White's statement reflects the _____ model.
   a. behavioral
   b. psychodynamic
   c. cognitive
   d. biological

Ans: b
Page: 49
Obj: 8
Type: C

42. Classical conditioning is a form of associative learning. What exactly is associated?
   a. Internal models of the world and behavior
   b. Responses to new stimuli
   c. A behavior and its consequence
   d. Unconscious motivations and internal needs

Ans: c
Page: 49
Obj: 8
Type: A

43. If a loud siren is sounded, any newborn infant will automatically scream. In classical conditioning terminology, the siren is
   a. a conditioned response.
   b. an unconditioned response.
   c. an unconditioned stimulus.
   d. a conditioned stimulus.

Ans: d
Page: 49
Obj: 8
Type: C

44. Which statement about classical conditioning is *accurate*?
   a. It was first described by Edward Thorndike.
   b. It assumes that behavior is controlled by its consequences.
   c. It involves associations between voluntary responses and genetics.
   d. It was discovered accidentally by Ivan Pavlov.

Ans: a
Page: 49
Obj: 8
Type: A

45. In his original experiments, Pavlov paired a bell tone with the presentation of food. After a while, the bell tone alone could provoke salivation. When this happened,
   a. the bell became a conditioned stimulus.
   b. the animal learned a new operant.
   c. the animal showed a neurotic pattern of behavior.
   d. the salivation became an unconditioned response.

Ans: d
Page: 49
Obj: 8
Type: F

46. Which statement about classical conditioning is *accurate*?
   a. The conditioned response is a response the organism makes automatically when in the presence of the UCS.
   b. Classical conditioning does not occur unless the associated stimuli are reinforced.
   c. A reliable pairing of the UCS and the UCR leads to learning.
   d. Classical conditioning involves involuntary responses.

Ans: c
Page: 49
Obj: 8
Type: F

47. Watson and Rayner's classic experiment with "Little Albert" was designed to explain the development of
    a. cognitive disorders.
    b. neuroses.
    c. phobias.
    d. depression.

Ans: a
Page: 49
Obj: 8
Type: C

48. Classical conditioning is limited in its usefulness because
    a. most human behavior is voluntary, not involuntary.
    b. it provides few ways to treat individuals.
    c. it is unable to explain basic psychopathologies such as phobias and depression.
    d. it is unable to explain extreme emotional reactions.

Ans: b
Page: 49
Obj: 8
Type: A

49. Erin's problem is that she talks incessantly and in a disjointed manner. This is an example of voluntary behaviors, so therapy based on _____ principles is *least* likely to be helpful.
    a. cognitive
    b. classical conditioning
    c. modeling
    d. operant conditioning

Ans: c
Page: 50
Obj: 9
Type: F

50. Unlike behaviors in classical conditioning, operant behaviors are
    a. learned by observing others.
    b. unconscious.
    c. voluntary and controllable.
    d. instinctive.

Ans: b
Page: 50
Obj: 9
Type: A

51. A psychologist says, "Most disorders involve the absence or presence of behaviors that people can control. For example, poor social skills are key factors in most interpersonal problems." This psychologist sees disorder as a problem related to
    a. inaccurate schemas.
    b. operant behaviors.
    c. unconditioned stimuli and unconditioned responses.
    d. inappropriate modeling.

Ans: d
Page: 50
Obj: 9
Type: C

52. Which quote is *most* similar to Thorndike's "law of effect"?
    a. "Emotions are a function of beliefs, not events."
    b. "Emotions are the outgrowth of passive associations we make with positive and negative stimuli in the world."
    c. "Most of our behavior is motivated by factors of which we are not conscious."
    d. "We do more of whatever behavior pays off."

Ans: a
Page: 50
Obj: 9
Type: C

53. Thorndike is to the law of effect as Skinner is to
    a. reinforcement.
    b. cognitive learning.
    c. modeling.
    d. classical conditioning.

Ans: b
Page: 50
Obj: 9
Type: A

54. Which of the following is the *best* example of operant conditioning?
    a. A man gets nauseated when he smells the same kind of food that once caused him food poisoning.
    b. A man asks for a raise because, in the past, his requests were successful.
    c. A woman has been frightened by thunderstorms all her life.
    d. A child watches a friend steal from a store, so he thinks he might steal sometime in the future.

Ans: c
Page: 50
Obj: 9
Type: F

55. In classical conditioning, behaviors are controlled by events that _____ the response, whereas in operant conditioning, they are controlled by events that _____ the response.
    a. intensify; reduce
    b. follow; precede
    c. precede; follow
    d. increase; decrease

Ans: a
Page: 50
Obj: 9
Type: C

56. According to operant conditioning, self-injurious behavior may be learned through the use of
    a. positive reinforcement.
    b. unconditioned stimuli.
    c. maladaptive schemas.
    d. modeling.

Ans: c
Page: 50
Obj: 9
Type: C

57. A kindergarten teacher wants to reduce the amount of aggressiveness children display in her class and on the playground. Using operant conditioning principles, the teacher should
    a. use negative reinforcers to decrease the behavior.
    b. pair aggressiveness with some pleasant stimulus.
    c. eliminate the reinforcement associated with aggressiveness.
    d. encourage the children to get the aggressiveness out of their systems.

Ans: c
Page: 51
Obj: 9
Type: C

58. _____ increases the frequency of a behavior because it removes or reduces an aversive (punishing) event.
    a. Positive reinforcement
    b. An unconditioned stimulus
    c. Negative reinforcement
    d. Modeling

Ans: a
Page: 51
Obj: 9
Type: A

59. When Stanley is afraid of meeting a woman, he finds an excuse to run off by himself. The immediate effect of running away is to make him feel less anxious and more at ease. Stanley's behavior illustrates
    a. the role of negative reinforcers in avoidance behavior.
    b. the fact that shaping can result in maladjusted behavior.
    c. the role of partial reinforcement in abnormal behavior.
    d. the power of positive reinforcement.

Ans: b
Page: 52
Obj: 10
Type: C

60. Unlike operant or classical conditioning, in observational learning
    a. direct reinforcement is necessary to establish behavior.
    b. new behaviors can be learned by watching others.
    c. reinforcement must precede the person's action.
    d. reinforcers are not necessary to establish or maintain behavior.

Ans: a
Page: 52
Obj: 10
Type: A

61. After viewing a television program that shows how children can call 911 to respond to an emergency, three-year-old Tina knew how to call 911 when she saw the curtains catch fire in her kitchen. The *best* explanation for how Tina learned this response is
    a. observational learning.
    b. classical conditioning.
    c. operant conditioning.
    d. id and superego functioning.

Ans: d
Page: 52
Obj: 10
Type: C

62. All of the following are strengths of the behavioral models *except*
    a. they emphasize the impact of environment on behavior.
    b. they have questioned the adequacy of the biological model.
    c. they have required strict adherence to scientific methodology.
    d. they highlight the subjective life of the individual.

Ans: c
Page: 52
Obj: 10
Type: A

63. When John was growing up, he saw his older brother severely beaten by their father after the brother was caught drinking a beer. Since then, John has never had a beer in his life. What form of learning does this *best* illustrate?
    a. Classical conditioning
    b. Instrumental learning
    c. Observational learning
    d. Operant conditioning

Ans: b
Page: 52
Obj: 10
Type: C

64. Observational learning differs from classical conditioning and operant learning in that
    a. it requires direct rewards for learning to occur.
    b. it requires neither direct rewards nor punishments for learning to occur.
    c. new behaviors are acquired at a faster rate.
    d. it requires direct punishments for learning to occur.

Ans: a
Page: 53
Obj: 11
Type: A

65. A depressed person hears this from his therapist: "Your interpretation of the events in your life bring on the depression. If you can see yourself as less of a failure and more of a success, the depression will lift." The therapist probably supports the _____ approach to abnormal behavior.
    a. cognitive
    b. operant conditioning
    c. psychodynamic
    d. family systems

Ans: c
Page: 53
Obj: 11
Type: F

66. *Mediating process, schema,* and *irrational thoughts* are all terms that are used in the _____ model of psychopathology.
    a. family systems
    b. behavioral
    c. cognitive
    d. multicultural

Ans: c
Page: 53
Obj: 11
Type: F

67. Cognitive theorists emphasize that disturbed individuals
    a. come from disturbed families.
    b. live in stressful environments.
    c. have irrational and maladaptive thoughts.
    d. are deficient in interpersonal skills.

Ans: a
Page: 53
Obj: 11
Type: F

68. Automatic thoughts and overgeneralizations are to _____ as the A-B-C theory of personality and irrational beliefs are to _____.
   a. Beck; Ellis
   b. Beck; Minuchin
   c. Ellis; Beck
   d. Satir; Ellis

Ans: b
Page: 53
Obj: 11
Type: A

69. Dr. Alcott makes the following statement about Janet's depression: "Your depression may be due to your misperception of this unfortunate situation and your tendency to blame yourself for events that are beyond your control. What we need to do is help you to recognize and modify your irrational beliefs." Dr. Alcott's comments are characteristic of the
   a. behavioral model.
   b. cognitive model.
   c. humanistic model.
   d. psychodynamic model.

Ans: d
Page: 54
Obj: 11
Type: A

70. Dr. Danvers is a firm believer in Ellis's A-B-C theory of personality. Given that, we would *never* expect Dr. Danvers to say,
   a. "People are less troubled by events in their lives, but rather by their thinking about these events."
   b. "Belief that an event is unfortunate leads to a healthier consequence than belief that an event is a catastrophe."
   c. "Our reactions are due to our beliefs, both rational ones and irrational ones."
   d. "Depression is something you are most likely born with and can never really escape."

Ans: a
Page: 56
Obj: 12
Type: A

71. Dr. Weinberg is a humanistically oriented psychotherapist. Which of the following comments about cognitive therapy is she *most* likely to make?
   a. "Therapists who attack irrational beliefs merely intimidate their clients."
   b. "Therapists who use RET are too passive; they should be more like teachers than listeners."
   c. "Cognitive therapists put too much emphasis on childhood experiences and not enough on choices one makes in life."
   d. "Thoughts are not observable, so they have no place in science."

Ans: a
Page: 56
Obj: 13
Type: C

72. These approaches developed as a reaction against the deterministic and mechanistic quality of psychoanalytic thinking. They emphasize the subjective world of the individual. What is being described?
   a. Humanistic and existential approaches
   b. Cognitive approaches
   c. Multicultural models
   d. Behavioral models

Ans: b
Page: 56
Obj: 13
Type: A

73. Dr. Abdul says to his students "There are two key things to understand about this therapeutic approach. First, the best way to understand an individual's behavior is to see the world from that person's point of view. Second, people are able to make free choices in life." To which theoretical approach is Dr. Abdul referring?
   a. psychodynamic
   b. humanistic and existential
   c. cognitive
   d. behavioral

Ans: c
Page: 56
Obj: 13
Type: F

74. The humanistic perspective is *most* associated with which pair of names?
   a. Thorndike and Skinner
   b. Ellis and Beck
   c. Maslow and Rogers
   d. Adler and Jung

Ans: a
Page: 56
Obj: 13
Type: A

75. Shelly says, "I think that everyone has an inherent tendency to strive toward their full potential. It shows in our creativity and delight in discovering new things." Shelly's thoughts illustrate
   a. Maslow's term "self-actualization."
   b. Rogers's principle "the law of effect."
   c. Freud's view of unconscious influences on our development.
   d. Ellis's concept of rational beliefs.

Ans: d
Page: 57
Obj: 13
Type: C

76. According to Rogers, behavior disorders are the result of
   a. insufficient discipline of children.
   b. a lack of direction from authority figures such as one's parents.
   c. fixation at early psychosexual stages.
   d. incongruence between self-concept and potential.

Ans: c
Page: 57
Obj: 13
Type: A

77. A mother says to her daughter, "I value you regardless of your behavior. I may disapprove of what you do, but I will still respect and love you." According to Rogers, this mother is
   a. increasing the incongruence between the child's self-concept and the child's behavior.
   b. expressing conditions of worth toward her daughter.
   c. providing unconditional positive regard.
   d. teaching the girl irrational beliefs.

Ans: c
Page: 58
Obj: 13
Type: F

78. According to Rogers, which of the following would be most important in a therapeutic relationship?
   a. well-developed counseling techniques.
   b. an ability to help guide the client.
   c. the therapist's attitude.
   d. insight into the client's problems.

Ans: a
Page: 58
Obj: 13
Type: A

79. A client says, "I am terrified to speak with strangers, but I feel so lonely I could die." The therapist says, "It sounds like you have two emotions: fear and loneliness." This therapist is using the technique of _____, usually associated with _____ theory.
   a. reflecting feelings; person-centered
   b. modeling; behavior
   c. free association; psychoanalytic
   d. confrontation; cognitive

Ans: b
Page: 58
Obj: 13
Type: C

80. Which of the following would a person-centered therapist *rarely if ever* do?
   a. Reflect the feelings of the client as they occur
   b. Tell a client how to think about a problem
   c. Develop a warm, person-to-person relationship
   d. Rely on the client's strengths and potential

Ans: d
Page: 56
Obj: 13
Type: F

81. In humanistic therapy, who is *most* responsible for change in the direction of health?
   a. The client's family
   b. The wider culture
   c. The therapist
   d. The client

Ans: a
Page: 58
Obj: 13
Type: F

82. This perspective is not really a coherent school of thought. It is more like a set of attitudes that emphasize the individual's quest for meaning and personal responsibility for choices. Which model is being described?
   a. Existential
   b. Cognitive
   c. Psychodynamic
   d. Behavioral

Ans: b
Page: 58
Obj: 13
Type: C

83. The existential and humanistic approaches differ from one another in that the existentialists emphasize
   a. the need for society to control and restrict the antisocial impulses of individuals.
   b. responsibility to society as well as personal responsibility.
   c. the importance of the therapist's interpretation of the client's difficulties in life.
   d. optimism.

Ans: d
Page: 58
Obj: 13
Type: C

84. Dr. Castillo says, "I look at psychopathology in terms of human suffering and the alienation that individuals now feel in an increasingly impersonal world. We are responsible for our actions, but responsible to others as well." Dr. Castillo's remarks *best* illustrate the _____ approach.
   a. humanistic
   b. cognitive
   c. neo-Freudian
   d. existential

Ans: c
Page: 57
Obj: 13
Type: A

85. Tuyet-Hoa says, "I tend to focus on the individual and how that person can reach his or her full potential. I am optimistic that people can fulfill themselves when they are free of society's burdening expectations." Tuyet-Hoa's ideas sound *most* like
   a. Ellis's A-B-C theory of personality.
   b. Thorndike's "law of effect."
   c. humanistic thinking.
   d. existential thinking.

Ans: c
Page: 59
Obj: 13
Type: C

86. The humanistic and existential approaches have been *most* successful at
   a. explaining the relationship between inheritance and stress.
   b. creating a coherent theory of behavior.
   c. describing the human condition.
   d. developing a scientific body of evidence for its concepts.

Ans: a
Page: 58
Obj: 14
Type: C

87. Joseph is a hardheaded scientist who puts high value on objective investigation and the clear definition of terms. The model of psychopathology he is *least* likely to value is
   a. humanistic and existential.
   b. biological.
   c. classical conditioning.
   d. cognitive.

Ans: b
Page: 59
Obj: 14
Type: C

88. Are traditional psychoanalytic therapy and humanistic psychotherapies effective in helping severely disturbed people?
   a. Only humanistic psychotherapies are effective; traditional psychoanalytic therapy is not.
   b. No, neither are designed to help these people.
   c. Yes, both are designed to help these people.
   d. Only traditional psychoanalytic therapy is effective; humanistic psychotherapies are not.

Ans: a
Page: 59
Obj: 15
Type: C

89. A therapist says, "You cannot fully understand people unless you understand their interactions and communications in their homes." This therapist probably supports the _____ model.
   a. family systems
   b. neo-Freudian
   c. behavioral
   d. cognitive

Ans: a
Page: 59
Obj: 15
Type: C

90. In contrast to psychologists with biological or medical model orientations, a psychologist with a family systems orientation would
   a. view the client's problem as a problem of the entire family.
   b. identify the source of psychopathology within the person diagnosed with a mental disorder.
   c. emphasize the importance of biochemical imbalances in the brain.
   d. reject the notion that interactions within the family produce psychopathology.

Ans: d
Page: 60
Obj: 16
Type: C

91. One limitation of the family systems approach is that
   a. id processes are overemphasized but ego and superego processes are ignored.
   b. little research has been done to test the basic elements of the model.
   c. research has failed to support the theory's central idea that family relationships contribute to the development of mental disorders.
   d. cultural differences in family structure are not considered.

Ans: d
Page: 61
Obj: 17
Type: A

92. Dr. Prince says, "European Americans will become a numerical minority in the United States in the next several decades. Multicultural models, which emphasize racial and ethnic issues but do not examine gender or religious preferences, have developed in response to demographic changes." Which portion of Dr. Prince's statement is *inaccurate*?
   a. It is incorrect to say that European Americans will become a minority.
   b. It is incorrect to say that multicultural models developed because of changes in population diversity.
   c. It is incorrect to say that multicultural models emphasize ethnic and racial issues.
   d. It is incorrect to say that multicultural models do not examine gender and religious issues.

Models of Abnormal Behavior

Ans: c
Page: 61
Obj: 17
Type: C

93. Which statement would a supporter of the multicultural model *most* likely oppose?
     a. European American concepts of mental health should be balanced with non-Western concepts.
     b. Unless we see how culture influences pathology, we will make mistakes in diagnosis and treatment.
     c. Lower academic performance by African Americans is probably due to their genetic inheritance.
     d. Everyone has a culture.

Ans: a
Page: 61
Obj: 17
Type: C

94. Before contemporary multicultural models were developed, racial differences in rates of mental disorder were explained in terms of
     a. cultural deprivation.
     b. automatic thoughts.
     c. therapists' biases in diagnosis.
     d. double binds.

Ans: b
Page: 61
Obj: 18
Type: C

95. Changes in the DSM-IV acknowledge that different populations show disorders in different ways, suggesting that the _____ model of psychopathology is growing in influence in the mental health profession.
     a. behavioral
     b. multicultural
     c. family systems
     d. psychoanalytic

Ans: c
Page: 61
Obj: 17
Type: C

96. The newest edition of the DSM has an appendix describing unique disorders. It also offers a special outline for clinicians to help them understand the impact of social background on the individual. These changes show the influence of the _____ model.
     a. cognitive
     b. observational learning
     c. multicultural
     d. family systems

Ans: a
Page: 61
Obj: 17
Type: A

97. A psychologist who supports the multicultural model would *most* likely say that
     a. some cultures value family identity as much as the individual.
     b. Western cultures value "belongingness" over individualism.
     c. European American therapists place too little importance on the problems within the person.
     d. almost all non-Western cultures value individuality over collectivity.

Ans: b
Page: 63
Obj: 17
Type: C

98. A reasonable criticism of the multicultural model is that
     a. it relies too heavily on scientific evidence for its assumptions.
     b. it lacks empirical validation of its assumptions.
     c. it is too old to explain contemporary mental health problems.
     d. it seeks to find universal explanations for mental health problems.

Ans: c
Page: 64
Obj: 18
Type: C

99. As practicing clinicians learn more about human behavior, they see that
     a. behavioral explanations are superior to the others.
     b. cultural factors are more important than biological or psychological factors.
     c. biological, psychological, and cultural factors are all important.
     d. most of the models are so different that there is little room for their integration.

Ans: d
Page: 67
Obj: 18
Type: F

100. If we take current trends as a way of predicting the future, mental health professionals appear to be moving toward
   a. refused to treat their clients from more than one theoretical viewpoint.
   b. abandoned the biological model completely.
   c. abandoned the multicultural model completely.
   d. integrating contrasting views to develop a more eclectic approach.

ESSAY QUESTIONS

1. Compare and contrast the psychodynamic model and the humanistic-existential model on the following issues: the origins of abnormal behavior, the role of conscious experience in everyday behavior, determinism, and methods of treatment.

2. Briefly describe the biological model of psychopathology. Be sure to include a discussion of brain structure and communication among brain structures and the role each may play in the development of psychological problems.

3. Imagine that a client from a non-European family comes to a psychological clinic for help. How would therapists endorsing a family systems approach see the person's problems differently than a multicultural psychologist? How might they see them similarly?

SAMPLE ANSWERS

1. Psychoanalytic thinkers see early childhood experiences as critical for all mental disorders. Traumatic experiences during the first three psychosexual stages can fixate the individual at that stage, arresting emotional development and leading to characteristic symptoms. These experiences are often out of the person's awareness, and unconscious impulses can threaten to overwhelm ego controls. Defenses against these sources of anxiety both protect the person and, if used excessively, generate psychological and physical symptoms. Humanistic thinkers also see childhood as influential. Specifically, Rogers claimed that the natural tendency to live up to one's potential (the actualizing tendency) can be thwarted when parents and others place conditions on their expression of love for the child. Incongruence between the individual's way of seeing himself or herself and actual experience is the core reason for mental disorders.

   Psychoanalysts place much greater emphasis on the unconscious than do other theorists. They see conscious experience as often being a distortion of underlying, truer feelings and impulses. Humanistic theorists believe that people are more capable of making conscious choices that are in their own best interests. They also place great importance on knowing the subjective reality of the client.

   Because early and unconscious experiences drive behavior, psychoanalysts are inclined to see current behavior as determined by history and forces out of the individual's control. Humanists disagree and claim that we have the freedom to make choices and that we also must take responsibility for those choices.

   These differences lead naturally to differences in treatment strategies. Psychoanalytic therapy seeks to make the unconscious conscious by using dream analysis, free association, and other techniques including projective tests. Humanistic therapists provide clients with unconditional positive regard—a supportive environment in which they can fully experience feelings and thoughts. Rogers's person-centered therapy is nondirective and uses reflection of feeling to help clients solve their own dilemmas.

2. According to the biological model, abnormal behavior is the result of biological or physical factors. More specifically, this model suggests that abnormal behavior may be due to problems with brain structure or functioning, neurotransmitter or hormonal problems, or inherited factors. Two major factors thought to play a role in producing abnormalities are the structure of the brain and communication between brain structures. One of the primary areas of the brain, responsible for sensory processing, motor control, and higher mental functioning, is the cerebral cortex. The cerebral cortex is comprised of four areas: the frontal lobe, which is responsible for motor responses and for higher mental functions such as thinking and planning; the temporal lobe, which is involved in language processing and memory and perception; the parietal lobe, which is important in processing information about pain, pressure, and body temperature; and the occipital lobe, which is responsible for processing visual information. In addition to the areas of the cerebral cortex, the brain can be divided into three main sections: the forebrain, the midbrain, and the hindbrain. The forebrain is comprised of the two cerebral hemispheres, the thalamus, and the hypothalamus. The thalamus is necessary for the relaying of information between other regions of the central nervous system and the cerebral cortex. The hypothalamus regulates hunger, thirst, and body temperature. The midbrain coordinates information between the forebrain and the hindbrain. The hindbrain contains the pons (which is involved in sleeping, waking, and dreaming), the medulla (which regulates the heart rate and breathing), and the reticular activating system (which is responsible for the arousal of other parts of the brain when necessary). Any type of abnormalities in these structures, due to injury, birth complications, or prenatal exposure to toxins, can result in direct physical and/or psychological problems.

    Messages are communicated from one area of the brain to another via neurotransmitters. More specifically, a message in the form of an electrical impulse moves through a neuron until, when it reaches the end of the axon, it triggers the neuron to release chemicals called neurotransmitters into the synaptic cleft. These neurotransmitters are taken up by the next neuron, transformed into a new electrical impulse, and carried through that cell body. This process of neurotransmission can go awry in several ways. There may be too much or too little of the neurotransmitter substance, there may be too many or too few receptors for the amount of neurotransmitter released, there may be other neurons present that might inhibit the neural connections, and there may be problems with the interrelationships among different neurotransmitter substances. All these problems may lead to psychopathology.

3. A family systems theorist will see the individual's behavior as stemming from a family context. This person's problems will be seen as being affected by the family and, in turn, affecting other family members. The individual's behavior may be a symptom of unhealthy family dynamics. Three approaches to family therapy might be taken: communications, strategic, and structural. The communications approach to treatment would look at how the client and family convey messages. The strategic approach would emphasize power relationships among family members. The structural approach would investigate the degree to which there are over- or under-involved relationships among family members.

    The multicultural theorist would emphasize the cultural norms of the client's background. Particularly if the family is Asian, the degree of collectivity versus independence would be highlighted. It would be important to accept the legitimacy of the client's culture and examine whether discrimination by the majority culture contributes to the individual's distress.

    Both models would focus more on the individual's larger context (family or society) than would other models. The problems of the individual would be reevaluated as problems that occur in larger groups.

CHAPTER 3
Assessment and Classification of Abnormal Behavior

LEARNING OBJECTIVES

1. Define the term *psychodiagnosis* and describe its functions. (p. 73)

2. Identify the characteristics of good tests, including reliability and validity. Define *reliability*, and differentiate among test-retest, internal, and interrater reliability. Define *validity*, and differentiate among predictive, criterion-related, construct, and content validity. (pp. 73–74)

3. Define *assessment* and discuss its role in clinical psychology. Describe and discuss various psychological assessment techniques and their strengths and limitations, including observation of behavior, clinical interviews, and tests and inventories. (pp. 74–87; Table 3.1)

4. Describe the nature and purposes of projective personality tests, including the Rorschach, Thematic Apperception Test (TAT), sentence-completion test, and draw-a-person test. Discuss the strengths and weaknesses of projective tests. (pp. 77–80)

5. Describe the nature and purposes of self-report inventories, including the Minnesota Multiphasic Personality Inventory (MMPI-2). Discuss the strengths and weaknesses of personality inventories. (pp. 80–82; Figure 3.1)

6. Describe the purposes and characteristics of the Wechsler and Stanford-Binet intelligence tests and the Kaufman Assessment Battery for Children (K-ABC). Discuss the strengths and limitations of these tests. (pp. 82-85)

7. Describe methods for assessing cognitive impairments due to brain damage (*organicity*), including the WAIS-III, Bender-Gestalt Visual-Motor Test, Halstead-Reitan Neuropsychological Test Battery, and Luria-Nebraska Neuropsychological Battery. (pp. 85-86)

8. Describe neurological procedures for detecting brain damage, including CAT and PET scans, EEGs, MRIs, and functional MRIs. (pp. 86–87)

9. Discuss ethical issues involved in assessment, particularly how cultural differences may influence clinical judgments. (pp. 87–89; Critical Thinking)

10. Explain the goals of classifying abnormal behaviors and review the history of classification systems. Discuss how validity problems have been raised and dealt with. (pp. 90-91)

11. Describe the characteristics of the DSM-IV-TR, including its five axes, the broad categories of mental disorders, and how the DSM-IV-TR places diagnosis in a cultural context. (pp. 91–9; Mental Health and Society)

12. Discuss the objections to the DSM classification system and the arguments supporting its use. (pp. 94–98)

13. Describe four problems associated with classification and labeling and the research related to these problems. Discuss how the findings of Rosenhan (1973) relate to the impact of labeling. (pp. 98–100; Mental Health and Society)

MULTIPLE–CHOICE QUESTIONS

Ans: a
Page: 73
Obj: 1
Type: A

1. A clinician has collected data about a client based on observations, interview material, and psychological test results. As a first step in the treatment process, the clinician evaluates this information and formulates a(n)
   a. psychodiagnosis.
   b. classification system.
   c. model.
   d. assessment instrument.

Ans: b
Page: 73
Obj: 1
Type: F

2. Condensing an individual's behavior patterns into a psychodiagnosis has four functions. Which of the following is *not* one of them?
   a. It facilitates communication among mental health professionals.
   b. It encourages the therapist to consider the causes of abnormal behavior from multiple perspectives.
   c. It clarifies the therapist's understanding of the client's situation.
   d. It suggests for the therapist possible treatment programs.

Ans: c
Page: 73
Obj: 1
Type: A

3. Dr. Norton says, "Classification facilitates communication between clinicians and assists the development of abnormal psychology as a science. Its benefits include guiding the clinician toward certain treatments and helping organize data about a client." What is *incorrect* about Dr. Norton's statement?
   a. That classification helps organize data about a client
   b. There is nothing incorrect in Dr. Norton's statement.
   c. That classification assists the development of science
   d. That classification guides the clinician toward certain treatments

Ans: a
Page: 73
Obj: 2
Type: C

4. A psychologist gives the same test to a client twice. The testings are separated by six days. If the test results are quite dissimilar, we could say that the test has weak
   a. test-retest reliability.
   b. interrater reliability.
   c. internal consistency.
   d. predictive validity.

Ans: d
Page: 74
Obj: 2
Type: C

5. Which term is defined as a test's ability to foretell some criterion in the future?
   a. Internal consistency
   b. Test-retest reliability
   c. Construct validity
   d. Predictive validity

Ans: b
Page: 74
Obj: 2
Type: C

6. Dr. Frederick is developing a new test for eating disorders. She finds that people who score high on a test actually engage in more binge eating and other forms of abnormal eating behaviors than people who score low on the test. These results indicate that the test
   a. has good construct validity.
   b. has good criterion-related validity.
   c. has high test-retest reliability.
   d. has good internal consistency.

Ans: d
Page: 74
Obj: 2
Type: C

7. All the following assessment procedures illustrate an aspect of validity *except*
    a. a test that measures depression and appears to have items that cover all the different symptoms of depression.
    b. a test that measures counselor aptitude that, when given to prospective counselors, accurately predicts those who will and those who will not perform well in a counseling vocation.
    c. a test that measures attention-deficit hyperactivity disorder and accurately identifies children who currently have difficulty in the classroom.
    d. a test that measures disordered eating behaviors and attitudes that yields similar scores when completed two weeks apart.

Ans: c
Page: 74
Obj: 2
Type: C

8. A psychologist wants to assess the construct validity of a new test. Which of the following illustrates the concept?
    a. Show that scores at Time 1 predict behavior at Time 2.
    b. Show that all portions of the test produce similar results.
    c. Show that the test results for a group correlate with related measures of a phenomenon.
    d. Show that scores on the test are consistent over time.

Ans: a
Page: 74
Obj: 3
Type: F

9. What is the *best* description of assessment?
    a. Making conclusions based on comprehensive information
    b. Beginning treatment in order to judge the client's prognosis
    c. Making a diagnosis using the DSM-IV-TR
    d. Interviewing, but not using psychological tests

Ans: c
Page: 74
Obj: 3
Type: A

10. Dr. Peterson has collected clinical observations, neurological test data, psychological test scores, and interview material on Mrs. Davis. If Dr. Peterson is doing this for the purpose of drawing conclusions that will lead to a diagnosis of Mrs. Davis, we can infer that Dr. Peterson is
    a. a psychoanalyst.
    b. using reliable and valid measures.
    c. doing an assessment.
    d. using the DSM-IV-TR.

Ans: d
Page: 74
Obj: 3
Type: C

11. An important goal of the assessment process is to
    a. use the information purely for research purposes.
    b. label the individual with a mental illness diagnosis.
    c. give advice to the individual about how to treat their problem.
    d. develop a diagnosis.

Ans: b
Page: 74
Obj: 3
Type: F

12. Psychological assessment includes gathering information on all but one of the following issues. Which one is usually *excluded*?
    a. Emotional functioning
    b. Brain chemistry
    c. Traits
    d. Skills

Ans: a
Page: 75
Obj: 3
Type: C

13. A psychologist notices that a male client rarely makes eye contact and pulls at his ear when he seems nervous. What type of assessment is the psychologist doing?
    a. Observation
    b. Projective testing
    c. Structured interviewing
    d. Controlled testing

Ans: d
Page: 75
Obj: 3
Type: C

14. Naturalistic observations are
    a. typically conducted in controlled environments.
    b. primarily conducted in clinics or laboratories.
    c. usually done by research psychologists.
    d. more characteristic of a clinician's work than a researcher's.

Ans: c
Page: 75-76
Obj: 3
Type: A

15. A psychologist notes that a female client is wearing a heavy wool sweater and cap on a hot summer day. The client walks with a limp and mumbles to herself. The psychologist
    a. should interpret these objective signs without regard to the individual's culture.
    b. should conduct testing or interviewing and disregard the information about the client's appearance.
    c. should assess the diagnostic significance of these observations with interview and test information.
    d. should disregard these observations in order to make an unbiased assessment.

Ans: b
Page: 75
Obj: 3
Type: A

16. Dr. Heyer is a behavioral therapist working with a ten-year-old boy named Lee. The boy's parents and school teachers complain that Lee is disobedient and unruly. What assessment method should Dr. Heyer use to *most accurately* assess the degree to which Lee is excessively active and disobedient?
    a. Personality testing
    b. Observation
    c. Interview method
    d. Questionnaire

Ans: c
Page: 76
Obj: 3
Type: F

17. Reactivity is primarily a difficulty associated with
    a. psychological testing.
    b. using the DSM-IV-TR.
    c. observation.
    d. neuropsychological assessments.

Ans: d
Page: 76
Obj: 3
Type: A

18. Keisha giggles and laughs in an interview with the psychologist because she does not want to be seen as the depressed and anxious person she is inside. This illustrates the problem of
    a. low interrater reliability.
    b. self-fulfilling prophesies after diagnosis.
    c. weak psychometrics.
    d. reactivity in observation.

Ans: c
Page: 76
Obj: 3
Type: F

19. In what way is interviewing superior to observation alone?
    a. In interviewing, assessors can notice the client's facial expressions, body posture, and dress.
    b. In interviewing, the style or training of the assessor has little impact on the data collected.
    c. In interviewing, assessors can collect data on the client's life history and personality.
    d. In interviewing, assessors can see the client face to face.

Ans: a
Page: 76-77
Obj: 3
Type: A

20. Dr. Chiu is a psychiatrist; Mr. Vega is a social worker. We can imagine that because of their differences in training, they will differ in what they emphasize in interviews. Dr. Chiu will probably focus on _____, while Mr. Vega will focus on _____.
    a. biological problems; the socioeconomic environment
    b. unconscious impulses; psychometrics
    c. past concerns; future plans
    d. biological problems; psychometrics

Ans: b
Page: 76
Obj: 3
Type: C

21. When Tyrone sees a new client, he conducts highly unstructured interviews hoping to learn about underlying psychological processes and the dreams the client has. We can guess that Tyrone endorses the _____ perspective.
    a. cognitive
    b. psychodynamic
    c. biological
    d. behavioral

Ans: d
Page: 76-77
Obj: 3
Type: F

22. What aspect of interviewing *increases* the consistency of assessment information?
    a. Doing the interview in a naturalistic setting
    b. Using projective techniques
    c. Increasing the reactivity of the person being interviewed
    d. Increasing the structure of the interview

Ans: c
Page: 77
Obj: 3
Type: F

23. According to Kleinmuntz, which of the following is a source of error in interviewing?
    a. A psychoanalytic approach
    b. High structure
    c. Anxiety in the interviewee
    d. The cultural similarity of the interviewer and interviewee

Ans: a
Page: 77
Obj: 3
Type: F

24. Standardized instruments that assess personality, social skills, and intellectual abilities (among other things) are called
    a. psychological tests and inventories.
    b. neuropsychological assessments.
    c. mental status examinations.
    d. structured interviews.

Ans: b
Page: 77
Obj: 4
Type: C

25. Most personality tests share two characteristics: They _____, and they _____.
    a. have high reliability; are highly structured
    b. provide a standard situation for collecting data; use norms to make inferences about the individual
    c. are low in structure; focus on unconscious conflicts within the interviewee
    d. can be done in controlled or naturalistic settings; are unaffected by the perspective of the person doing the testing

Ans: a
Page: 77
Obj: 3
Type: F

26. Dr. Rose, a clinical psychologist, is administering a batter of psychological tests to a client to gain insight into the client's current issues. If Dr. Rose is using the most popular measures, in addition to an intellectual achievement, she would also be using:
    a. an evaluation of personality-psychopathology.
    b. a neuropsychological assessment.
    c. an adaptive-functional behavior assessment.
    d. a mental status examination.

Ans: b
Page: 77
Obj: 4
Type: A

27. Nicole is asked to sculpt anything she would like out of modeling clay and then tell a story about her creation. If this is a psychological test, it is a _____ test.
    a. self-report inventory
    b. projective personality
    c. cognitive impairment
    d. standardized

Ans: c
Page: 77
Obj: 4
Type: F

28. Tests that use ambiguous stimuli in order to reveal a multifaceted view of the person's functioning are called
    a. self-report inventories.
    b. physiological tests.
    c. projective personality tests.
    d. tests of cognitive impairment.

Ans: a
Page: 77
Obj: 4
Type: F

29. Psychoanalysts are interested in unconscious needs and motives. Therefore, they are *most* likely to use _____ in assessing clients.
    a. projective personality tests
    b. self-report inventories
    c. highly structured interviews
    d. tests for cognitive impairment

Ans: c
Page: 78
Obj: 4
Type: F

30. In the _____, inner motives and conflicts are revealed by what is seen in inkblots and whether color plays a role in these responses.
    a. Minnesota Multiphasic Personality Inventory-2 (MMPI-2)
    b. structured diagnostic interview (SDI)
    c. Rorschach technique
    d. Thematic Apperception Test (TAT)

Ans: d
Page: 78
Obj: 4
Type: A

31. Dr. West is scoring an individual's responses to a projective personality test on the basis of Exner's research-based system. Included in the scoring is whether the test-taker's responses included color and perceived movement. The test Dr. West is scoring is called the
    a. WAIS-R.
    b. TAT.
    c. MMPI-2.
    d. Rorschach test.

Ans: b
Page: 78
Obj: 4
Type: F

32. The Rorschach inkblot technique is associated with the _____ perspective on abnormal behavior.
    a. family systems
    b. psychodynamic
    c. biogenic
    d. behavioral

Ans: c
Page: 79
Obj: 4
Type: F

33. The TAT is considered a projective personality test because it
    a. asks test-takers to respond to inkblots.
    b. presents incomplete sentences that test-takers finish.
    c. presents pictures of people in ambiguous situations.
    d. relies on direct questions about specific situations.

Ans: a
Page: 79
Obj: 4
Type: A

34. A psychologist says, "I'm going to show you some pictures. Please make up a story about what is going on in each picture, what led up to it, and how it will turn out in the end." What test is the psychologist administering?
    a. TAT
    b. Rorschach test
    c. WAIS-R
    d. MMPI-2

Ans: d
Page: 79
Obj: 4
Type: F

35. Which statement about the Draw-a-Person test is *accurate*?
    a. Its purpose is to assess the individual's artistic skill.
    b. It is considered a self-report inventory.
    c. Research shows that it has very strong validity.
    d. The size, position, and details of drawings are analyzed.

Ans: c
Page: 79
Obj: 4
Type: C

36. Generally speaking, the reliability of projective tests is
    a. unknown; it has never been subjected to research study.
    b. quite strong.
    c. rather weak.
    d. better than that of structured interviews.

Ans: b
Page: 80
Obj: 5
Type: A

37. Rose is being given a self-report inventory to assess her general personality traits. What kinds of questions or tasks is she likely to be given?
    a. She will be asked to draw pictures of herself and the rest of her family members.
    b. She will be asked to agree or disagree with statements such as "I am attractive" and "I sometimes feel shy."
    c. She will be shown pictures of people and asked to write a story describing them and the situations they face.
    d. She will be asked to answer arithmetic, vocabulary, and general knowledge questions.

Ans: a
Page: 80
Obj: 5
Type: C

38. These tests require test-takers to answer specific written questions. They are scored in a predetermined way, and scores are readily compared with those from a standardization sample. What kind of tests are being described?
    a. Self-report inventories
    b. Psychodiagnostic tests
    c. Neuropsychological tests
    d. Projective personality tests

Ans: b
Page: 80
Obj: 5
Type: F

39. Which of the following occurred in the revision of the MMPI into the MMPI-2?
    a. It removed the validity scales that tried to detect faking.
    b. It refined wording and eliminated outdated items.
    c. It was changed from an objective test into a projective test.
    d. It included new scales to measure intelligence and creativity.

Ans: c
Page: 80
Obj: 5
Type: F

40. Which personality test includes ten clinical scales as well as three validity scales to check for faking or defensiveness in the test-taker?
    a. Beck Depression Inventory
    b. WAIS-R
    c. MMPI-2
    d. TAT

Ans: d
Page: 80
Obj: 5
Type: C

41. In utilizing MMPI scores, trained and experienced clinicians usually focus on the
    a. content scores.
    b. DSM diagnosis derived from the individual's responses.
    c. validity scores.
    d. pattern of scores from an entire profile.

Ans: d
Page: 80
Obj: 5
Type: A

42. A psychologist says, "The fixed alternatives for answers prevent test-takers from presenting a true picture of themselves." What kind of assessment tool is being criticized?
    a. Unstructured interviews
    b. Projective personality tests
    c. Naturalistic observation
    d. Personality inventories

Ans: a
Page: 80
Obj: 5
Type: A

43. A critic of personality inventories says, "These tests have no way of detecting faking or defensiveness in the individuals who take them. Worse, they never include norms for responses of people from different cultural groups." Which response to these criticisms is *accurate*?
    a. The MMPI-2 has both of the features the critic says are absent.
    b. The critic is correct about the problem of faking but not about norms from different cultures.
    c. The critic is confusing the problems of projective tests with those of inventories.
    d. Current research supports what the critic is saying.

Ans: c
Page: 80
Obj: 5
Type: A

44. The administrator of a mental health center wants to increase test reliability and cut the costs of assessing clients. Which change would lead to reduced costs?
    a. Use batteries of psychological tests instead of single tests.
    b. Use interviewing only.
    c. Use personality inventories instead of projective tests.
    d. Use neuropsychological and projective tests only.

Ans: d
Page: 82
Obj: 6
Type: F

45. The intelligence test that yields both a performance and a verbal IQ and is used predominantly with adults is the
    a. WISC-III.
    b. MMPI-2.
    c. Stanford-Binet test.
    d. WAIS-R.

Ans: a
Page: 82
Obj: 6
Type: F

46. Which statement about intelligence tests is *accurate*?
    a. Scores on these tests correlate with brain wave patterns.
    b. Scores on these tests accurately predict future success in life.
    c. They are based on psychodynamic concepts including unconscious motivation and defense against anxiety.
    d. It is clear that they measure innate, rather than learned, intelligence.

Ans: a
Page: 82
Obj: 6
Type: F

47. What is known about the relationship between IQ scores and physiological measures of brain function?
    a. IQ scores are correlated with the rate of glucose metabolism in the brain.
    b. Brain wave patterns and IQ scores are unrelated.
    c. There is negative correlation between IQ scores and brain wave patterns.
    d. Both measures are too unreliable to be used in research.

Ans: c
Page: 84
Obj: 6
Type: A

48. Teachers in a school are interested in finding a psychological test that predicts future achievement and identifies individuals with strong social competence. Which statement *best* reflects what is known about the existence of such a test?
    a. Few psychologists believe that there is a test that can do either of the things the teachers want.
    b. Projective tests do a good job of predicting achievement; IQ tests predict social competence.
    c. There is debate about whether IQ tests can predict achievement, but many psychologists agree they are poor at identifying social competence.
    d. There is debate about whether IQ tests can predict achievement, but most psychologists agree they can measure social competence.

Ans: b
Page: 84
Obj: 6
Type: A

49. Dr. Colina is a Mexican-American psychologist who attacks intelligence tests for being culturally biased against minorities, being excessively reliable, and producing self-fulfilling prophecies. What is *unusual* or *inaccurate* about Dr. Colina's objections?
    a. Minority psychologists do not claim the tests are biased.
    b. Tests cannot be criticized for being excessively reliable.
    c. Few psychologists would suggest that labels lead to self-fulfilling prophecies.
    d. Tests do not lead to self-fulfilling prophecies.

Ans: d
Page: 84
Obj: 6
Type: F

50. Although IQ tests are controversial, one thing is clear:
    a. Test scores accurately predict the future achievements of people from a wide range of cultures.
    b. IQ tests have poor reliability because they are not scored in a standardized way.
    c. IQ tests measure innate, rather than learned, intelligence.
    d. Test scores have been used in discriminatory ways.

Ans: c
Page: 84
Obj: 6
Type: F

51. The K-ABC and the System of Multicultural Pluralistic Assessment (SOMPA) are alike in that they
    a. assess innate intelligence rather than social intelligence.
    b. are self-report personality inventories.
    c. are less culturally dependent intelligence tests than the WISC-R.
    d. do not require the test-taker to solve problems.

Ans: b
Page: 84-85
Obj: 6
Type: A

52. Pablo has a serious speech impairment and is of Hispanic heritage. To test him for intelligence, a psychologist would best use the
    a. Bender-Gestalt Visual-Motor Test.
    b. K-ABC.
    c. Stanford-Binet test.
    d. WISC-R.

Ans: a
Page: 85
Obj: 7
Type: C

53. A clinical psychologist in a hospital is given this note: "Please assess Mr. Rollens for organicity." This note means that
    a. Mr. Rollens is presumed to have brain damage.
    b. the psychologist should use the Rorschach test in assessing Mr. Rollens.
    c. Mr. Rollens is overly worried that his internal organs are deteriorating.
    d. the psychologist should use a structured interview.

Ans: b
Page: 80
Obj: 7
Type: F

54. All of the following tests can be used to assess brain damage *except*
    a. Bender-Gestalt.
    b. MMPI-2.
    c. PET scan.
    d. Luria-Nebraska.

Ans: b
Page: 82
Obj: 7
Type: C

55. A psychologist is interested in assessing a person for organic brain disorder and looking at how the person approaches intellectual tasks. A good test to use for these purposes is
    a. a projective test.
    b. an intelligence test.
    c. the MMPI-2.
    d. the electroencephalograph (EEG).

Ans: c
Page: 85
Obj: 7
Type: A

56. Jack is being tested for suspected brain damage by being shown designs made up of lines and dots. He is asked to copy the designs on a blank sheet of paper. Jack is taking which test?
    a. Luria-Nebraska Neuropsychological Battery
    b. MMPI-2
    c. Bender-Gestalt Visual-Motor Test
    d. WAIS-R

Ans: b
Page: 85-86
Obj: 7
Type: A

57. Oscar is suspected of having brain damage. He is given more than ten psychological tests to assess memory, abstract concept formation, auditory perception, and attention. The whole testing process takes more than six hours. It is likely that Oscar was given the
    a. Luria-Nebraska Neuropsychological Battery.
    b. Halstead-Reitan Neuropsychological Test Battery.
    c. positron emission tomography (PET) test.
    d. MMPI-2.

Ans: d
Page: 85-86
Obj: 7
Type: F

58. Which statement about the Halstead-Reitan and the Luria-Nebraska neuropsychological batteries is *accurate*?
    a. Both tests are based on psychodynamic concepts.
    b. Both tests require individuals to have CAT and PET scans taken.
    c. The Halstead-Reitan is a much shorter version of the Luria-Nebraska.
    d. Separate versions of the tests assess brain damage in children and adults.

Ans: a
Page: 85-86
Obj: 7
Type: A

59. Dr. Frances says, "With the Luria-Nebraska Neuropsychological Battery, we can accurately pinpoint damaged areas of the brain just by using psychological tests. A version of the battery can be used with children. On top of that, the testing takes only two and one-half hours, much less time than the Halstead-Reitan battery." What portion of Dr. Frances's statement is *inaccurate*?
    a. No portion of the statement is inaccurate.
    b. It is inaccurate to say that the Luria-Nebraska can accurately pinpoint brain damage.
    c. It is inaccurate to say that there is a version for children.
    d. It is inaccurate to say that the testing takes only two and one-half hours.

Ans: c
Page: 87
Obj: 8
Type: C

60. Unlike the Halstead-Reitan and the Luria-Nebraska tests, EEGs and MRIs are
    a. self-report inventories.
    b. used to assess organic brain damage.
    c. neurological medical procedures.
    d. given in batteries of tests.

Ans: b
Page: 86
Obj: 8
Type: A

61. Dr. Cohen says to her patient, "We believe there may be problems with the way your brain functions. We're going to do a test that uses a radioactive substance that we can trace as it's metabolized in your brain." What procedure is Dr. Cohen describing?
    a. Luria-Nebraska Neurophysiological Battery
    b. PET scan
    c. EEG
    d. CAT scan

Ans: a
Page: 87
Obj: 8
Type: A

62. A psychologist says, "The pictures that come from the testing are amazing—clear and detailed depictions of brain structures. Not only that, they do not require giving radioactive substances to patients." The psychologist is talking about
    a. an MRI.
    b. an electroencephalograph.
    c. a PET scan.
    d. a Halstead-Reitan Neuropsychological Test Battery.

Ans: d
Page: 87
Obj: 9
Type: F

63. Which of the following is *not* a common criticism of psychological testing?
    a. Tests may be inaccurate and lead to serious misdiagnosis.
    b. Testing can be an invasion of privacy.
    c. Test results can be used in ways that hurt the client.
    d. Test results rarely differ between ethnic groups.

Ans: a
Page: 88
Obj: 9
Type: A

64. A company that wants to market computer assessment would *best* advertise its product as a substitute for
    a. clinical interviewing.
    b. naturalistic observation.
    c. projective personality testing.
    d. PET and CAT scan testing.

Ans: b
Page: 88
Obj: 9
Type: C

65. Computer assessment has all the following advantages over face-to-face assessment *except* it
    a. provides superior standardization of scoring.
    b. allows for individual differences in the wording of questions.
    c. may increase client motivation and attention.
    d. is less expensive.

Ans: a
Page: 88
Obj: 9
Type: C

66. Which of the following is a reason for caution about computerized assessment?
    a. The validity of computerized assessments is still unknown.
    b. There is little consistency between computer assessments and those made by trained professionals.
    c. Research shows that clients will avoid using computers.
    d. Computers cannot be programmed to use standardized ways of asking or recording responses.

Ans: c
Page: 88-89
Obj: 9
Type: A

67. Mr. Chen is a Chinese American who is separately interviewed by Dr. Taylor, a European American therapist, and Dr. Wong, a Chinese American therapist. Based on research by Li-Repac (1980) that compared the clinical judgments of Chinese American and European American therapists, we could predict that
    a. Mr. Chen will be seen as more ambitious, honest, and friendly by Dr. Taylor than by Dr. Wong.
    b. Mr. Chen will reveal more about himself to Dr. Taylor than he will to Dr. Wong.
    c. Mr. Chen will be seen as more depressed and inhibited by Dr. Taylor than by Dr. Wong.
    d. both therapists will agree in their clinical judgments, as long as they use valid psychological measures.

Ans: c
Page: 90
Obj: 10
Type: F

68. The goal of _____ is to provide distinct categories for different patterns of behavior.
    a. assessment
    b. neuropsychological testing
    c. a classification system
    d. psychometrics

Ans: b
Page: 90
Obj: 10
Type: F

69. Early studies of the DSM found that
    a. reliability was strong but validity was weak.
    b. there was low interrater reliability.
    c. few clinicians were willing to see disorders as biologically based.
    d. reliability was worst for the general categories of disorders.

Ans: d
Page: 90
Obj: 10
Type: A

70. Dr. Cooper says, "What abnormal psychology needs is a system of categories for different patterns of behavior that can be agreed on by all professionals." Dr. Cooper is asking for
    a. a valid method of assessment.
    b. a more reliable battery of psychological tests.
    c. ethical use of assessment.
    d. a reliable classification system.

Ans: c
Page: 90
Obj: 10
Type: C

71. Dr. Erving, a strict behaviorist, says of the traditional classification systems, "I like both Kraepelin's system and the DSM because they rely on the medical model, which is based on behavioral principles." What is unusual about what Dr. Erving says?
    a. Kraepelin's classification system is very recent.
    b. The DSM is strongly opposed to a medical model.
    c. Behaviorists oppose the medical model.
    d. Behaviorists like the DSM but object to Kraepelin's system.

Ans: a
Page: 90
Obj: 10
Type: F

72. Much of the unreliability of the original version of the DSM was due to
   a. the diagnostic categories used.
   b. a lack of professional training among the psychiatrists who used it.
   c. the different theoretical perspectives that psychologists maintain.
   d. the fact that the DSM had strict guidelines for the behavioral criteria that were to be used in making a diagnosis.

Ans: c
Page: 90
Obj: 10
Type: C

73. Etiology is to _____ as prognosis is to _____.
   a. objective; subjective
   b. future behavior; past behavior
   c. cause; future behavior
   d. assessment; classification

Ans: d
Page: 91
Obj: 11
Type: F

74. Which of the following is *not* included in the DSM-IV-TR?
   a. Disorders that do not fully meet DSM-IV-TR criteria for a particular disorder may be identified as "not otherwise specified."
   b. Following a diagnosed disorder, clinicians may select specifiers that indicate the severity of a disorder, or its remission status.
   c. Information about an individual's psychosocial functioning during the past year is typically indicated in a DSM-IV-TR diagnosis.
   d. Etiology of the disorder is specified for almost all disorders in the DSM-IV-TR.

Ans: b
Page: 91
Obj: 11
Type: A

75. Which statement below about DSM-IV-TR is *accurate*?
   a. It assumes that mental disorders have a biological cause and are best treated with medication.
   b. It relies on no theory and lists the criteria to be used before making a diagnosis.
   c. It has discarded the use of exact behavioral criteria for making a diagnosis.
   d. It has gone from having no theoretical slant to one that is highly psychoanalytic.

Ans: b
Page: 91
Obj: 11
Type: A

76. A psychologist says, "It recommends that individuals be evaluated on five dimensions. Its reliability is currently being studied by having thousands of clinicians make diagnoses based on videotaped clients." What is the psychologist talking about?
   a. MMPI-2
   b. DSM-IV-TR
   c. Composite International Diagnostic Interview
   d. Axis I

Ans: d
Page: 91
Obj: 11
Type: C

77. In the DSM-IV-TR, Axis I is used to indicate
   a. underlying personality disorders.
   b. the individual's level of functioning.
   c. the stresses the individual has experienced recently.
   d. the chief clinical syndrome.

Ans: d
Page: 91
Obj: 11
Type: C

78. Wanda's psychotherapist thinks she has a personality disorder as well as a mental disorder. Using the DSM-IV-TR, the psychotherapist should
   a. indicate the mental disorder but not the personality disorder.
   b. indicate the personality disorder but not the mental disorder.
   c. list the mental disorder on Axis I and consider the personality disorder as a stressor (Axis III).
   d. list the mental disorder on Axis I and the personality disorder on Axis II.

Ans: b
Page: 91
Obj: 11
Type: A

79. Tonya is extremely anxious, partly because she was recently diagnosed as having a potentially life-threatening heart defect. She was raised in many foster homes and was extremely paranoid as a child. Which information about Tonya is correctly paired with the relevant DSM-IV-TR dimension?
    a. Axis V—raised in foster homes
    b. Axis I—anxiety disorder
    c. Axis II—heart defect
    d. Axis III—paranoid personality

Ans: c
Page: 91
Obj: 11
Type: A

80. Ted is a 65-year-old man who has recently gone through many stressful experiences. Would his recent level of stress be included in a DSM-IV-TR diagnosis?
    a. No, the DSM-IV-TR includes only childhood stress.
    b. Perhaps, if it led to an illness.
    c. Yes, the DSM-IV-TR rates life stress on Axis IV.
    d. No, the DSM-IV-TR does not rate life stress.

Ans: d
Page: 92
Obj: 11
Type: A

81. Harold is addicted to cocaine and nicotine. His wife, Janet, often fakes having physical or psychological symptoms so that she can get attention from others. According to the DSM-IV-TR,
    a. Janet has schizophrenia.
    b. Harold has a personality disorder.
    c. neither Harold nor Janet has a mental disorder.
    d. Harold has a substance-related disorder.

Ans: a
Page: 94
Obj: 11
Type: F

82. A client who has some of the symptoms of depression but not all that are required by the DSM-IV-TR to qualify for the disorder "depression" is considered
    a. to be suffering from "depression, not otherwise specified."
    b. a person without a mental disorder.
    c. a malingerer.
    d. to be suffering from the disorder "mild depression."

Ans: c
Page: 94
Obj: 11
Type: A

83. At the completion of a diagnostic evaluation, Angel was told that she had two different disorders: major depression and alcohol dependence. In this example, major depression and alcohol dependence disorder are said to be
    a. mixed disorders.
    b. reified.
    c. comorbid.
    d. collateral.

Ans: a
Page: 94
Obj: 11
Type: C

84. The DSM-IV-TR is different from the DSM-III-R in that it
    a. provides a description of relevant cultural features for each disorder.
    b. relies far less on behavioral criteria for determining diagnoses.
    c. eliminated about one-half of the categories for disorders.
    d. increased to five the number of dimensions that are rated.

Ans: b
Page: 94
Obj: 11
Type: C

85. Which statement about the DSM-IV-TR is *accurate*?
    a. It has dramatically reduced the number of general categories of disorder.
    b. It indicates cultural variations in symptoms and describes disorders unique to a particular cultural group.
    c. It assumes that each disorder has its own set of neurobiological causes or pattern of neurotransmitter imbalances.
    d. It interprets each disorder's symptoms in terms of psychoanalytic or family systems concepts.

Ans: c
Page: 94
Obj: 11
Type: F

86. Because the DSM-IV-TR is based on research findings, we can expect
    a. it to yield unbiased diagnoses.
    b. a decrease in validity.
    c. an increase in reliability.
    d. a decrease in its usefulness.

Ans: b
Page: 95
Obj: 11
Type: F

87. A survey of psychologists asked them how they felt about the DSM system. Results indicated that the majority
    a. rejected the DSM because it does not emphasize a medical model enough.
    b. rejected the DSM's view that mental disorders are a subset of medical disorders.
    c. believed that the DSM's reliance on behavioral criteria was unnecessary.
    d. preferred the DSM because it supports the medical model of disorders.

Ans: d
Page: 95
Obj: 12
Type: F

88. Which of the following is a criticism of the DSM-IV-TR made by most psychologists?
    a. It has eliminated the five-axis concept in favor of a single diagnostic label.
    b. It fails to acknowledge the possibility of medical causes for disorders.
    c. It assumes that stimulus control is a major component in mental disorders.
    d. It overemphasizes the medical approach.

Ans: a
Page: 97
Obj: 12
Type: A

89. Vera has this cyclical pattern of symptoms: A week before her period, she is persistently angry and anxious, has body aches, and has marked interpersonal conflicts that interfere with work and social relationships. According to the DSM-IV-TR, Vera has
    a. the proposed condition "premenstrual dysphoric disorder."
    b. "adjustment disorder."
    c. a gynecological disorder called "raging hormones."
    d. no mental disorder at all.

Ans: c
Page: 97
Obj: 12
Type: A

90. Dr. Reynolds is a strong feminist. What is her opinion of the proposed condition "premenstrual dysphoric disorder" likely to be?
    a. She would argue that it helps reduce the stigma of being a woman with a mental disorder.
    b. She will favor its inclusion in future editions of the DSM.
    c. She would prefer that it be seen as a physiological condition, not a mental disorder.
    d. She would prefer that it not be seen as a problem at all.

Ans: a
Page: 98
Obj: 12
Type: F

91. Which statement *best* summarizes Millon's (1983) position on the DSM?
    a. He believes that, as we learn more, each DSM edition will be an improvement.
    b. He believes that all classification systems dehumanize and should be abandoned.
    c. He believes that a behavioral classification system would reduce the bias against women.
    d. He believes that the DSM cannot be substantially improved.

Ans: d
Page: 98
Obj: 13
Type: A

92. A psychologist says, "Classification does not have to rely on a medical model. Rather, we can look at the factors that maintain problem behaviors and classify accordingly." This psychologist
    a. is arguing for the abandonment of all assessment methods.
    b. would tend to ignore the situational causes of behavior disorders.
    c. favors using the DSM system.
    d. favors a behavioral classification scheme.

Ans: b
Page: 98
Obj: 13
Type: C

93. Which statement about the behavioral classification approach is *accurate*?
    a. It tends to have weaker reliability than the DSM.
    b. It tends to have better reliability than the DSM.
    c. It relies heavily on the medical model.
    d. It is more widely used than the DSM-IV-TR.

Ans: d
Page: 99
Obj: 13
Type: C

94. The results of the Rosenthal and Jacobson (1968) study of schoolchildren underscore what objection to classification?
    a. Classification tends to be highly unreliable.
    b. Classification tends to give psychopathology an all-or-nothing quality.
    c. Classification is rarely based on empirical research.
    d. Classification may create a self-fulfilling prophecy.

Ans: a
Page: 99
Obj: 13
Type: F

95. In the Rosenthal and Jacobson (1968) study, some children were randomly assigned the label of "bloomers." This label
    a. increased these children's IQs because their teachers believed the label.
    b. made the teachers see mental disorder where there wasn't any.
    c. made the teachers see normality when the children were actually abnormal.
    d. reduced these children's IQs because they became lazy.

Ans: b
Page: 99
Obj: 13
Type: F

96. In the Rosenthal (1973) study, hospital staff looked at normal writing by the pseudopatients as "excessive note-taking." This finding supports the view that classification
    a. can help professionals understand the causes of abnormal behavior.
    b. can cause people to interpret many activities of a labeled person as pathological even if the behaviors are normal.
    c. can make "normal" people believe the label they are given and cause a change in their behavior.
    d. can blur the lines that divide normal from abnormal.

Ans: c
Page: 99
Obj: 13
Type: F

97. Which of the following occurred in the Rosenthal (1973) study involving pseudopatients being admitted to a mental hospital?
   a. Pseudopatients were given warm and individualized care.
   b. Although the patients were fooled by the pseudopatients, the professionals quickly realized that they were not disturbed.
   c. Although some patients detected the pseudopatients, the professional staff did not.
   d. The hospital staff disagreed on the diagnosis to be given the pseudopatients.

Ans: d
Page: 100
Obj: 12
Type: A

98. A supervisor at a managed-care organization looks at a DSM-IV-TR diagnosis supplied by a clinician. The supervisor is likely to
   a. think the diagnosis supplies excessive information about the client, infringing on rights of privacy.
   b. feel the diagnosis relies too heavily on behavioral classification.
   c. reject the diagnosis as being too unreliable.
   d. think the diagnosis supplies less information about functioning than is necessary to make treatment decisions.

Ans: a
Page: 100
Obj: 12
Type: F

99. If managed-care organizations want more detailed information about the functioning of clients in home, work, and other environments, they will probably
   a. request more precise measures of client functioning.
   b. require more use of neuropsychological assessment devices.
   c. support the DSM system wholeheartedly.
   d. reject the idea of Axis V in the DSM-IV-TR.

Ans: d
Page: 99
Obj: 13
Type: A

100. Last year Mr. Plimpton, the high school principal, was fired from his job because it became known that he had, at one time, been diagnosed as being depressed. This illustrates
   a. the lack of reliability in the labeling process.
   b. that people who are labeled change their own behavior.
   c. the negative effects of a medical model.
   d. that labels can cause people to treat individuals differently even when they are perfectly normal.

ESSAY QUESTIONS

1. Clinical assessment uses four methods of assessment. Briefly describe how each would be used in collecting information on the following hypothetical client:

   Mara is a sixteen-year-old who is angry and anxious at home and in school but seems relatively happy among her friends when shopping or doing other leisure activities. She seems extremely bright to her teachers but is receiving poor grades because she seems distracted and unable to remember information. Her interest in boys has been almost obsessive recently; she fantasizes about being saved from her horrible parents by a guy who will marry her and take her away.

2. What three criteria are commonly used to evaluate psychological assessment procedures? Describe each criterion in detail, and apply each of the criteria to the assessment of a problem such as severe anxiety.

3. What are the components of the DSM classification system? What new information is included in the DSM-IV-TR?

SAMPLE ANSWERS

1. The four assessment methods are observation, interview, psychological tests, and neurological tests. In Mara's case, the psychologist could collect direct observations of her in the school, home, and office environments to see whether there is consistency in her behaviors and emotions. The psychologist would look at Mara's dress, facial expressions, posture, activity level, speech, and voice tone to get a full picture of her emotional state in different settings. Observations by others—teachers, parents, friends, and Mara herself—could deepen the psychologist's appreciation of her situation. A nondirective interview would allow Mara to express what she is feeling and emphasize the problems she thinks are most important. Using a more structured interview, the psychologist would present her with a set of questions to assess her mental status (does she really believe her fantasies are based in fact?) and get a clearer idea about her diagnosis. Interviews with parents, teachers, and friends could reveal how consistent her problems are and how distressing. Psychological tests could range from projective tests such as the TAT and Rorschach to self-report inventories such as the MMPI-2 and Beck Depression Inventory. The projectives would reveal unconscious motives; the MMPI-2 would show general personality patterns; the Beck would assess the degree of her depression. Intelligence tests like the WAIS-R might be given to see whether her poor grades are due to a lack of intellectual capacity or a learning disability. Neurological tests might also reveal a cognitive impairment that accounts for her poor memory and attention span.

2. The three criteria commonly used to evaluate assessment procedures are reliaiblity, validity, and utility. *Reliability* refers to the consistency or repeatability of results. There are three different types of reliaiblity: test-retest, internal consistency, and interrater. *Test-retest reliability* refers to the consistency of a test over time. For example, if you take a test measuring your intelligence one week and the test has good test-retest reliability, your score should be about the same if you take the test again the following week. The second type of reliability is *internal consistency*. This type of reliability refers to the consistency among test items. In other words, to what extent do the items in a test measure the same construct? The third type of reliability is *interrater reliability*, which refers to consistency or agreement among scorers or observers. For example, if two researchers were observing children on a playground and counting the frequency with which they engaged in aggressive behavior, then the observers should have similar frequency counts for their assessment to be considered to have good interrater reliability.

    Validity addresses the issue of the extent to which a test measures what it is supposed to. There are three main types of validity: content validity, criterion-related validity, and construct validity. *Content validity* means that the items of an assessment device are representative examples of the domain(s) the test measures. For example, if a test measures anxiety and yet the questions asked about a person's social activities, it would not have adequate content validity. A second type of validity is *criterion-related validity*. With this type of validity, the scores on a measure are compared with a criterion thought to be related to the construct measured by the test. The criterion can be some future event (if so, it is called *predictive validity*) or some current event (if so, it is called *concurrent validity*). For example, if I had a test that was supposed to measure how successful one was going to be in college, I might give my test to a group of high school seniors. Then four years later I would compare their scores on the test with their college GPA to see if my test had good predictive validity. For *construct validity*, test results must be related to the theoretical construct (or concept) the test is supposed to measure. The third criterion is *utility*, or usefulness. For an assessment to be useful it must be reliable and valid, and provide information that cannot be obtained more simply, cheaply, or quickly using another procedure.

3. The *Diagnostic and Statistical Manual of Mental Disorders* is the dominant classification system for abnormal behavior. It guides the clinician in diagnosing an individual and acquiring related useful information. It comprises five dimensions, or axes. Axes I and II are involved in making a diagnosis. Axis I identifies the major clinical syndromes, such as specific forms of schizophrenia or substance abuse. Axis II lists personality disorders and developmental disorders including mental retardation. Detailed diagnostic criteria based on research findings and expert clinical judgments help the clinician make diagnoses on Axes I and II. Axis III lists any physical conditions that may contribute to Axis I or Axis II disorders. For instance, a thyroid condition (Axis III) might contribute to major depression (Axis I). On Axis IV, the clinician identifies psychosocial or environmental problems (stressors) that may affect the clinical syndrome. Axis V rates the individual's current global level of functioning on a 1–100 scale.

    The most recent edition of the DSM (DSM-IV-TR) emphasizes cross-cultural assessment more than previous editions did. If culture, age, or gender have been shown to influence the behavioral features of a disorder, they are listed. It also contains an outline of syndromes that are unique to particular cultural groups. Finally, it offers guidelines for sensitively addressing the cultural backgrounds of clients.

CHAPTER 4

The Scientific Method
in Abnormal Psychology

LEARNING OBJECTIVES

1. Explain the roles of skepticism and replication in science. Discuss the current status of scientific "facts" in abnormal psychology that have received subsequent investigation, including facilitated communication and the identification of an alcoholism gene. (pp. 103–104; Critical Thinking)

2. Discuss the characteristics of the scientific method in clinical research, including the proper stating of hypotheses, operational definitions, and the need for reliable and valid measures and observations. (pp. 105–106; Mental Health & Society)

3. Describe the concepts of base rates, statistical significance, and clinical significance. (pp. 106-109)

4. Identify the components of a basic experiment, and describe the need for placebos, blind and double-blind research designs. (pp. 109–112)

5. Discuss the characteristics of correlational studies and their strengths and limitations, specifically their ambiguous conclusions with respect to causality. Use the Sanders and Giolas (1991) study to discuss how correlational research can be improved. (pp. 112–115)

6. Describe analogue and field studies, and discuss their strengths and limitations. (pp. 115–116)

7. Define the nomothetic and idiographic orientations toward research. Discuss the characteristics and limitations of case studies and single-participant experiment designs. (pp. 116–118)

8. Discuss the biological research strategies, including genetic linkage studies, biological markers, iatrogenic effects, genetic penetrance, pathognomonic symptoms, and biological challenge tests. (pp. 118–120; Critical Thinking)

9. Describe various research strategies used in the study of abnormal behavior, including epidemiological research. Differentiate between prevalence and incidence. (pp. 120–122)

10. Discuss the ethical issues in conducting research and the American Psychological Association's guiding principles on ethics, including the use of animals, and research with culturally diverse populations. (pp. 122–123)

MULTIPLE–CHOICE QUESTIONS

Ans: d
Page: 103
Obj: 1
Type: F

1. Research on facilitated communication
   a. has not been done.
   b. has failed to include control groups.
   c. has shown that it is an effective treatment for mentally retarded people.
   d. has shown that it does not exist.

Ans: a
Page: 104
Obj: 1
Type: C

2. Why was it necessary to interpret the initial finding of a relationship between the A1 allele of DRD2 and alcoholism with great caution?
   a. Those alcoholics with the gene may not be representative of alcoholics generally.
   b. More people in the control group showed the allele than alcoholics in the experimental group.
   c. Scientists cannot identify the allele with any reliability.
   d. Alcoholism is not a common disorder.

Ans: b
Page: 104
Obj: 1
Type: A

3. Your neighbor tells you, "My children are so hyperactive after they eat certain foods. I understand that scientists have proved that foods and food additives cause hyperactivity." What response to your neighbor is *most* accurate?
   a. "Actually, no one has ever studied this thoroughly, so no one really knows."
   b. "Not really; when well-designed studies have been done, food and additives have had no impact on hyperactivity."
   c. "Not exactly; it seems that hyperactivity is caused primarily by food allergies."
   d. "You are right; double-blind research has shown that foods and food additives cause hyperactivity."

Ans: c
Page: 104
Obj: 1
Type: C

4. What conclusion can be reached from research findings reported in the mass media as conclusive?
   a. Usually the findings from initial research are replicated.
   b. Newspapers often get the facts wrong.
   c. Initial findings reported by newspapers often are not replicated.
   d. Newspapers are the best sources of scientific information.

Ans: d
Page: 104
Obj: 1
Type: C

5. What lesson can be learned from the studies reported in newspapers claiming that an alcoholism gene had been discovered?
   a. Control groups must have a significant percentage of people with the same genetic characteristics as the experimental, alcoholic group.
   b. The methods used in the initial study of a topic should be used over and over to replicate findings.
   c. The best research samples are small but homogeneous.
   d. Comparisons with nonalcoholic psychiatric samples are needed before saying that a gene is specific for alcoholism.

Ans: a
Page: 104
Obj: 1
Type: F

6. A newspaper headline in 1990 might have read, "Specific Gene Causes Alcoholism and Other Addictions." What did news stories report in 1991 and 1992?
   a. Later research showed that many nonaddicted people have the gene, too.
   b. It is just as likely that alcoholism causes the gene as the other way around.
   c. The researchers who reported these results were later found to have faked them.
   d. Later research found that there was no such gene.

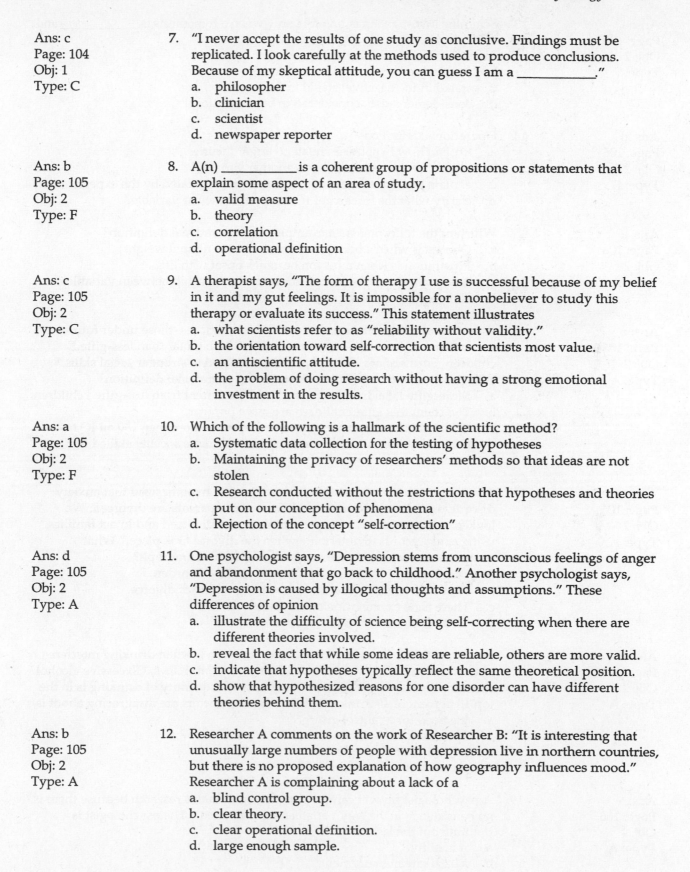

Ans: c
Page: 104
Obj: 1
Type: C

7. "I never accept the results of one study as conclusive. Findings must be replicated. I look carefully at the methods used to produce conclusions. Because of my skeptical attitude, you can guess I am a _____."
    a. philosopher
    b. clinician
    c. scientist
    d. newspaper reporter

Ans: b
Page: 105
Obj: 2
Type: F

8. A(n) _____ is a coherent group of propositions or statements that explain some aspect of an area of study.
    a. valid measure
    b. theory
    c. correlation
    d. operational definition

Ans: c
Page: 105
Obj: 2
Type: C

9. A therapist says, "The form of therapy I use is successful because of my belief in it and my gut feelings. It is impossible for a nonbeliever to study this therapy or evaluate its success." This statement illustrates
    a. what scientists refer to as "reliability without validity."
    b. the orientation toward self-correction that scientists most value.
    c. an antiscientific attitude.
    d. the problem of doing research without having a strong emotional investment in the results.

Ans: a
Page: 105
Obj: 2
Type: F

10. Which of the following is a hallmark of the scientific method?
    a. Systematic data collection for the testing of hypotheses
    b. Maintaining the privacy of researchers' methods so that ideas are not stolen
    c. Research conducted without the restrictions that hypotheses and theories put on our conception of phenomena
    d. Rejection of the concept "self-correction"

Ans: d
Page: 105
Obj: 2
Type: A

11. One psychologist says, "Depression stems from unconscious feelings of anger and abandonment that go back to childhood." Another psychologist says, "Depression is caused by illogical thoughts and assumptions." These differences of opinion
    a. illustrate the difficulty of science being self-correcting when there are different theories involved.
    b. reveal the fact that while some ideas are reliable, others are more valid.
    c. indicate that hypotheses typically reflect the same theoretical position.
    d. show that hypothesized reasons for one disorder can have different theories behind them.

Ans: b
Page: 105
Obj: 2
Type: A

12. Researcher A comments on the work of Researcher B: "It is interesting that unusually large numbers of people with depression live in northern countries, but there is no proposed explanation of how geography influences mood." Researcher A is complaining about a lack of a
    a. blind control group.
    b. clear theory.
    c. clear operational definition.
    d. large enough sample.

Ans: a Page: 105 Obj: 2 Type: F	13. Scientific investigation is possible only when a hypothesis is _____ and variables are _____. 　a.　stated clearly; measurable 　b.　operationally defined; left undefined 　c.　stated in the negative; stated in the positive 　d.　considered causal; considered to be correlational
Ans: d Page: 106 Obj: 2 Type: F	14. Operational definitions 　a.　explain how hypotheses relate to larger theories. 　b.　state how one variable affects another variable. 　c.　explain how independent variables are manipulated by the experimenter. 　d.　clarify what the researcher means by a particular variable.
Ans: a Page: 106 Obj: 2 Type: A	15. Which of the following is an example of an operational definition? 　a.　Obesity is when a person is 20 percent over normal weight. 　b.　Frustration is when a person becomes upset with life. 　c.　A hypothesis is a conjecture about the relationship between variables. 　d.　A theory is a set of explanatory concepts.
Ans: c Page: 106 Obj: 2 Type: A	16. A portion of a research report says, "Gifted children—those under fourteen and with an IQ over 130—are more likely to be popular than less-gifted children. Furthermore, their popularity is related to stronger social skills." What portion of the statement illustrates an operational definition? 　a.　More-gifted children are believed to be different from less-gifted children. 　b.　The claim that gifted children are more popular. 　c.　Gifted children are under fourteen and score more than 130 on IQ tests. 　d.　Gifted children are both more popular and more socially skilled than others.
Ans: a Page: 106 Obj: 2 Type: A	17. A research report includes this paragraph: "We hypothesized that anxiety disorders are more frequent in children whose parents are divorced. We looked at the frequency of anxiety problems in divorced and intact families, using court records to determine when the divorce took place." What component of scientific research is *missing* in this paragraph? 　a.　There is no operational definition of anxiety disorder. 　b.　There is no reliable way of determining timing of divorce. 　c.　There is no examination of base rates. 　d.　There is no clearly stated hypothesis.
Ans: b Page: 106 Obj: 2 Type: A	18. Dr. Appel says, "Excessive alcohol consumption is when drinking interferes with social and occupational functioning." Dr. Baker says, "Excessive alcohol consumption is when a person's frequency and quantity of drinking is in the top 10 percent of all drinkers." What the two doctors are disagreeing about is 　a.　the need for a control group. 　b.　operational definitions. 　c.　reliability of measurement. 　d.　the need for base rates.
Ans: a Page: 106 Obj: 2 Type: A	19. A psychologist says, "I cannot place any faith in this research because there is no consistency in the way variables are measured." The psychologist is pointing out the lack of 　a.　reliability. 　b.　a base rate measurement. 　c.　validity. 　d.　statistical significance.

Ans: d
Page: 106
Obj: 2
Type: A

20. A researcher finds that when people report their sexual activity on a mailed questionnaire, they indicate higher levels of bizarre fantasies than when they are questioned face to face. This indicates that these methods of measuring sexual activity
    a. have high base rates.
    b. are high in validity.
    c. have high reliability.
    d. have low reliability.

Ans: c
Page: 106
Obj: 2
Type: C

21. Reliable measures _____; valid measures _____.
    a. have operational definitions; do not have operational definitions
    b. measure what they are supposed to; are consistent
    c. are consistent; measure what they are supposed to
    d. are consistent; are manipulated by the experimenter

Ans: d
Page: 106
Obj: 2
Type: A

22. For some strange reason, a music teacher gives students a vocabulary test before deciding what the right musical instrument is for each. The vocabulary test gives consistent results, but the students are rarely happy with the instrument they play. The problem is that the vocabulary test
    a. is valid but not reliable.
    b. has excessive reliability.
    c. is neither reliable nor valid.
    d. is reliable but not valid.

Ans: b
Page: 106
Obj: 2
Type: C

23. A psychologist announces that her diagnostic system for depression is very reliable. We can predict that the system
    a. involves the use of base rates.
    b. gives the same results if taken more than once.
    c. accurately identifies people who have depression.
    d. uses clinical tests rather than answers to questionnaire items.

Ans: d
Page: 106
Obj: 3
Type: F

24. _____ represent a way to appropriately compare how often some behavior or other phenomenon occurs in two or more groups.
    a. Correlations
    b. Reliable measurements
    c. Operational definitions
    d. Base rates

Ans: a
Page: 1047
Obj: 3
Type: C

25. A researcher reports that 38 percent of people who take a particular medication complain of headaches. To claim that headaches are a side effect of the medication, the researcher must
    a. find out the base rate of headaches in nonmedicated populations.
    b. show that the medication works on the condition it was designed for.
    c. do an experiment in which two groups are given the medication.
    d. show a correlation between dosage of the drug and headache intensity.

Ans: d
Page: 107
Obj: 3
Type: A

26. Suppose that one-third of a sample of teenage girls thought they were too fat despite being normal weight. If these thoughts were taken as a sign of eating disorders, the problem would be that
    a. no boys were included in the sample.
    b. there is too small a sample on which to base the conclusion.
    c. there is confusion about what reliability and validity mean.
    d. there are no base rates for control and eating disorder populations.

Ans: c
Page: 109
Obj: 3
Type: A

27. A large school district introduces a new reading program into one-half of its first-grade classrooms. Three years later, the reading scores of the 10,000 children in the new program average 3 points higher on a 100-point test than the scores of the 10,000 children who did not get the program. Although 3 points is statistically significant, the problem with saying that the program was a great success is that
    a. the samples are too small to assess clinical significance.
    b. the reading test is probably not reliable.
    c. 3 points on the reading score is probably not clinically significant.
    d. there was no control group.

Ans: b
Page: 109
Obj: 3
Type: F

28. Which statement about clinical and statistical significance is *accurate*?
    a. Clinical significance is influenced by reliability; statistical significance is influenced by validity.
    b. Large samples can produce statistical significance without showing clinical significance.
    c. Statistical significance has greater practical value than clinical significance.
    d. If there is statistical significance, we can assume there is clinical significance.

Ans: a
Page: 109
Obj: 3
Type: F

29. When is clinical significance *most* likely to be minimal while statistical significance is quite large?
    a. When the sample size is very large
    b. When the sample size is very small
    c. When research measures are reliable and valid
    d. When base rates are very small

Ans: b
Page: 109
Obj: 3
Type: A

30. Dr. Kendall is treating a group of people diagnosed with anxiety disorders. At the completion of the treatment program, analyses indicate that the clients are showing statistically significant changes as a result of treatment. Many of the clients, however, still report feeling strong symptoms of anxiety. Which of the following statements is *accurate*?
    a. Dr. Kendall needs to assess clinical significance by applying the correct statistics.
    b. Although the treatment group showed statistically significant changes, the clinical significance of the results is questionable.
    c. A study is clinically significant if it is statistically significant.
    d. Dr. Kendall's treatment is successful because it has been shown to produce statistically significant changes.

Ans: d
Page: 109
Obj: 4
Type: C

31. If the results of a study are due to factors other than those included in the research investigation, the study is said to have poor
    a. external validity.
    b. statistical significance.
    c. directionality.
    d. internal validity.

Ans: c
Page: 109
Obj: 4
Type: C

32. A researcher believes that depressive symptoms will be reduced when family members give attention to competent behavior and express disinterest when depressive behavior is exhibited. In this example, attention is the _____ and depressive symptoms are the _____.
    a. baseline; normative comparison
    b. dependent variable; independent variable
    c. independent variable; dependent variable
    d. experimental variable; control variable

Ans: d
Page: 109
Obj: 4
Type: F

33. The _____ is the *best* way to test cause-and-effect relationships.
    a. case study
    b. placebo
    c. correlational study
    d. experiment

Ans: a
Page: 110
Obj: 4
Type: F

34. In an experiment, this group is as similar as possible to the experimental group except that it is not exposed to the independent variable. It is the
    a. control group.
    b. placebo group.
    c. dependent variable group.
    d. randomized group.

Ans: b
Page: 109
Obj: 4
Type: F

35. In the Thom et al. (2000) study of the treatment of anxiety and panic attacks subjects were randomly assigned to one of two experimental groups or a control group. Thom and her colleagues found that patients in the experimental groups had fewer anxiety attacks. A dependent variable in this study was the
    a. number of subjects in each group.
    b. number of anxiety attacks.
    c. three groups.
    d. type of treatment used.

Ans: c
Page: 109
Obj: 4
Type: A

36. Dr. Malcolm is developing a new personality inventory. In his validation study, he ensures that his participants include individuals from every state, an equal number of men and women, individuals from all ethnic and racial backgrounds, and individuals from both rural and urban areas. Dr. Malcolm is trying to ensure that his study is
    a. internally valid.
    b. internally and externally valid.
    c. externally valid.
    d. reliable.

Ans: b
Page: 110
Obj: 4
Type: C

37. To study the effectiveness of a new antianxiety drug, researchers randomly assign equally anxious people to two groups, one getting Drug X and the other getting no drug. The researchers mistakenly conclude that Drug X works because people in the drug group show fewer signs of anxiety than the others. What is the mistake?
    a. They never introduced an independent variable.
    b. They did not create a placebo control group.
    c. They never did a pretest of anxiety symptoms.
    d. They did not operationally define what the experimental group was.

Ans: a
Page: 110
Obj: 4
Type: A

38. In a study of the effectiveness of cognitive therapy on anxiety, fifty anxious patients are divided into two groups. One group gets cognitive therapy, the other a fake kind of therapy that should have no benefit. However, the patients can tell that the second form of treatment is fake. The study is weak because
    a. its placebo condition did not control for expectancy effects.
    b. it did not include an independent variable.
    c. it confuses experimental designs with correlational designs.
    d. it did not have a placebo condition.

Ans: d
Page: 110
Obj: 4
Type: C

39. The effect caused by a placebo results from
    a. pathognomonic processes.
    b. an effect of the drug.
    c. the control group.
    d. expectation of relief.

Ans: b
Page: 111
Obj: 4
Type: F

40. In a double-blind research study,
    a. behavior is measured before and after the introduction of an independent variable.
    b. neither the subjects nor those who work directly with them know who is in the experimental condition.
    c. the subjects know which condition they are in, but the experimenters do not.
    d. subjects are randomly assigned to one of two conditions that are similar in every way possible.

Ans: a
Page: 112
Obj: 5
Type: C

41. All of the following are characteristic of correlational studies *except*
    a. that they help understand cause and effect.
    b. that they help understand the strength of a relationship between variables.
    c. that when two variables are highly related, knowledge about one variable can be used to make predictions about the other variable.
    d. that they are helpful in generating hypotheses for experimental research.

Ans: b
Page: 112
Obj: 5
Type: A

42. Suppose the results of a correlational study examining the association between poverty and psychotic behavior show a correlation coefficient of $r = 0.80$. One possibility is that poverty causes psychotic behavior. Another possibility is that
    a. the study was actually an experiment.
    b. a third variable causes both poverty and psychotic behavior.
    c. poverty and psychotic behavior are unrelated.
    d. the correlation is actually negative.

Ans: d
Page: 112
Obj: 5
Type: F

43. In _____ studies, variables are not manipulated. Instead, the researcher measures the extent to which changes in one variable are accompanied by changes in a second variable.
    a. analogue
    b. experimental
    c. epidemiological
    d. correlational

Ans: a
Page: 112
Obj: 5
Type: C

44. A researcher believes that the higher a person's creativity, the greater the person's likelihood of showing mood swings. Research to test this idea
    a. could use the correlation coefficient.
    b. would require an experimental design.
    c. could not use the correlational method.
    d. would require a double-blind design.

Ans: c
Page: 112
Obj: 5
Type: C

45. Suppose the only thing you know about a research study is that its statistical result is $r = -0.74$. What could you deduce?
   a. It was an experiment in which the independent variable had an effect.
   b. It is not only statistically significant but also clinically significant.
   c. It was a correlational study where scores on one variable decreased as scores on the other increased.
   d. It was a correlational study where no relationship was found between the first variable and the second.

Ans: d
Page: 112
Obj: 5
Type: F

46. Which of the following is the *strongest* correlation?
   a. +0.11
   b. +1.89
   c. +0.66
   d. −0.80

Ans: c
Page: 112
Obj: 5
Type: C

47. The higher the scores on Factor A, the lower the scores on Factor B. If this inverse relationship were strong, it would be measured as a _____ correlation.
   a. positive
   b. fractional
   c. negative
   d. zero

Ans: a
Page: 112
Obj: 5
Type: C

48. A researcher studies a group of elderly people and finds that, as a group, the better their memory performance, the lower their anxiety level. What can be said about this research?
   a. It was a correlational study.
   b. The results show that memory loss causes anxiety.
   c. It was an experiment.
   d. The results show a perfect positive correlation.

Ans: d
Page: 1112
Obj: 5
Type: C

49. What type of study would yield information on whether or not persons who are abused as children develop mental disorders in adulthood?
   a. Meta-analysis
   b. Experiment
   c. Case study
   d. Correlational

Ans: d
Page: 114
Obj: 5
Type: A

50. Results of the Sanders and Giolas (1991) study showed a significant positive correlation between scores on the Dissociative Experiences Scale and a questionnaire on child abuse. The authors concluded that this supports "the view that dissociation represents a reaction to early negative experience." What is one problem with this conclusion?
   a. It suggests that dissociation causes child abuse.
   b. It assumes there is a negative correlation when there was actually a positive correlation.
   c. It suggests that child abuse is the same thing as dissociation.
   d. It assumes there is a cause-and-effect relationship.

Ans: b
Page: 114
Obj: 5
Type: F

51. Which of the following is a problem with the Sanders and Giolas (1990) study of dissociative experiences and child abuse?
    a. It used an experimental design but did not make cause-and-effect inferences from the data.
    b. It failed to use valid research instruments.
    c. It did not include a placebo control group.
    d. It was unethical to subject individuals to abuse to see if they had more dissociative experiences.

Ans: c
Page: 115
Obj: 5
Type: C

52. Unlike an experiment, the results of a correlational study
    a. identify third variables that account for associations among variables.
    b. do not include dependent variables.
    c. cannot tell you about cause-and-effect relationships.
    d. are not dependent on the validity of research instruments.

Ans: a
Page: 115
Obj: 6
Type: A

53. Which of the following is an example of analogue research?
    a. Studying the effects of alcohol ingestion on pregnant rats in order to obtain further evidence to prevent fetal alcohol syndrome in human children
    b. Studying the effects of RET therapy on a population of depressed individuals
    c. Studying the effects of an art class on a group of heterogeneous school children in order to determine factors that enhance creativity
    d. Studying the effects of antipsychotic drugs on people diagnosed with schizophrenia

Ans: d
Page: 115
Obj: 6
Type: C

54. Often, when new drugs are developed, their effects are first tested on animals rather than on humans. The use of animals as substitutes for humans in research is often referred to as
    a. descriptive research.
    b. substitution research.
    c. quasi-experimental research.
    d. analogue research.

Ans: d
Page: 115
Obj: 6
Type: C

55. Analogue studies are used when researchers
    a. are interested in the causal relationship of one variable to another.
    b. are able to use only a single subject who must act as his or her own control.
    c. are interested in the effects of expectation on behavior.
    d. cannot practically or ethically observe behaviors as they occur in real life.

Ans: a
Page: 115
Obj: 6
Type: A

56. To assess the possible benefits of a new kind of therapy for highly anxious patients, a researcher uses college students when they are fearful prior to an exam. This kind of research is called a(n) _____ study.
    a. analogue
    b. correlational
    c. epidemiological
    d. single-subject design

Ans: c
Page: 116
Obj: 6
Type: F

57. When researchers feel that an analogue study is too contrived to accurately represent what goes on in real life, a _____ is often used.
    a. case study
    b. historical study
    c. field study
    d. correlational study

Ans: d
Page: 116
Obj: 6
Type: C

58. Contrived situations are to _____ studies as naturalistic observations are to _____ studies.
    a. field; correlational
    b. correlational; experimental
    c. field; epidemiological
    d. analogue; field

Ans: b
Page: 115
Obj: 6
Type: C

59. What is the primary drawback to using analogue studies?
    a. Although the results of such studies often are statistically significant, they lack clinical significance.
    b. Although such research offers high levels of control, external validity suffers.
    c. Although the external validity of such research is strong, internal validity is usually weak.
    d. It is difficult to gain the statistical significance needed for such studies to provide meaningful results.

Ans: d
Page: 116
Obj: 6
Type: A

60. To learn about the social skills of adolescents, a researcher goes to a shopping mall and records interactions of opposite-sex pairs of teens. This research study illustrates a(n)
    a. single-subject correlation.
    b. analogue study.
    c. longitudinal study.
    d. field study.

Ans: b
Page: 116
Obj: 6
Type: A

61. To better understand bulimia among college students, a researcher lives in a female freshman dorm for the fall semester to observe and interview students about their stresses, attitudes, and eating behaviors. This is an example of a(n) _____ study.
    a. analogue
    b. field
    c. experimental
    d. case

Ans: c
Page: 116
Obj: 6
Type: A

62. To better understand bulimia among college students, a researcher lives in a female freshman dorm for the fall semester to observe and interview students about their stresses, attitudes, and eating behaviors. A limitation of this field study is
    a. its lack of correlational design.
    b. the fact that it is actually a longitudinal study.
    c. the possibility that the researcher's presence influenced behavior.
    d. that it will have little external validity.

Ans: a
Page: 116
Obj: 6
Type: C

63. Which of the following *best* illustrates a field study?
    a. Caregivers of people with heart conditions are observed and interviewed at home.
    b. Mice are observed before and after they are deprived of sleep.
    c. A group of people are tested for intelligence when they are twenty, thirty, and forty years old.
    d. The brain wave patterns of autistic children are compared with those of nonautistic children.

Ans: d
Page: 116
Obj: 7
Type: C

64. Experiments with large groups of subjects reflect the _____, whereas single-subject studies reflect the _____.
  a. idiographic orientation; biogenic orientation
  b. scientific method; armchair approach
  c. armchair approach; idiographic orientation
  d. nomothetic orientation; idiographic orientation

Ans: c
Page: 116
Obj: 7
Type: C

65. Idiographic research is *most* effective
  a. in laboratory, analogue studies with nonhuman subjects.
  b. at showing clear cause-and-effect relationships.
  c. in applied clinical work.
  d. when it uses large numbers of subjects.

Ans: b
Page: 117
Obj: 7
Type: C

66. Dr. Quillen treats a chronic smoker by first recording the number of cigarettes smoked daily, then offering monetary rewards for each day that one fewer cigarette is smoked. Because the client's own behavior serves as a control, this kind of study is called a(n)
  a. analogue study.
  b. single-subject experiment.
  c. correlational study.
  d. field study with one subject.

Ans: d
Page: 117
Obj: 7
Type: C

67. The case study and the single-subject experiment are two examples of
  a. epidemiological research.
  b. experimental studies.
  c. the nomothetic research approach.
  d. single-subject studies.

Ans: c
Page: 117
Obj: 7
Type: A

68. Dr. Cummins publishes an article describing a man who abused alcohol for twenty-five years before becoming abstinent after having a religious conversion experience. This article illustrates a
  a. nomothetic study.
  b. field study.
  c. case study.
  d. single-subject experiment.

Ans: b
Page: 117
Obj: 7
Type: F

69. _____ studies are especially valuable for studying rare phenomena and for evaluating the course of a disorder and its treatment.
  a. Field
  b. Case
  c. Nomothetic
  d. Correlational

Ans: b
Page: 117
Obj: 7
Type: C

70. Dr. Goldstein wants to investigate the effects of positive reinforcement on the behavior of people with a rare disorder. The research design that is *best* suited to this is the
  a. genetic linkage study.
  b. single-subject experiment.
  c. survey study.
  d. correlational field study.

Ans: c
Page: 117
Obj: 7
Type: C

71. Unlike the case study, the single-subject experiment
    a. cannot determine cause-and-effect relationships.
    b. is based on the nomothetic research orientation.
    c. is better able to assess cause-and-effect relationships.
    d. is a correlational design.

Ans: d
Page: 121
Obj: 7
Type: C

72. Which of the following is a research design *not* based on the idiographic orientation?
    a. Case study
    b. Genetic linkage study
    c. Single-subject experiment
    d. Epidemiological survey

Ans: a
Page: 117
Obj: 7
Type: C

73. Kira is involved in a research study consisting of four phases. Her behavior is monitored under baseline conditions and then after her mother gives her rewards for specific behaviors. In the third stage, she goes back to baseline, and in the fourth, her mother again rewards her. What kind of research is this?
    a. Single-subject experiment
    b. Longitudinal
    c. Case study
    d. A field study

Ans: d
Page: 118
Obj: 8
Type: C

74. In a genetic linkage study, which of the following information would be important?
    a. Whether behavior changes when individuals are exposed to a particular chemical or diet
    b. Whether the experimenter knows who is in the experimental group
    c. The nationwide prevalence of the disorder under study
    d. The number of family members who have the same disorder as the proband

Ans: a
Page: 118
Obj: 8
Type: F

75. An individual who is closely related to a person with a disorder is called a(n) _____ in a biological research study.
    a. proband
    b. case
    c. incidence
    d. marker

Ans: b
Page: 118
Obj: 8
Type: A

76. A researcher has identified seventy individuals with a relatively rare psychological disorder. These individuals are asked to identify blood relatives, who are contacted by the researcher to see if they have the same disorder. What kind of research study is being performed?
    a. Single-subject experiment
    b. Genetic linkage study
    c. Biological challenge test
    d. Correlational case study

Ans: c
Page: 119
Obj: 8
Type: A

77. A researcher is doing a genetic linkage study on sexual dysfunction. First a sample of individuals with sexual dysfunction (probands) and their family members are identified. If the disorder *does* have a genetic component
   a. probands will develop the disorder earlier in life than their family members with close blood relationships.
   b. probands and family members will have abnormal neurotransmitter levels.
   c. the closer the blood relationship, the more likely it is that family members will have sexual dysfunction.
   d. the closer the blood relationship, the less likely it is that family members will have sexual dysfunction.

Ans: b
Page: 119
Obj: 8
Type: C

78. Greg is involved in a research study because he has a rare form of psychopathology. All his blood relatives are being contacted to see if they, too, have this disorder. Greg is probably involved in a(n) _____ research study.
   a. single-subject experiment
   b. genetic linkage
   c. iatrogenic
   d. field

Ans: a
Page: 119
Obj: 8
Type: C

79. Differences in brain size, hormone levels, eye movements, or responses to specific medications that are consistently associated with a particular diagnosis are the result of studies identifying
   a. biological markers.
   b. iatrogenic effects.
   c. base rates for a behavior.
   d. genetic linkages.

Ans: b
Page: 119
Obj: 8
Type: A

80. Dr. Bundy reports, "In 90 percent of a sample of antisocial personalities, we found an unusual brain wave pattern; in a control group, this brain wave occurred in only 5 percent. Furthermore, over half of the fathers of antisocials showing this pattern had a similar brain wave pattern. None of the fathers in the control group did." Dr. Bundy's report
   a. is an example of an analogue experiment.
   b. illustrates a convincing biological marker study.
   c. is unconvincing because it did not include base rates for the brain wave pattern.
   d. rejects the notion that biology contributes to antisocial personality disorder.

Ans: d
Page: 120
Obj: 8
Type: A

81. Mrs. Yarnell was given large doses of antipsychotic medications that had side effects including twitches and dizziness. These side effects were misinterpreted as additional psychopathology. Such a mistaken diagnosis illustrates
   a. the value of single-subject experiments.
   b. a negative effect of experimentation on humans.
   c. the power of biological markers.
   d. an iatrogenic condition.

Ans: b
Page: 120
Obj: 8
Type: A

82. People with schizophrenia who are given large doses of certain medications begin to smack their lips and grimace. They look as though they are getting worse instead of better. The fact that treatment leads to these additional symptoms illustrates
   a. that the medication is pathognomonic for schizophrenia.
   b. iatrogenic effects.
   c. analogue effects.
   d. the need for double-blind research designs.

Ans: a
Page: 120
Obj: 8
Type: F

83. Hypnosis can make individuals more suggestible and increase the production of false but confident recollections of sexual abuse and trauma. This demonstrates
   a. iatrogenic effects.
   b. incomplete penetrance of the disorder.
   c. the unreliability of DSM categories for the disorder.
   d. none of the above.

Ans: c
Page: 120
Obj: 8
Type: F

84. _____ refers to the degree to which a genetic characteristic is manifested by individuals carrying a specific gene.
   a. Iatrogenic
   b. Epidemiological
   c. Penetrance
   d. Pathognomonic

Ans: d
Page: 120
Obj: 8
Type: F

85. If a biological or psychological symptom is specific for a disorder, it is said to be
   a. inherited.
   b. iatrogenic.
   c. idiographic.
   d. pathognomonic.

Ans: b
Page: 120
Obj: 9
Type: A

86. A study of childhood depression examines six-year-olds for symptoms of depression, then reassesses these individuals when they are eight and twelve years old. What kind of research is this?
   a. Historical research
   b. Longitudinal research
   c. Epidemiological research
   d. Case study research

Ans: a
Page: 120
Obj: 9
Type: F

87. A researcher interested in sex differences in the diagnosis of childhood disorders reviews teachers' comments on report cards issued to boys and girls during the 1930s and compares them with teachers' comments on report cards during the 1980s. This study illustrates
   a. historical research.
   b. survey research.
   c. program evaluation.
   d. longitudinal research.

Ans: d
Page: 120
Obj: 9
Type: C

88. Fifty survivors of an airliner crash are given questionnaires to fill out two weeks, six weeks, and thirty weeks after the crash. This study combines what types of research?
   a. Longitudinal and historical
   b. Case study and analogue
   c. Single-subject experiment and survey
   d. Longitudinal and survey

Ans: c
Page: 121
Obj: 9
Type: A

89. The town of Mayberry wants to know if a new suicide prevention telephone line has reduced the number of suicides in town. What kind of research should the town do to find out?
   a. Case study
   b. Analogue research
   c. Program evaluation
   d. Historical research

Ans: d
Page: 121
Obj: 9
Type: F

90. A survey of therapists by Yapko (1994) found that
   a. most therapists surveyed had extremely accurate knowledge about memory, but gave inaccurate responses concerning hypnosis.
   b. most therapists surveyed had extremely accurate knowledge about hypnosis, but gave inaccurate responses concerning memory.
   c. most therapists surveyed had extremely accurate knowledge about both memory and hypnosis.
   d. most therapists surveyed had extremely inaccurate knowledge about both memory and hypnosis.

Ans: b
Page: 121
Obj: 9
Type: F

91. _____ examines the rate and distribution of mental disorders in the population.
   a. Historical research
   b. Epidemiology
   c. The single-subject study
   d. Analogue research

Ans: c
Page: 121
Obj: 9
Type: A

92. Dr. Chin is interested in the number of new cases of posttraumatic stress disorder occurring in military personnel each year. The doctor's research illustrates
   a. a search for prevalence statistics.
   b. the value of the field study.
   c. epidemiology.
   d. the case study method.

Ans: a
Page: 121
Obj: 9
Type: C

93. Prevalence is to _____ as incidence is to _____.
   a. total number of cases; new cases during a particular unit of time
   b. control over extraneous variables; lack of control over extraneous variables
   c. total number of cases; control for expectations
   d. new cases in a unit of time; causes of disorder

Ans: b
Page: 122
Obj: 9
Type: A

94. A school psychologist was concerned with the number of children being diagnosed with attention-deficit hyperactivity disorder (ADHD). If she were interested in learning how many new cases of ADHD had been diagnosed within the last two years, she would look at
   a. variable rates.
   b. incidence rates.
   c. sampling rates.
   d. prevalence rates.

Ans: a
Page: 122
Obj: 9
Type: C

95. Roughly 5 percent of all adults in Country A are hospitalized with a diagnosis of alcoholism; only 1 percent of those in Country B are. It is *inaccurate* to assume that Country A's rate of alcoholism is 5 times larger than Country B's because
   a. Country A may have a different definition of alcoholism than Country B.
   b. the biological markers for alcoholism can be different in one country versus another.
   c. the research does not take into account iatrogenic effects.
   d. epidemiology cannot be done across different cultures.

Ans: d
Page: 122
Obj: 10
Type: F

96. Which statement concerning ethical psychological research is *accurate*?
   a. Treatment can never be withheld from individuals as a way of establishing a control group.
   b. Deception can never be used.
   c. Deception must be used frequently because faking is very common.
   d. The value of any research design must outweigh its possible risks to participants.

Ans: c
Page: 122
Obj: 10
Type: A

97. Dr. Barnes says this about psychological research: "Pain may be inflicted on subjects, but deception may not be used. Research must protect participants while it enables researchers to contribute to the long-term welfare of humans and other animals." Which portion of Dr. Barnes's statement is *inaccurate*?
   a. It is inaccurate to say that psychology is interested in the welfare of humans and other animals.
   b. It is inaccurate to say that pain may be inflicted on subjects.
   c. It is inaccurate to say that deception cannot be used.
   d. It is inaccurate to say that research must protect participants.

Ans: b
Page: 122
Obj: 10
Type: F

98. One safeguard against unethical research is the fact that research
   a. does not permit animals to be used as subjects.
   b. participants should be fully informed of the risks involved.
   c. requires operational definitions.
   d. is usually idiographic.

Ans: a
Page: 122
Obj: 10
Type: F

99. According to the American Psychological Association guidelines for ethical research, should research subjects be free to withdraw from a study at any time?
   a. Yes, in all cases.
   b. In cases where deception was used, yes, but in all other cases, no.
   c. No, the importance of their data overshadows their temporary discomfort.
   d. In most cases, no, but if they are becoming mentally disordered, it is allowable.

Ans: c
Page: 122
Obj: 10
Type: C

100. Which statement concerning ethical psychological research is *accurate*?
   a. Deception can never be used.
   b. Treatment can never be withheld from individuals as a way of establishing a control group.
   c. The value of any research design must outweigh its possible risks to participants.
   d. Informed consent must be given to each research subject unless deception is planned by the researcher.

ESSAY QUESTIONS

1. Suppose you are interested in the relationship between stress and overeating. Describe two research studies on the topic, one a laboratory experiment and the other a correlational study. Provide operational definitions of *stress* and *overeating*. Discuss the strengths and weaknesses of each form of research.

2. What is the idiographic orientation to research? Describe two of the research methods that use this orientation. Discuss the strengths and weaknesses of this approach.

3. Describe three principles delineated by the American Psychological Association for the protection of human participants in research.

SAMPLE ANSWERS

1. In an experiment, the researcher manipulates a variable, the independent variable, and randomly assigns subjects to at least two groups: one where the independent variable is present and one (the control group) where it is not. The independent variable in the proposed study is *stress*. This could be operationally defined as the threat of being negatively evaluated by another person. This is, of course, only one possible definition. In a hypothetical experiment, one-half of the subjects might be led to believe they were negatively evaluated by an audience (stress) and the other half would receive no such indication (control/no stress). Subjects would be allowed to eat as much of some snack foods that were made available as they wished. Average differences in the amounts eaten by experimental and control subjects would then be calculated.

   In a correlational study, subjects might be asked how many stressful events had occurred in their lives over the past thirty days. Again, this is one of an infinite number of operational definitions of *stress*. Each person would also be asked how much he or she ate in the past twenty-four hours (another definition of *eating*). If reported eating increased as reported stress increased, we could assume a positive correlation between the two variables.

   The experiment would allow inferences about cause and effect (stress caused eating), but the correlational study would not allow such inferences since eating might induce stress or both eating and stress might be influenced by a third variable. The experiment's weakness would be the artificiality of the situation, reducing our confidence in generalizing results to the "real world." The weakness of the correlation is not only the inability to make causal inferences but also inaccuracies that come from self-reports.

2. The idiographic orientation emphasizes the in-depth examination of one subject rather than the more surface-level examination of larger samples. Clinical studies most often use idiographic techniques because they can be valuable for making therapeutic decisions. Unlike nomothetic studies in the laboratory, idiographic studies can examine rare phenomena (important in abnormal psychology), demonstrate novel diagnostic or treatment approaches, or compile detailed information on an individual.

   One idiographic strategy is the case study, in which one person's life is examined in great detail using clinical information (observations, psychological tests, biographical and historical information, and interviews). When systematic experimental procedures are impractical, it is an excellent source of information. The single-subject experiment is another strategy. Individuals' behavior is observed and compared at baseline (before any independent variable is introduced) and afterward. Often this strategy evaluates the impact of a treatment. To be sure that behavior change occurred because of the treatment, conditions are returned to baseline to see if behavior reverts to its original level. If so, the treatment is seen as the explanation for changes and is reinstituted. Biological research strategies such as genetic linkage and biological marker studies also use the idiographic approach since they examine the presence of disorders or specific indicators that may or may not be causal in family members as well as probands (individuals who have the disorder).

All idiographic studies have the advantage of examining a person within the richness of his or her life and in great detail. However, all idiographic studies are weak in generalizability: It is difficult to know whether the behavior of these individuals is representative of others. Further, unexpected and undesirable effects of treatment may occur in some individuals; these are called iatrogenic effects.

3. Three principles include informed consent, debriefing, and right to withdraw from the research.
   a. Before participating in research, all individuals must be told about the study and give their informed consent. Specifically, researchers must reveal all aspects of the research that might reasonably be expected to influence a person's willingness to participate, especially any risks that may result from participation.
   b. When information must be withheld from participants in order to test an experimental hypothesis, the researcher must subsequently debrief all participants (i.e., provide all participants with a clear statement of the rationale and methods of the study and any deception used).
   c. Participants must be told that they can terminate their involvement in the study at any time and that such termination will not hurt them in any way.

CHAPTER 5
Anxiety Disorders

LEARNING OBJECTIVES

1. Describe the nature and cognitive, behavioral, and somatic manifestations of anxiety in anxiety disorders and list the five major groups of anxiety disorders. (pp. 127-130; Figure 5.1)

2. Describe the symptoms and discuss the prevalence of panic disorder. (pp. 130-132)

3. Describe the symptoms and frequency of generalized anxiety disorder. (p. 132)

4. Discuss the psychodynamic, cognitive-behavioral, and biological theories of cause for panic disorder and generalized anxiety disorder. (pp. 132-136)

5. Compare the biochemical and behavioral treatment approaches for panic disorder and generalized anxiety disorder and discuss their relative efficacy in treating these disorders. (pp. 136-137)

6. Discuss the symptoms and prevalence of phobias, including agoraphobia, specific phobia, and social phobia. (pp. 137-142; Tables 5.1 & 5.2)

7. Discuss the psychodynamic, behavioral, cognitive, and biological theories for the cause of phobias. (pp. 142-146)

8. Discuss the biochemical and behavioral treatment of phobias, including systematic desensitization, exposure, and modeling therapy. (pp. 146-149; Mental Health & Society)

9. Distinguish between obsessions and compulsions and describe the symptoms and prevalence of obsessive-compulsive disorder. (pp. 149-152; Table 5.3)

10. Discuss the psychodynamic, behavioral, and biological theories of the cause of obsessive-compulsive disorder. (pp. 152-155)

11. Describe and discuss the biological, behavioral, and cognitive treatment of obsessive-compulsive disorder. (pp. 155-156)

12. Differentiate between acute stress disorders (ASD) and posttraumatic stress disorders (PTSD) and the DSM-IV's criteria for their diagnoses. (pp. 155-156; Table 5.4)

13. Discuss the causes and treatment of PTSD, including prolonged exposure and eye movement desensitization and reprocessing. (pp. 160-163)

MULTIPLE–CHOICE QUESTIONS

Ans: d
Page: 127
Obj: 1
Type: F

1. Feelings of apprehension that can produce seemingly illogical and restrictive patterns of behavior are the major characteristics of
   a. traumatic disorders.
   b. somatoform disorders.
   c. dissociative disorders.
   d. anxiety disorders.

Ans: c
Page: 130
Obj: 1
Type: C

2. Which of the following is *not* a criterion for defining anxiety disorders?
   a. The anxiety results from an attempt to master other symptoms.
   b. The anxiety is observed only in specific situations.
   c. The anxiety serves an adaptive function.
   d. The anxiety itself is the major disturbance.

Ans: d
Page: 128
Obj: 1
Type: A

3. Both Luis and Pablo experience anxiety at work and school. Luis tends to face his stressors and uses relaxation or problem solving to reduce stress. Pablo is often overwhelmed by anxiety and finds that it interferes with his work and school performance. Do either of these men show signs of anxiety disorder?
   a. Both Luis and Pablo show signs of anxiety disorder.
   b. Neither Luis nor Pablo shows signs of anxiety disorder.
   c. Only Luis shows signs of anxiety disorder.
   d. Only Pablo shows signs of anxiety disorder.

Ans: a
Page: 130
Obj: 1
Type: A

4. Holly describes herself this way: "I am always tense and worried. Sometimes I get so frightened, I feel like I'll die. I get terribly embarrassed by my behavior, but I can't control it." Holly is probably suffering from what type of disorder?
   a. Anxiety disorder
   b. Avoidance disorder
   c. Malingering
   d. Somatoform disorder

Ans: b
Page: 122
Obj: 1
Type: F

5. When anxiety manifests itself in a person cognitively, we can tell because the person
   a. does anything to avoid the object of fear.
   b. is preoccupied with worrisome thoughts.
   c. tends to think about positive events.
   d. shows shallow breathing and muscular tension.

Ans: b
Page: 130
Obj: 1
Type: A

6. On the first day of class, Marilyn learns that one requirement is giving an oral presentation. She is so fearful of public speaking she immediately drops the class. By dropping the class, Marilyn illustrates the _____ component of anxiety.
   a. physiological
   b. behavioral
   c. somatic
   d. cognitive

Ans: a
Page: 130
Obj: 1
Type: F

7. Which of the following is *not* one of the five groups of anxiety disorders?
   a. Somatization disorder
   b. Panic disorder
   c. Obsessive-compulsive disorder
   d. Posttraumatic stress disorder

Ans: b
Page: 130
Obj: 2
Type: A

8. When Yuri must talk on the phone with strangers, he becomes short of breath, his heart beats very fast, and he trembles so much he fears he will die. What Yuri is experiencing is called
    a. panic disorder.
    b. a panic attack.
    c. free-floating anxiety.
    d. acute traumatic stress.

Ans: c
Page: 130
Obj: 2
Type: F

9. There are three kinds of panic attacks. They are
    a. biogenic, psychogenic, and sociogenic.
    b. those caused by interpersonal situations, those caused by environmental change, and those caused by intrapsychic distress.
    c. situationally bound, situationally predisposed, and unexpected.
    d. those associated with agoraphobia, those associated with depression, and those not associated with another disorder.

Ans: a
Page: 130
Obj: 2
Type: C

10. Alma has recurrent terrifying episodes that last twenty minutes. Her heart beats so fast she thinks she is having a heart attack, she sweats profusely, and she feels a sense of doom. For more than a month she has feared having another episode. An appropriate diagnosis is
    a. panic disorder.
    b. panic attack.
    c. agoraphobia.
    d. generalized anxiety disorder.

Ans: d
Page: 131
Obj: 2
Type: C

11. Which diagnosis is *most* closely associated with panic disorder?
    a. Posttraumatic stress disorder (PTSD)
    b. Obsessive-compulsive disorder
    c. Specific phobia
    d. Agoraphobia

Ans: c
Page: 131
Obj: 2
Type: A

12. The public health director of a southwestern American city is concerned about providing services for people with panic disorder. Based on the research, her treatment services should be designed for
    a. Mexican Americans, who are at very high risk for it.
    b. large populations, since the lifetime prevalence is roughly 12 percent.
    c. two or three times as many women as men.
    d. people who have no problem with leaving their homes to get care.

Ans: a
Page: 132
Obj: 2
Type: F

13. Which statement about the prevalence of panic attacks and panic disorder is *accurate*?
    a. Panic attacks are relatively common; panic disorder is relatively rare.
    b. Panic attacks are more common in women; panic disorder is more common in men.
    c. Panic attacks are relatively rare; panic disorder is relatively common.
    d. Panic attacks rarely occur during adolescence; panic disorder almost always occurs during adolescence.

Ans: a
Page: 130
Obj: 3
Type: A

14. Dr. McAllister says, "Free-floating anxiety occurs only in generalized anxiety disorder (GAD), but the anxiety is less intense than in panic disorder. People with GAD often do not know exactly what they are afraid of, but the themes are often finances, work performance, and rejection." What portion of this statement is *inaccurate*?
   a. It is inaccurate to say that free-floating anxiety occurs only in GAD.
   b. It is inaccurate to say that anxiety in GAD is milder than in panic disorder.
   c. It is inaccurate to say that people with GAD often do not know exactly what they are afraid of.
   d. It is inaccurate to say that people with GAD are afraid of finances, work performance, and rejection.

Ans: c
Page: 130
Obj: 3
Type: F

15. Free-floating (nonspecific) anxiety is a characteristic of
   a. posttraumatic stress disorder.
   b. neurotic disorders.
   c. generalized anxiety and panic disorders.
   d. simple phobias.

Ans: c
Page: 132
Obj: 3
Type: A

16. John describes himself as feeling tense, nervous, and on edge. He says that he seems to worry about everything, including finances, the health of his wife and children, his job performance, and the quality of his spiritual life. What diagnosis would John *most likely* be given?
   a. Panic disorder
   b. Agoraphobia
   c. Generalized anxiety disorder
   d. Obsessive-compulsive disorder

Ans: c
Page: 132
Obj: 3
Type: A

17. Laurel has been diagnosed with generalized anxiety disorder. To meet the criteria for making this diagnosis,
   a. she must have a specific situation that she fears and avoids.
   b. she must fear leaving home.
   c. her symptoms must have lasted for six months or more.
   d. she must have had four or more panic attacks in the past year.

Ans: b
Page: 132
Obj: 3
Type: C

18. Dr. Nakamura thinks that his client might be suffering from generalized anxiety disorder. Which fact would rule out that diagnosis (make it impossible)?
   a. The client worries over both minor and major events but experiences only mild anxiety.
   b. The client has experienced anxiety symptoms for about one month.
   c. The client is a divorced, unemployed woman.
   d. The client has never shown symptoms of agoraphobia.

Ans: d
Page: 133
Obj: 4
Type: C

19. In the psychodynamic explanation for generalized anxiety disorder, it is assumed that
   a. anxiety has been associated with a specific stimulus in the environment.
   b. the ego is much stronger than the id.
   c. the source of the anxiety is usually known to the person suffering from the disorder.
   d. the person uses repression to defend against unconscious impulses.

Ans: a
Page: 133
Obj: 4
Type: F

20. Psychoanalysts believe that defenses are _____ in generalized anxiety disorder than in _____.
    a. less effective; other anxiety disorders
    b. more conscious; phobias
    c. more displaced; other anxiety disorders
    d. more effective; phobias

Ans: a
Page: 133
Obj: 4
Type: C

21. Dr. Mahoney is a cognitive-behavioral therapist treating a client with panic disorder. Which of the following is the doctor likely to focus upon?
    a. The client's thoughts before and during fearful episodes
    b. The client's family history of panic disorder
    c. The client's response to sodium lactate
    d. The client's early childhood experiences with sexuality

Ans: d
Page: 134
Obj: 4
Type: A

22. Which explanation for panic disorder would *most likely* be offered by a cognitive-behavioral theorist?
    a. "A malfunction in the receptors monitoring oxygen in the blood causes the patient to feel that he or she is suffocating when, in fact, he or she isn't."
    b. "If intense unconditioned stimuli are paired with many environmental stimuli, the disorder is likely to develop."
    c. "When ego defenses have weakened because of overuse, forbidden sexual impulses threaten to break into consciousness, causing an attack."
    d. "When small changes in the body are misinterpreted as dreadful events, these beliefs start a positive-feedback loop that brings on an attack."

Ans: c
Page: 134
Obj: 4
Type: A

23. A researcher is investigating the impact of negative thoughts on the biological symptoms of anxiety. Past research suggests that the researcher will find that
    a. only those with panic disorder are affected by negative thoughts.
    b. very few patients with panic disorder are influenced by negative thoughts.
    c. negative thoughts will increase heart rate in many people.
    d. negative thoughts are the effect of anxiety, not the cause of it.

Ans: a
Page: 133-134
Obj: 4
Type: A

24. "Over-attentiveness to internal bodily sensations may act as internal triggers for short, intense episodes of anxiety." The person who agrees with this statement would support the _____ perspective on the disorder, called _____.
    a. biological; generalized anxiety disorder
    b. cognitive-behavioral; panic disorder
    c. cognitive-behavioral; generalized anxiety disorder
    d. biological; agoraphobia

Ans: a
Page: 135
Obj: 4
Type: F

25. Dysfunction in the locus ceruleus is believed to be associated with
    a. panic disorders.
    b. obsessive-compulsive disorder.
    c. social phobias.
    d. generalized anxiety disorder.

Ans: c
Page: 136
Obj: 4
Type: C

26. Research evidence on the genetic transmission of anxiety disorders has suggested that
    a. anxiety disorders have a strong genetic component.
    b. genetic testing can locate the predisposition for anxiety disorders.
    c. anxiety disorders have a moderate degree of family transmission.
    d. anxiety disorders have no degree of family transmission.

Ans: d
Page: 136
Obj: 4
Type: C

27. What does the research investigating genetic contributions to anxiety disorders suggest about the role of inheritance?
    a. Concordance rates for most anxiety disorders are very high.
    b. There is no evidence of genetic inheritance for any of the anxiety disorders.
    c. Approximately 50 percent of the variance in anxiety disorders is due to genetic factors.
    d. There is some evidence of a modest genetic inheritance for panic disorders, but only a small influence for GAD.

Ans: d
Page: 136
Obj: 4
Type: A

28. Paulina, thirty-eight, has been diagnosed with generalized anxiety disorder. She is worried that her sons and daughters will also develop this disorder because they will have inherited it from her. Based on research evidence, you could tell her that
    a. her children will develop the disorder only if they are sensitive to sodium lactate or carbon dioxide exposure.
    b. the likelihood is high they will have the disorder because genetic factors are the major cause.
    c. they will probably inherit a dysfunction of the locus ceruleus, which in turn will foster the disorder.
    d. there have been few studies done, but it seems that genetics plays less of a role than in panic disorder.

Ans: d
Page: 136
Obj: 4
Type: F

29. Concerning generalized anxiety disorder (GAD) and panic disorder, inheritance plays
    a. a stronger role in GAD than in panic disorder.
    b. only a very weak role in both.
    c. a very strong role in both.
    d. a stronger role in panic disorder than in GAD.

Ans: c
Page: 136
Obj: 5
Type: C

30. A psychiatrist is treating Barbara with medication for panic disorder. She is not sure what drug she is taking, but she knows it works. It is a good bet that the drug is
    a. an antipsychotic.
    b. benzodiazepines.
    c. an antidepressant.
    d. a central nervous system stimulant such as amphetamine.

Ans: a
Page: 136
Obj: 5
Type: F

31. The fact that panic disorder is successfully treated with antidepressants and anti-anxiety medications indicates that
    a. there may be different forms of the disorder.
    b. neurotransmitters are not involved in the cause of the disorder.
    c. there is little problem of relapse after people stop taking the drugs.
    d. biological factors are probably of minor importance in the disorder.

Ans: d
Page: 136
Obj: 5
Type: C

32. Karen suffers from panic disorder and has been taking antidepressant medication. We can expect that
   a. her anxiety will be permanently reduced after she stops taking the medication.
   b. the medication will increase the rate of panic attacks.
   c. the medication was of no use in treating her.
   d. her anxiety will return when she stops taking the medication.

Ans: b
Page: 136
Obj: 5
Type: F

33. The most commonly prescribed anti-anxiety drugs are
   a. barbiturates.
   b. benzodiazepines.
   c. sedatives.
   d. SSRIs.

Ans: c
Page: 136
Obj: 5
Type: A

34. A psychiatrist is worried about her patient with generalized anxiety disorder. The patient got relief from anxiety when first put on a medication but now needs larger and larger doses and is dependent on the medication. The medication is probably
   a. sodium lactate.
   b. an antidepressant like imipramine.
   c. a benzodiazepine like Valium or Librium.
   d. a central nervous system stimulant like amphetamine.

Ans: b
Page: 137
Obj: 5
Type: A

35. Dr. Swensen says this about treating panic disorder: "Treatment should involve positive coping statements, methods of avoiding symptoms, and relaxation skills. Behavioral approaches like this have higher success rates than treatments that rely on medication." What portion of Dr. Swensen's statement is *inaccurate*?
   a. It is inaccurate to say that treatment involves positive coping statements.
   b. It is inaccurate to say that clients should avoid symptoms.
   c. It is inaccurate to say that relaxation training is a behavioral approach.
   d. It is inaccurate to say that behavioral approaches have higher success rates than medication.

Ans: c
Page: 137
Obj: 5
Type: F

36. _____ is the only consistently validated treatment for GAD.
   a. Medication
   b. Psychoanalysis
   c. Cognitive behavioral therapy
   d. Behavioral therapy

Ans: d
Page: 137
Obj: 6
Type: F

37. There are three categories of phobias:
   a. cognitive, behavioral, and somatic.
   b. agoraphobic, panic, and social.
   c. general, specific, and situational.
   d. specific, social, and agoraphobic.

Ans: b
Page: 137
Obj: 6
Type: F

38. Which of the following disorders is *most* common?
   a. Posttraumatic stress disorder
   b. Phobias
   c. Generalized anxiety disorder
   d. Obsessive-compulsive disorder

Ans: d
Page: 137
Obj: 6
Type: A

39. Larry is so afraid of being alone in public places that he cannot bring himself to leave his house. The mere thought of leaving produces overwhelming panic. Larry probably suffers from
    a. obsessive-compulsive disorder.
    b. generalized anxiety disorder.
    c. social phobia.
    d. agoraphobia.

Ans: c
Page: 138
Obj: 6
Type: F

40. Agoraphobia seems to be *most* closely related to which of these disorders?
    a. Posttraumatic stress disorder
    b. Obsessive-compulsive disorder
    c. Panic disorder
    d. Dissociative disorder

Ans: b
Page: 138
Obj: 6
Type: A

41. Gina has been diagnosed with agoraphobia. If we ask her how the symptoms of the disorder started, we can expect she will say that
    a. she had previous problems with obsessive-compulsive disorder.
    b. they were preceded by panic attacks.
    c. she had never had any problems with anxiety before.
    d. they came on suddenly without any apparent reason.

Ans: c
Page: 138
Obj: 6
Type: F

42. Recent research on agoraphobia suggests that
    a. a genetic marker on chromosome 5 is the likely cause.
    b. repressed memories are the key causal factors.
    c. cognitions may play a major causal role.
    d. the disorder is inherited from the mother.

Ans: b
Page: 139
Obj: 6
Type: A

43. Shane is ready to break up with Kayla. He is extremely frustrated with her and does not know what to do. One of his favorite activities is to eat out and try new restaurants. Kayla, however, hates eating in restaurants. She has told Shane that she loses her appetite at the mere thought of having to eat out. When he pushed her for an explanation, Kayla explained that she is afraid that she might spill something on herself or do something equally foolish. Even though she knows how frustrated Shane is with her, Kayla cannot bring herself to eat in a restaurant. What diagnosis would be the *most appropriate* for Kayla's fears?
    a. Agoraphobia
    b. Social phobia
    c. Specific phobia
    d. Xenophobia

Ans: d
Page: 139
Obj: 6
Type: A

44. Patrick is a musical conductor, but he is terrified of giving performances and speaking to the audience between pieces. He is perfectly comfortable during rehearsal sessions but sometimes has to cancel concerts because of his fears. According to the DSM-IV-TR, Patrick probably has
    a. agoraphobia due to earlier panic attacks.
    b. a social phobia of the generalized type.
    c. generalized anxiety disorder.
    d. a social phobia of the performance type.

Ans: d
Page: 140
Obj: 6
Type: F

45. An extreme and irrational fear of a specific object such as snakes or crowded elevators is a definition of a
   a. specific obsession.
   b. social compulsion.
   c. social phobia.
   d. specific phobia.

Ans: b
Page: 140
Obj: 6
Type: F

46. Based on cross-cultural research, which of the following individuals is most likely to be diagnosed with an anxiety disorder:
   a. Yeh, a Taiwanese woman.
   b. Kim, a Korean woman.
   c. Chang, a Chinese man.
   d. Nicole, a Canadian woman.

Ans: b
Page: 141
Obj: 6
Type: C

47. A pediatrician is interested in the types of phobias that typically begin in childhood. Research would tell this doctor that
   a. agoraphobia usually begins in early childhood.
   b. animal phobias begin in childhood.
   c. all phobias begin in childhood.
   d. none of the common phobias begin in childhood.

Ans: c
Page: 141
Obj: 6
Type: A

48. Imagine a classroom of one hundred college students, half male and half female. What can be expected concerning the likelihood of the students reporting specific phobias?
   a. Males will report more phobias than will females.
   b. Males will be less likely to lie about their phobias than will females.
   c. Females will report more phobias than men.
   d. Males and females will report phobias at nearly the same rate.

Ans: d
Page: 142
Obj: 7
Type: A

49. A psychoanalytic therapist would explain the agoraphobic's fear of leaving the house as
   a. an exaggerated fear stemming from a single panic attack.
   b. the excessive use of the defense mechanism called projection.
   c. a symbolic fear of castration.
   d. an unconscious way of preventing the acting out of sexual desires.

Ans: d
Page: 142
Obj: 7
Type: C

50. Tamisha is so afraid of knives that she cannot enter a kitchen. Her psychoanalytic therapist would probably diagnose her with _____ and explain the problem in terms of _____.
   a. generalized anxiety disorder; faulty reasoning
   b. agoraphobia; pairing knives and pain
   c. social phobia; repression and denial
   d. specific phobia; unresolved aggressive conflicts

Ans: a
Page: 143
Obj: 7
Type: F

51. The case of little Hans is used by psychoanalysts to explain
   a. phobias.
   b. obsessive-compulsive disorder.
   c. generalized anxiety disorder.
   d. posttraumatic stress disorder.

Ans: d
Page: 144
Obj: 7
Type: A

52. Tina is fearful of dogs. She has never had a bad experience with dogs, but her father was injured by a dog when he was a young boy. Tina's father goes to great lengths to avoid contact with dogs. What behavioral theory *best explains* Tina's fear of dogs?
   a. Classical conditioning
   b. Avoidance response
   c. Operant conditioning
   d. Modeling

Ans: c
Page: 144
Obj: 7
Type: A

53. In a research study, cancer patients, prior to undergoing chemotherapy, were given a drink in a container with a bright orange lid. After pairing the drink with chemotherapy, the patients experienced distress and nausea when presented with the container. This study supports a(n) _____ theory of phobias.
   a. observational learning
   b. psychodynamic
   c. classical conditioning
   d. cognitive-behavioral

Ans: c
Page: 144
Obj: 7
Type: F

54. Behaviorists give three reasons for phobias: modeling, negative information, and direct conditioning experiences. Children with strong fears of animals, medical procedures, and criticism were more likely to report the cause of their fears to be:
   a. modeling.
   b. negative information.
   c. conditioning experiences.
   d. none of the three reasons.

Ans: a
Page: 144
Obj: 7
Type: F

55. Phobias seem to run in families. Assuming that this conclusion comes from family studies, why can't we state that the disorder is caused by genetics?
   a. Because it is just as likely that children model the behavior of their parents
   b. Because classical conditioning can account for these results
   c. Because we do not know how genetics influences the central nervous system
   d. Because preparedness influences the likelihood of defective genes being transmitted to offspring

Ans: b
Page: 145
Obj: 7
Type: A

56. Dr. Vannucci says, "Some individuals have high social anxiety and interpret others' actions more negatively than other individuals; they overestimate the chances of unpleasant things happening generally. This is the background for developing a phobia." Dr. Vannucci probably supports the _____ perspective on phobias.
   a. classical conditioning
   b. cognitive-behavioral
   c. operant conditioning
   d. modeling

Ans: b
Page: 146
Obj: 7
Type: F

57. The fact that some people fear harmless animals diminishes the capacity for the _____ explanation to account for all phobias.
   a. substitution
   b. preparedness
   c. classical conditioning
   d. modeling

Ans: d
Page: 147
Obj: 8
Type: A

58. Jesse has a social phobia; Lisa suffers from agoraphobia. Based on research, what will be the *most* effective treatments for Jesse and Lisa?
    a. Jesse is best treated with antidepressants, Lisa with beta blockers.
    b. Jesse and Lisa are best treated with antidepressants.
    c. Jesse is best treated with antidepressants, Lisa with behavioral treatment.
    d. Both will benefit most from behavioral methods.

Ans: a
Page: 147
Obj: 8
Type: F

59. Which of the following is not one of the flaws that hampers the evaluation of using drugs to treat phobias?
    a. Too few studies have been conducted.
    b. Most of the studies rely on self-reports as measures of success.
    c. Few studies use control groups.
    d. The treatment conditions often encourage patients to expose themselves to the fear producing situation, thereby confounding the research.

Ans: b
Page: 147
Obj: 8
Type: C

60. Julie suffers from agoraphobia. Her therapist urges her to take longer and longer walks outside the home with the therapist. What kind of therapy is Julie receiving?
    a. Cognitive restructuring
    b. Exposure therapy
    c. Systematic desensitization
    d. Substitution therapy

Ans: a
Page: 148
Obj: 8
Type: A

61. Ahmad has a specific phobia about elevators. His therapist teaches him how to relax and then has him relax when he is in a building with elevators. Then he practices being relaxed when pushing an elevator button and finally when taking an elevator ride. What kind of therapy did Ahmad experience?
    a. Systematic desensitization
    b. Modeling
    c. Cognitive graduated exposure
    d. Flooding

Ans: d
Page: 147-148
Obj: 8
Type: F

62. Monitoring automatic thoughts, generating alternative rational responses, and developing problem-solving skills are components of _____ therapy for phobias.
    a. systematic desensitization
    b. modeling
    c. gradual exposure
    d. cognitive

Ans: b
Page: 149
Obj: 8
Type: C

63. Maya has a phobia about elevators. Her therapist has her watch other people getting into elevators and coping with crowds inside them. Maya becomes less fearful because she sees how others behave. The therapy being described can be called
    a. cognitive-behavioral.
    b. modeling.
    c. psychoanalytic.
    d. flooding.

Ans: d
Page: 149
Obj: 8
Type: A

64. Melissa's parents are distressed with her microphobia (fear of germs). They have tried several different treatments unsuccessfully, and are now discussing an experimental procedure in which Melissa will wear a helmet with video monitors that produce computer-generated three-dimensional images that will immerse her in a realistic setting, so she will feel like she is actually being exposed to germs. At first she will be able to control her interactions with the germs, but this will later be controlled by the therapist. What type of therapy is this?
a. modeling.
b. systematic desensitization.
c. cognitive-behavioral therapy.
d. virtual reality.

Ans: b
Page: 149
Obj: 9
Type: C

65. Sam has persistent and distressing thoughts of germs; he cannot eat without washing his hands three times before and three times after every meal. Although his hands are raw from the washings, he is overwhelmed with anxiety if he doesn't wash this way. Sam's problems illustrate
a. posttraumatic stress disorder.
b. obsessive-compulsive disorder.
c. agoraphobia.
d. generalized anxiety disorder.

Ans: a
Page: 149
Obj: 9
Type: A

66. Jack has been diagnosed with obsessive-compulsive disorder. He has persistent thoughts that are upsetting and engages in ritualistic actions to reduce anxiety. He feels that he has control over his thoughts and actions but chooses not to stop them. What aspect of Jack's case is *unusual*?
a. Few obsessive-compulsives feel they have control over their thoughts and actions.
b. Few obsessive-compulsives have upsetting thoughts.
c. Few obsessive-compulsives engage in ritualistic actions.
d. Few obsessive-compulsives are male.

Ans: b
Page: 150
Obj: 9
Type: A

67. Peter was on the verge of being fired for tardiness because he is continuously late to work. Peter explains that after leaving his house when he has driven approximately five miles, he becomes concerned that he has hit someone in the road. He feels compelled to turn around and drive back to the spot where he believed he may have hit someone, and although he searches the area, he has never found any evidence of hitting someone. He repeats this sequence of events an average of ten to twenty times each morning, causing him to be late for work. What diagnosis would best fit Peter's experiences?
a. Specific phobic disorder
b. Obsessive-compulsive disorder
c. Peter's behavior is clearly psychotic and does not fit any of the anxiety disorders.
d. Generalized anxiety disorder

Ans: a
Page: 150
Obj: 9
Type: A

68. Suppose you could not get a television advertising jingle out of your head. Unwanted and persistent, the stupid melody ran through your mind for days and weeks without end. This would be similar to
a. the obsessions seen in obsessive-compulsive disorder.
b. the fear seen in generalized anxiety disorder.
c. the compulsions seen in obsessive-compulsive disorder.
d. the avoidance seen in social phobias.

Ans: b
Page: 152
Obj: 9
Type: C

69. Ginny must check four times whether each door and window in her eight-room house is locked before she will leave. In Ginny's mind, this checking has a magical quality—it seems to ward off danger—even though she knows it is absurd and very time-consuming. Ginny's behavior illustrates
    a. the obsessions usually seen in generalized anxiety disorder.
    b. the compulsions usually seen in obsessive-compulsive disorder.
    c. the systematic desensitization that is usually seen in agoraphobia.
    d. the rituals usually seen in panic disorder.

Ans: d
Page: 151-152
Obj: 9
Type: A

70. Angel is worried that her intrusive, unacceptable thoughts are signs of obsessive-compulsive disorder. Research would tell her that
    a. unless the thoughts are bizarre, she does not have the disorder.
    b. she probably has the disorder because it is defined by intrusive thoughts.
    c. she cannot have the disorder unless she engages in compulsive behaviors.
    d. such thoughts are quite common and their mere existence is not very meaningful in diagnosing the disorder.

Ans: c
Page: 152
Obj: 9
Type: F

71. Research shows that in obsessive-compulsives, compulsions
    a. cause little distress if not done "correctly."
    b. rarely change from one ritual act to another.
    c. most commonly involve washing, checking, and repeating acts.
    d. tend to increase anxiety; refraining from compulsions reduces anxiety.

Ans: a
Page: 152
Obj: 10
Type: A

72. "An unwelcome thought (an obsession) is a tolerable substitute for a more anxiety-provoking thought or impulse." This quote best illustrates the _____ perspective on obsessive-compulsive disorder.
    a. psychodynamic
    b. cognitive
    c. humanistic
    d. sociocultural

Ans: b
Page: 153
Obj: 10
Type: F

73. Psychoanalysts would say that obsessive-compulsives overuse the defense mechanism called
    a. projection.
    b. undoing.
    c. rationalization.
    d. sublimation.

Ans: a
Page: 153
Obj: 10
Type: A

74. Cheryl washes her hands again and again, fearing that she is contaminated with urine or feces. She sees a psychoanalyst for treatment. The psychoanalyst is most likely to write which of the following notes about Cheryl's case?
    a. "Guarding against own unacceptable urges; uses reaction formation as a general defense."
    b. "Engages in superstitious behavior; probably associating handwashing with some previous situation where it led to reinforcement."
    c. "Neurotransmitter not functioning properly; needs medication."
    d. "Consciously uses distracting thoughts to reduce anxiety over cleanliness."

Ans: d
Page: 153
Obj: 10
Type: F

75. Undoing, reaction formation, and isolation are all defense mechanisms associated with
    a. the preparedness theory of agoraphobia.
    b. behavioral approaches to preventing relapse in phobias.
    c. effectively using support groups when treating posttraumatic stress disorder.
    d. the substitution theory of obsessive-compulsive disorder.

Ans: b
Page: 154
Obj: 10
Type: A

76. A psychologist who supports a cognitive-behavioral approach would be likely to say which of the following when explaining the cause of obsessive-compulsive disorder?
    a. "Excessive use of defense mechanisms helps the person redirect his or her unacceptable impulses into more acceptable behaviors."
    b. "Thoughts and actions that reduce anxiety are done repetitively."
    c. "Some individuals' personalities need high levels of autonomic nervous system arousal, and repetitive thoughts and behaviors satisfy that need."
    d. "Certain thoughts and actions are the result of abnormal activity in particular brain centers."

Ans: b
Page: 154
Obj: 10
Type: A

77. Behaviorists explain obsessive-compulsive disorder in terms of anxiety reduction. For which case is this explanation *least* adequate?
    a. Max, who distracts himself from work responsibilities by compulsively cleaning his desk
    b. Sarah, who repeatedly thinks about dying in a flaming car wreck
    c. Tia, who repeatedly checks her door locks because her father warned her about criminals in the neighborhood
    d. Vernon, who is normally quite nervous but who calms down when he engages in ritualistic actions

Ans: a
Page: 154
Obj: 10
Type: A

78. Wanda is obsessed with the thought of strangling her daughter. Even though she has never done this, she believes her thoughts are as bad as if she actually carried out the act (which she says she does not want to do). This demonstrates which cognitive characteristic of OCD?
    a. morality bias
    b. probability bias.
    c. disconfirmatory bias.
    d. fear bias.

Ans: d
Page: 154
Obj: 10
Type: A

79. V.J. suffers from obsessive-compulsive disorder. According to the biological perspective, he is likely to
    a. show preparedness in the objects he uses for compulsive behavior.
    b. show abnormally low levels of metabolism in the locus ceruleus.
    c. have an excess of the neurotransmitter serotonin.
    d. show increased metabolic activity in the frontal lobe of the left hemisphere.

Ans: c
Page: 155
Obj: 11
Type: F

80. Drugs that most successfully treat obsessive-compulsive disorder
    a. greatly increase the anxiety level of the patient.
    b. use the patient's sensitivity to sodium lactate.
    c. affect serotonin levels.
    d. act as minor tranquilizers.

Ans: b
Page: 155
Obj: 11
Type: A

81. Hugo suffers from obsessive-compulsive disorder and has been given an antianxiety drug by his psychiatrist. What are the chances that the drug will be helpful in eliminating unwanted thoughts and rituals?
   a. These drugs decrease both thoughts and actions in almost all cases.
   b. These drugs do not decrease the frequency of these symptoms.
   c. If the drugs are of the type that decreases serotonin, they can be helpful.
   d. These drugs can decrease thoughts but not ritualistic actions.

Ans: b
Page: 155
Obj: 11
Type: A

82. A compulsive handwasher is in therapy in which the therapist conjures up several images of filthy clothes and dishes. The client gets the feeling of being "contaminated" but is not allowed to resort to the usual ritual of handwashing. This therapy is called
   a. desensitization and relapse prevention.
   b. exposure with response prevention.
   c. systematic desensitization.
   d. cognitive restructuring.

Ans: d
Page: 155-156
Obj: 11
Type: C

83. Behavioral therapists frequently utilize response prevention strategies because they believe that
   a. a new conditioned stimulus–conditioned response link will be formed.
   b. by challenging a client's cognitive distortions, new schemas will be developed.
   c. shaping will be the most effective way to modify behavior.
   d. blocking avoidant and escape responses will prevent negative reinforcement.

Ans: d
Page: 156
Obj: 11
Type: F

84. The treatment of choice for obsessive-compulsive disorder is a combination of
   a. antidepressants and anti-anxiety drugs.
   b. exposure and flooding.
   c. relaxation and insight psychotherapy.
   d. exposure and response prevention.

Ans: b
Page: 156
Obj: 11
Type: A

85. When her boyfriend asks her about today's therapy session, Jamie responds, "It wasn't very fun. My therapist had me sit right next to her trashcan, which was brimming full of garbage and half-eaten food. I could almost see the germs jumping right out at me. Now she wants me to touch something I think is contaminated at least once a day every day this week." Jamie is probably suffering from _____ and is being treated using _____.
   a. a specific phobia; exposure
   b. obsessive-compulsive disorder; exposure
   c. a specific phobia; systematic rational restructuring
   d. obsessive-compulsive disorder; systematic rational restructuring

Ans: a
Page: 156
Obj: 11
Type: F

86. In the treatment of obsessive-compulsive disorder, a two-stage therapy involving _____ and _____ has proved to be quite effective.
   a. exposure; response prevention
   b. dream analysis; transference
   c. cognitive restructuring; medication
   d. systematic desensitization; minor tranquilizers

Ans: d
Page: 155
Obj: 11
Type: F

87. The text discusses treatment of two African American women for OCD. Their treatment appeared to be complicated by all of the following problems except
   a. each believed she was the only black person to have the disorder.
   b. they felt a sense of isolation when they learned that no other blacks

attended local support groups.
c. the therapy was delivered by European American therapists in an academic setting.
d. cultural differences resulted in different responses to therapy than were seen by their European American counterparts.

Ans: a
Page: 155
Obj: 11
Type: A

88. Sharlisa has unwanted thoughts concerning her daughter being burned in a house fire. Her therapist has had her write down her irrational thoughts and challenge their logic. This form of treatment emphasizes
a. cognitive techniques.
b. exposure therapy.
c. response prevention.
d. flooding.

Ans: d
Page: 156
Obj: 11
Type: F

89. O'Kearney (1993) describes a case in which a woman with obsessive thoughts of gouging out her own eyes was successfully treated by
a. increasing her use of the defense mechanisms called undoing and reaction formation.
b. having her see actual eye surgery.
c. getting her to realize that losing one's eyesight is not a tragedy.
d. monitoring her obsessive thoughts and labeling them as illogical.

Ans: c
Page: 156-157
Obj: 12
Type: A

90. Jane has been experiencing a lot of difficulties since she lost her home in a tornado two months ago. Jane reports that she often relives the moment when she was in her cellar and heard her house being ripped off its foundation. She also reports that she used to love thunderstorms but now she feels overly frightened and panics every time the sky darkens. In addition, she describes herself as numb, not really being able to experience emotions. Jane's problems appear to best fit a diagnosis of
a. specific phobia of storms (astraphobia).
b. panic disorder.
c. posttraumatic stress disorder.
d. acute stress disorder.

Ans: b
Page: 156
Obj: 12
Type: F

91. "Reliving a traumatic experience and trying to avoid reminders of it for between two and thirty days and doing this within four weeks of the original stressor event" defines
a. posttraumatic stress disorder.
b. acute stress disorder.
c. generalized anxiety disorder.
d. simple stress disorder.

Ans: b
Page: 157
Obj: 12
Type: C

92. Norma has problems sleeping and is emotionally withdrawn from her family. She startles easily and has been this way since a specific incident occurred in her life. Norma is *most* likely to be diagnosed as having posttraumatic stress disorder if the event was
a. driving home in a snowstorm.
b. watching her mother die in a house fire.
c. the birth of her second child.
d. working overtime at a job she dislikes intensely.

Ans: c
Page: 156
Obj: 12
Type: A

93. Both Kurt and Magda survived airplane crashes. Both experience intrusive memories of the event. Why might one be diagnosed with acute stress disorder and the other with posttraumatic stress disorder?
    a. If one experienced anxiety and the other did not
    b. If one relived the experience and the other did not
    c. If one had symptoms for more than thirty days and the other did not
    d. If one experienced panic attacks and the other did not

Ans: a
Page: 158
Obj: 13
Type: F

94. Recent research on young adults living in Detroit, Michigan, examined the prevalence of posttraumatic stress disorder (PTSD). What was discovered?
    a. More women than men suffer from PTSD.
    b. Almost any time a person experiences a traumatic event, PTSD is the immediate reaction.
    c. One cannot use previous anxiety problems or family history to predict who will develop PTSD.
    d. Lifetime prevalence of exposure to traumatic events is so small (less than 1 percent) that PTSD is exceptionally rare.

Ans: c
Page: 159
Obj: 12
Type: A

95. Drazen was in Bosnia during the civil war there. He has daytime flashbacks of the bombing and is emotionally numb, withdrawing from friends and family. Although he is much calmer than he was before the war, symptoms have lasted for several months. What about Drazen's case is *unusual* for a person with posttraumatic stress disorder (PTSD)?
    a. It is unusual for people with PTSD to have flashbacks.
    b. It is unusual for people with PTSD to withdraw from others.
    c. It is unusual for people with PTSD to become calm.
    d. It is unusual for people with PTSD to have symptoms longer than thirty days.

Ans: c
Page: 160
Obj: 12
Type: A

96. Suppose you were the director of a rape crisis center. What could you expect in terms of the frequency of posttraumatic stress disorder (PTSD) among the clients who come to your center immediately and three months after being assaulted?
    a. Because PTSD is delayed, no one would meet the criteria for PTSD immediately; about 2 percent would suffer from PTSD at three months.
    b. About 10 percent would meet the criteria for PTSD immediately; about 50 percent would suffer from PTSD at three months.
    c. Almost every client would meet the criteria for PTSD immediately; about half would still suffer from it at three months.
    d. Because rape is quite common, there will be almost no cases of PTSD either immediately or three months after the assault.

Ans: b
Page: 160
Obj: 13
Type: F

97. All of the following appear to be important variables in developing PTSD except:
    a. The degree of trauma.
    b. Premorbid predisposing factors.
    c. The person's own coping styles.
    d. Whether the person has a supportive recovery environment.

Ans: c
Page: 158
Obj: 12
Type: F

98. Research from the National Comorbidity Survey on Americans aged 15-54, that examined the prevalence of posttraumatic stress disorder (PTSD), discovered
   a. less than 1 percent
   b. about 3 percent
   c. almost 24 percent
   d. over 50 percent

Ans: d
Page: 161
Obj: 13
Type: A

99. Mitchell, a Vietnam veteran, spends his therapy sessions describing the horrors of combat. His therapist has him recall all the details, focusing on the horrific events for extended periods of time. Mitchell's therapist is most likely utilizing a _____ approach and treating him for _____.
   a. humanistic; generalized anxiety disorder
   b. cognitive-behavioral; generalized anxiety disorder
   c. humanistic; posttraumatic stress disorder
   d. cognitive-behavioral; posttraumatic stress disorder

Ans: c
Page: 162-163
Obj: 13
Type: F

100. A friend who suffers from posttraumatic stress disorder is receiving eye movement desensitization therapy. She wants to know whether it is a good treatment for PTSD. You should say,
   a. "It has been used for thirty years and is the most effective treatment known."
   b. "It is a well-known treatment but should be used only to treat social phobia."
   c. "It is a recent development, and studies have called into question both its effectiveness and its theoretical foundation."
   d. "No one has ever shown it to be an effective treatment for PTSD."

ESSAY QUESTIONS

1. Phobic disorders are frequently grouped into three different categories. List these three categories (categories, not individual phobias such as "fear of heights"), and provide a description of the characteristics associated with each. Discuss briefly behavioral theories that explain how phobic disorders may be acquired and how phobic behavior may be maintained over many years.

2. Compare and contrast the conditioning, observational learning, and cognitive theories of the development of phobias.

3. Using research evidence, describe a comprehensive and effective method for treatment of obsessive-compulsive disorder.

SAMPLE ANSWERS

1. The three different phobic disorders are specific phobia, social phobia, and agoraphobia. *Specific phobia* is the unrealistic and excessive fear of a specific animal, object, or situation. Common examples include fear of needles, flying, elevators, bugs, dentists, and snakes. An individual with a specific phobia experiences anticipatory anxiety when aware of an impending situation that may force a confrontation with the feared object. When the individual is actually exposed to the feared object, there is almost always an intense and immediate anxiety response. *Social phobia* is persistent fear of being in a social situation in which one is exposed to scrutiny by others and a related fear of acting in a way that will be humiliating or embarrassing or where social disapproval may occur. Examples of social phobias include irrational reactions to eating in public places, using public

restrooms, public speaking, or attending social gatherings. Like the specific phobic, the social phobic experiences marked anxiety when anticipating the phobic situation and thus usually avoids such situations that interfere with his or her daily functioning. *Agoraphobia* is a marked fear of being alone or of being in public places where escape is difficult or where help is not readily available in the event of a panic attack. Often individuals with agoraphobia experience intense fear in shopping malls, in crowds, or in tunnels, bridges, or public vehicles. The primary characteristic of agoraphobia is severe phobic anxiety and phobic avoidance of the feared situation. Many agoraphobic individuals are housebound as a result of their avoidance and only venture forth when accompanied by a close and trusted companion.

Behavioral theories may be used to explain the acquisition and maintenance of phobic behaviors. Specifically, *classical conditioning* may explain the acquisition of phobias, while *operant conditioning* may explain the maintenance of phobic responses. *Social learning theory* also may explain the development of phobic behavior.

2. The first behavioral explanation for phobias was supplied by John B. Watson and emphasized classical conditioning. If a formerly neutral (conditioned) stimulus is paired with a conditioned stimulus that elicits fear, the conditioned stimulus will, in time, have the capacity to elicit fear itself. As in the Watson and Rayner (Little Albert) experiment, the sight of white fur was paired with a loud noise and came to produce crying on its own. However, attempts to replicate this early study were unsuccessful, and many people with phobias cannot recall any such conditioning experiences. Fully 71 percent of spider phobics report that another cause was evident—modeling someone else who was fearful. Indirect experience may account for as many or more phobias as direct conditioning. Conditioning is also limited by preparedness—the fact that some stimulus associations are more easily made than others. Therefore, biological predisposition may make the development of some phobias (machinery, for instance) less likely than others (small animals).

Observational learning agrees with the conditioning approach that phobias stem from experiences in the world and stimulus-response connections. However, observational learning argues that fears can be learned through indirect rather than direct conditioning. Experimental research suggests that fears can be learned this way, but surveys of people with phobias indicate that, in their memory, indirect conditioning was a factor in only a minority of cases.

An even more indirect way of developing phobias is to have a fear-inducing way of thinking. Some researchers argue that people with phobias have negative thoughts and develop fears when they "listen to themselves." Fears are dramatically reduced when such negative thoughts are challenged and removed.

It is possible that these three factors interact to explain many phobias. Whether by direct or indirect conditioning, people develop a fear response to specific stimuli. Those who are most vulnerable to such conditioning may have a predisposing tendency to think fearful and negative thoughts. Alternatively, once they have experienced a conditioning episode, those who adopt such negative thoughts make themselves more fearful and responsive to any further conditioning experiences.

3. Obsessive-compulsive disorder (OCD) has biological, behavioral, and cognitive components. A comprehensive therapy must address all three. Since OCD is an anxiety disorder, it might seem likely that antianxiety medications would be effective. Research shows this not to be the case. Instead, antidepressants such as clomipramine and fluvoxamine have been shown to reduce symptoms. Unfortunately, relief is often partial and relapse likely.

Research shows that a particularly effective treatment is a combination of exposure and response prevention, which addresses the behavioral aspects of the disorder. Individuals are presented with actual fear-arousing stimuli or imagine them vividly. This increases arousal markedly and generates a strong desire to engage in rituals. Instead of reducing the anxiety through compulsive behaviors (e.g., hand-washing), the client maintains the anxiety until it is extinguished. Repeated exposure to the anxiety-producing stimuli and being prevented from engaging in compulsive behaviors rapidly stops symptomatic behavior.

Because OCD also has a strong cognitive component, treatment should address clients' irrational thoughts. Case studies show that getting clients to identify their irrational thoughts and replace them with more rational ones can be an adjunct to behavioral treatment. OCD in a fourteen-year-old boy with irrational thoughts about bats and rabies was successfully treated this way.

CHAPTER 6
Dissociative Disorders and Somatoform Disorders

LEARNING OBJECTIVES

1. Discuss the fundamental characteristics involved in dissociative disorders, and list the four types of dissociative disorders. (pp. 167-168; Figure 6.1)

2. Discuss the characteristics of the four types of dissociative amnesia and the process by which they occur. (pp. 169–170)

3. Describe the characteristics of dissociative fugue and depersonalization disorder. (pp. 170–173)

4. Discuss the controversy over the validity of "repressed memories" and research that indicates the possibility of false memories. (pp. 170–171; Critical Thinking; First Person)

5. Describe the characteristics of dissociative identity (multiple personality) disorder and its prevalence. (pp. 173–175)

6. Discuss the diagnostic controversies concerning dissociative identity disorder. (pp. 175–176)

7. Discuss and distinguish the psychodynamic, behavioral, and iatrogenic (therapist-produced) explanations for dissociative disorders. (pp. 176–179)

8. Discuss the treatment of dissociative amnesia and fugue, depersonalization disorder, and dissociative identity disorder. (pp. 179–183; Mental Health & Society)

9. Describe the basic characteristics of somatoform disorders and distinguish them from malingering and factitious disorders. (pp. 173, 183–185; Mental Health & Society; Figures 6.4 & 6.4B)

10. List and describe the five subtypes of somatoform disorder, including somatization disorder, conversion disorder, pain disorder, hypochondriasis, and body dysmorphic disorder. (pp. 184–191; Table 6.1; Mental Health & Society)

11. Describe and discuss the causes of somatoform disorders from the psychodynamic, behavioral, sociocultural, and biological perspectives, and the diathesis-stress model. (pp. 192–195)

12. Describe and discuss the treatment of somatoform disorders with psychoanalytic, behavioral, and family systems therapies. (pp. 195–196)

MULTIPLE–CHOICE QUESTIONS

Ans: d
Page: 167
Obj: 1
Type: C

1. A psychologist says, "This person's problem is that a part of her consciousness—her memory—has split off from the rest of her consciousness, even though there is no evidence of brain damage." The psychologist is describing a person with
   a. an organic brain disorder.
   b. an anxiety disorder.
   c. a somatoform disorder.
   d. a dissociative disorder.

Ans: c
Page: 167
Obj: 1
Type: F

2. All of the following are examples of dissociative disorders *except*
   a. depersonalization disorder.
   b. dissociative identity disorder.
   c. conversion disorder.
   d. dissociative fugue.

Ans: a
Page: 167
Obj: 1
Type: C

3. In a classroom presentation, Kato reports, "Dissociative disorders are nonpsychotic conditions in which people develop physical problems even though there is no physiological cause. They are very rare." What error has Kato made?
   a. Dissociative disorders do not involve physical problems.
   b. Dissociative disorders are physiologically caused.
   c. Dissociative disorders are psychotic conditions.
   d. Dissociative disorders are relatively common.

Ans: d
Page: 167
Obj: 1
Type: A

4. In which of the following countries would you expect the government mental health officials to be most concerned about providing publically financed treatment for dissociative disorders because the reported prevalence was *highest*?
   a. England
   b. Scotland
   c. Japan
   d. United States

Ans: c
Page: 167
Obj: 1
Type: F

5. The symptoms of dissociative disorder and somatoform disorder generally ecome known through
   a. clinical observation.
   b. complaints by a patient's family members.
   c. self-reports.
   d. psychological testing.

Ans: a
Page: 168
Obj: 1
Type: C

6. Which of the following *best* illustrates the concept of dissociation?
   a. While traveling from home to work and thinking about an important meeting, Jonathan noticed that he traveled several miles without remembering anything about the drive.
   b. At a high school reunion, Kerry cannot remember the names of some of her former classmates.
   c. A nervous Marlene cannot remember her lines during the opening of a play.
   d. Even after two weeks in the hospital, Thomas remains unconscious following a motorcycle accident.

Ans: b
Page: 169
Obj: 2
Type: F

7. Which type of dissociative amnesia disorder is *correctly* paired with its chief characteristic?
    a. Generalized amnesia—partial loss of memory for a short period of time
    b. Localized amnesia—loss of all memory for a short period of time
    c. Localized amnesia—memory loss due to brain damage in a particular area of the cortex
    d. Selective amnesia—memory loss associated with fleeing a stressful event and developing a new identity

Ans: a
Page: 169
Obj: 2
Type: F

8. Which form of dissociative amnesia involves the inability to remember details of an incident and is quite commonly claimed by individuals charged with homicide?
    a. Selective amnesia
    b. Continuous amnesia
    c. Dissociative fugue
    d. Localized amnesia

Ans: c
Page: 169
Obj: 2
Type: A

9. Pedro has the most common form of dissociative amnesia. He was a witness to his father's murder but has no memory of the event. This illustrates
    a. depersonalization.
    b. fugue.
    c. localized amnesia.
    d. generalized amnesia.

Ans: a
Page: 170
Obj: 2
Type: A

10. Jane Doe had total memory loss of her previous life. Even when her parents identified her when she appeared on television, she claimed she could not remember them as her parents. Jane illustrates
    a. generalized amnesia.
    b. hypochondriasis.
    c. selective amnesia.
    d. somatization disorder.

Ans: b
Page: 170
Obj: 2
Type: F

11. _____ is similar to dissociative amnesia because recall is impaired after a specific event and can be retrieved later with professional help.
    a. Depersonalization disorder
    b. Posthypnotic amnesia
    c. Continuous amnesia
    d. Somatization disorder

Ans: d
Page: 170
Obj: 3
Type: A

12 Jerald wakes up in New Jersey, some four hundred miles from his home in New Hampshire. He cannot remember how he got there, and he has no memory of his former life. He establishes a new identity in New Jersey. This illustrates
    a. dissociative identity disorder.
    b. localized amnesia.
    c. depersonalization disorder.
    d. dissociative fugue.

Ans: c
Page: 170
Obj: 3
Type: A

13. Dante is diagnosed with dissociative fugue. He adopted a completely new identity while staying in his hometown. His amnesia lasted only a short time. What aspect of this case is *unusual* for dissociative fugue?
    a. It is unusual for a male to have a dissociative disorder.
    b. It is unusual for fugue to involve a completely new identity.
    c. It is unusual for people with fugue to remain in their hometown.
    d. It is unusual for dissociative fugue to last only a short time.

Ans: b
Page: 172
Obj: 3
Type: C

14. When comparing dissociative amnesia and dissociative fugue, which statement below is *accurate*?
    a. Dissociative fugue is a very common disorder, but dissociative amnesia is quite rare.
    b. In both dissociative fugue and dissociative amnesia, recovery tends to be abrupt and complete.
    c. Dissociative fugue is psychogenic in origin, but dissociative amnesia is not.
    d. Complete recovery from dissociative fugue is rare, but recovery from dissociative amnesia is common.

Ans: d
Page: 171
Obj: 4
Type: C

15. Are reports of formerly repressed memories authentic?
    a. Research suggests that they are authentic in 80 to 90 percent of cases.
    b. Research suggests that they are authentic in about half of all cases.
    c. Research suggests that such memories are primarily the result of popular writings and leading questions by therapists.
    d. No studies have scientifically examined the validity of such memories; thus, one must use caution in accepting them.

Ans: d
Page: 172
Obj: 3
Type: C

16. Teresa has an intense and terrifying feeling that she is no longer real and that she is looking at herself and the world from a distance. These feelings have caused major impairments in her work and personal life. The *most* likely diagnosis is
    a. dissociative amnesia.
    b. dissociative identity disorder.
    c. somatoform disorder.
    d. depersonalization disorder.

Ans: d
Page: 172
Obj: 3
Type: C

17. Colleen has been diagnosed with depersonalization disorder. Which of the following symptoms should be present?
    a. Vague and diverse physical complaints such as nausea and headache
    b. An inability to remember events just before and during a crisis
    c. Travel to another town and the establishment of a new identity
    d. Perceptions that her body is distorted or that life is unreal

Ans: c
Page: 172
Obj: 3
Type: C

18. Depersonalization disorder differs from other dissociative disorders in that it
    a. is caused by physiological abnormalities such as brain damage.
    b. involves total loss of memory of one's past.
    c. is relatively common.
    d. is rarely related to stressful events.

Ans: a
Page: 172
Obj: 3
Type: A

19. Caitlyn has been diagnosed with depersonalization disorder. We can guess that she would make which of the following statements?
    a. "I must be going crazy because it seems that my body is distorted and unreal."
    b. "I can remember going into the house when it was on fire, but I cannot remember getting out."
    c. "I found myself in a new city with a new identity and no recollection of who Caitlyn was."
    d. "I have strange feelings when people seem to know me but call me by the name Caitlyn; I don't even know who they are talking about."

Ans: b
Page: 171
Obj: 4
Type: C

20. Which statement about the validity of repressed memories is *accurate*?
    a. Because hypnosis is the main way repressed memories are uncovered, we can be fairly certain they are valid memories, as hypnosis uncovers material deeply buried in one's unconscious.
    b. Determining the validity of memories dating from an early age is very difficult.
    c. In almost every case, it has been shown that repressed memories of sexual abuse does not exist.
    d. Because people do not forget other traumatic events, repression must be the explanation for forgotten sexual abuse.

Ans: c
Page: 174
Obj: 5
Type: C

21. Delta is diagnosed as having dissociative identity disorder (DID). She was severely abused as a child and, in response, developed three distinct personalities, all of whom are aware of one another. What aspect of Delta's case is *unusual* for DID?
    a. She was severely abused as a child.
    b. She has more than two personalities.
    c. Her personalities are all aware of one another.
    d. She is a female.

Ans: b
Page: 174
Obj: 5
Type: A

22. Lyndsey has been diagnosed with dissociative identity disorder. She claims that she has fifteen different personalities, that each personality is aware of all the others, that each demonstrates quite different personality traits, and that the shifts from one personality to another occur quite abruptly. What is *unusual* about Lyndsey's description of her symptoms?
    a. The fact that she has fifteen different personalities.
    b. The fact that all the personalities are aware of one another.
    c. The fact that the personalities have such different characteristics.
    d. The fact that the transition from one personality to another is abrupt.

Ans: a
Page: 174
Obj: 5
Type: F

23. Which statement about the development of dissociative identity disorder is *accurate*?
    a. Child abuse is frequently reported as the trigger for the disorder.
    b. The start of the disorder is usually unrelated to family stresses.
    c. The disorder usually cannot be detected until middle age.
    d. Males are more likely to develop the disorder than females.

Ans: b
Page: 174
Obj: 5
Type: A

24. Jenna has been diagnosed with dissociative identity disorder. Which of the following facts in her case is *unusual* for such a disorder?
    a. She developed her first set of personalities when she was a child.
    b. She reports no history of physical or sexual abuse.
    c. She has feelings of anxiety and depression.
    d. She is highly suggestible and can be hypnotized.

Ans: c
Page: 174
Obj: 5
Type: F

25. Is there a gender difference in dissociative identity disorder?
     a. No, men and women of all cultures are equally likely to have the disorder.
     b. Yes, men are far more likely to have the disorder.
     c. Yes, but the increased prevalence of females having the disorder may be specific to the United States.
     d. Yes, females always have "male" personalities, while males always have "female" personalities.

Ans: d
Page: 174
Obj: 5
Type: C

26. The hypothesized origin of DID is that it is
     a. due to a biochemical imbalance in neurotransmitters.
     b. a modeled reaction.
     c. a form of malingering.
     d. a defense against intensely painful experiences.

Ans: b
Pages: 174
Obj: 5
Type: F

27. When compared with individuals in other diagnostic groups, females diagnosed with dissociative identity disorder
     a. report fewer alterations in consciousness.
     b. are more likely to have a history of trance states and sleepwalking.
     c. have lower levels of substance abuse.
     d. have lower IQ scores.

Ans: d
Page: 175
Obj: 5
Type: F

28. Goff and Simms (1993) compared case reports of dissociative identity disorder from the years before 1965 and from the 1980s. More recent cases tend to
     a. have fewer personalities.
     b. have their onset later in life.
     c. be quite rare in the United States.
     d. have a higher incidence of reported child abuse.

Ans: d
Pages: 175
Obj: 5
Type: F

29. Gleaves (1996) does not believe that dissociative identity disorder is due to iatrogenic factors for all of the following reasons except
     a. individuals with the disorder show a core set of symptoms
     b. most individuals with dissociative identity disorder are not hypnotized before the diagnosis is made.
     c. a distinct set of characteristics is found for patients diagnosed with dissociative identity disorder as compared with patients who do not have the disorder.
     d. dissociative identity disorder is well-documented in many countries around the world.

Ans: c
Page: 175
Obj: 6
Type: C

30. The fact that dissociation is a common result of both stress and hypnosis suggests that
     a. more people experience dissociative identity disorder than was previously believed because of increasing stress experienced in our society.
     b. hypnosis is a stressful experience for most people.
     c. dissociation may be a symptom of stress or the result of expectation rather than a sign of a disorder.
     d. dissociative identity disorder does not really exist.

Ans: c
Page: 176
Obj: 6
Type: C

31. Dr. Young asks these questions of a child: "Do you ever sort of space out? Does it ever happen that time goes by and you can't remember what you were doing during that time? Do you ever do things that surprise you and you later stop and ask yourself why you did that?" What problem is Dr. Young investigating?
    a. Conversion disorder
    b. Somatization disorder
    c. Dissociation
    d. Panic disorder

Ans: a
Page: 177
Obj: 6
Type: A

32. A friend of yours asks, "Isn't it easy to tell when a person is faking the symptoms of dissociative identity disorder?" An *accurate* answer would be,
    a. "No, even experts cannot distinguish real and faked amnesia."
    b. "No, there are no differences even in objective measures like EEG when people are in different personalities."
    c. "Yes, diagnosis is usually done after hypnosis, when people are most truthful."
    d. "Yes, differences in EEG tracing prove who is showing a different personality and who is not."

Ans: d
Page: 175
Obj: 6
Type: C

33. All of the following suggests that socio-cultural influences are involved in the diagnosis of dissociative identity disorder *except*
    a. an increase in DID diagnoses after 1973, the year the movie *Sybil* was made.
    b. a shift in diagnoses from males to females before and after 1965.
    c. DID is rarely diagnosed in countries other than the U.S. and Canada.
    d. the increased use of questionnaires with established reliability and validity.

Ans: d
Page: 175
Obj: 7
Type: C

34. Repression is to the _____ explanation for dissociative disorders as _____ is to the behavioral explanation.
    a. socio-cultural; projection
    b. family systems; contingent reinforcement
    c. psychodynamic; projection
    d. psychodynamic; avoidance

Ans: d
Page: 176
Obj: 7
Type: A

35. Dr. Hart is a psychoanalyst treating a patient with dissociative identity disorder. He will probably explain the loss of memory in his patient as being due to
    a. the attention the patient receives for being so forgetful.
    b. excessive id control and a lack of superego.
    c. a lack of conflicts within the patient's personality structure.
    d. extreme repression in the face of intense anxiety.

Ans: d
Page: 176
Obj: 7
Type: C

36. What is the perspective that explains the cause of dissociative disorders this way: "Extraordinary stress threatens the very existence of the ego and produces extraordinary repression"?
    a. Behavioral
    b. Biological
    c. Family systems
    d. Psychodynamic

Ans: b
Page: 178
Obj: 7
Type: A

37. Harvey is diagnosed with dissociative identity disorder. His mother severely abused him from the time he was six years old. The first of his personalities developed around seven. According to a psychoanalyst, the development of separate personalities served the purpose of
  a. increasing the variety in a dull and boring world.
  b. taking the pain of the abuse so that his core personality would survive.
  c. helping Harvey to remember his mother's viciousness when he grew older.
  d. getting Harvey additional attention from family members.

Ans: d
Page: 178
Obj: 7
Type: C

38. A psychologist says, "The disorder develops because, in the face of overwhelming stress, the person has the capacity to dissociate and wall off the traumatic experience. This happens when there is no support in the family." The psychologist probably holds a _____ perspective on _____.
  a. behavioral; dissociative identity disorder
  b. behavioral; somatoform disorder
  c. psychodynamic; hypochondriasis
  d. psychodynamic; dissociative identity disorder

Ans: a
Page: 178
Obj: 7
Type: C

39. According to psychodynamically oriented thinkers, traumatic events alone do not produce multiple personality. There must also be a
  a. capacity to dissociate.
  b. lack of superego function.
  c. lack of id.
  d. model for this behavior.

Ans: d
Page: 175
Obj: 7
Type: A

40. Dr. Kim believes that increases in the frequency of diagnosing dissociative identity disorder have occurred because of iatrogenic effects. Which argument would Dr. Kim *most* likely use?
  a. EEG patterns are consistently different when those diagnosed with the disorder experience different personalities.
  b. Therapists tend to see the disorder as a way of escaping from unpleasant interpersonal situations.
  c. Reports of child abuse cannot be influenced by instructions or expectations.
  d. Most therapists who diagnose the disorder use hypnosis and other memory retrieval methods that rely on suggestion.

Ans: d
Page: 178
Obj: 7
Type: A

41. A therapist says this about a person with dissociative amnesia: "Forgetting who you are is an avoidance mechanism for coping with unpleasant emotions." The therapist probably holds a
  a. diathesis-stress perspective.
  b. biomedical perspective.
  c. psychoanalytic perspective.
  d. behavioral perspective.

Ans: b
Page: 178
Obj: 7
Type: C

42. Dr. Penn believes that dissociative amnesias are due to avoidance of unpleasant emotional conflicts. People with this disorder run from stressful situations by blocking out all disturbing thoughts of them. Furthermore, they gain attention by developing these symptoms. Dr. Penn probably supports the _____ perspective.
    a. iatrogenic
    b. behavioral
    c. psychodynamic
    d. socio-cultural

Ans: c
Page: 178
Obj: 7
Type: C

43. Rule-governed and goal-directed experiences, displays of multiple role enactments, and social reinforcement are all key concepts in the _____ explanation for dissociative disorders.
    a. psychodynamic
    b. family systems
    c. socio-cognitive
    d. iatrogenic

Ans: c
Page: 179
Obj: 7
Type: C

44. Saying that dissociative identity disorder is iatrogenic means that it is
    a. caused by blocking the full expression of id impulses.
    b. a fictitious or made-up diagnosis.
    c. an unintended result of therapy.
    d. an unacceptable way of avoiding social responsibilities.

Ans: b
Page: 179
Obj: 7
Type: F

45. Because the origin of dissociative identity disorder in some cases may stem from the expectations and reinforcements of therapists, the disorder may be considered
    a. somatoform.
    b. iatrogenic.
    c. psychosomatic.
    d. a form of malingering.

Ans: c
Page: 179
Obj: 7
Type: F

46. Research by Spanos et al. (1985) using college students discovered that
    a. hypnosis plays no role in the ability to produce different personalities.
    b. few laypeople believe in the diagnosis of dissociative identity disorder.
    c. suggestions given under hypnosis influenced students to produce different personalities.
    d. only 3 percent of students could be influenced to produce different personalities.

Ans: d
Page: 180
Obj: 8
Type: A

47. Dr. Abdullah's new patient is diagnosed with dissociative fugue. Rather than doing in-depth psychotherapy, the doctor prescribes an antidepressant and provides emotional support. Why would Dr. Abdullah respond this way?
    a. The doctor probably sees the condition as iatrogenic.
    b. The doctor probably agrees with the psychodynamic perspective.
    c. The doctor probably knows that fugue is a hopeless condition that is untreatable.
    d. The doctor probably knows that fugue goes away spontaneously and that depression is the only significant treatable symptom.

Ans: a
Page: 180
Obj: 8
Type: F

48. Which symptoms are often found in association with fugue and dissociative amnesia?
   a. Stress and depression
   b. Conversion disorder and hysteria
   c. Hypochondriasis and phobia
   d. Depression and mania

Ans: b
Page: 181
Obj: 8
Type: C

49. The behavioral approach to treating depersonalization disorder would emphasize
   a. the use of hypnosis to uncover the hidden reasons for symptoms.
   b. alleviating feelings of anxiety or depression, or the fear of going insane.
   c. extinguishing the person's complaints about loss of memory.
   d. increasing the person's awareness of his or her different personalities.

Ans: c
Page: 181
Obj: 8
Type: F

50. Coons (1986) did follow-up research on twenty patients treated for dissociative identity disorder. The findings show that
   a. almost all of them were successfully reintegrated.
   b. most showed great improvement in the first months, but all relapsed within a year.
   c. none of them showed enough improvement to be employed.
   d. about one-third were unable to work due to their disorder.

Ans: c
Page: 178
Obj: 8
Type: C

51. Dr. Newman used hypnosis to help Marianne return to her childhood and uncover a hidden trauma that might be causing her symptoms. Her therapeutic orientation is probably
   a. humanistic/existential.
   b. cognitive.
   c. psychodynamic.
   d. behaviorist.

Ans: d
Page: 181
Obj: 8
Type: A

52. Donna is diagnosed as having dissociative identity disorder. She can expect that her therapist is likely to use _____ combined with psychotherapy to help her become aware of her different personalities.
   a. antidepressant medication
   b. biofeedback
   c. systematic desensitization
   d. hypnosis

Ans: a
Page: 181
Obj: 8
Type: A

53. A psychological training institute wants to teach young therapists how to treat patients with dissociative identity disorder. If the training uses the *most* common approach to treating the disorder, they will teach
   a. psychotherapy and hypnosis.
   b. flooding and response prevention.
   c. systematic desensitization and hypnosis.
   d. role playing and response prevention.

Ans: b
Page: 184
Obj: 9
Type: A

54. Joshua is a rehabilitation counselor whose job is to help disabled people become reemployed in another appropriate occupation. Joshua is concerned that there has been an increase in the number of people claiming to be disabled by stress or feigning physical injuries in order to receive government disability payments. What concept best identifies Joshua's concern?
   a. factitious disorder
   b. malingering
   c. moral anxiety
   d. collaborative empiricism

Ans: d
Page: 184
Obj: 10
Type: F

55. Which of the following is *not* a somatoform disorder?
    a. Body dysmorphic disorder
    b. Hypochondriasis
    c. Conversion disorder
    d. Factitious disorder

Ans: a
Page: 183
Obj: 10
Type: C

56. A psychologist says, "We know it is a psychological disorder because the physical symptoms have no physiological basis and the symptoms are not under voluntary control." What is the psychologist describing?
    a. Somatoform disorders
    b. Anxiety disorders
    c. Dissociative amnesia
    d. Dissociative disorders

Ans: a
Page: 184
Obj: 9
Type: C

57. What is the primary difference between factitious disorder and malingering?
    a. The feigning of symptoms in factitious disorder is motivated by a desire to assume the sick role, while the motivation in malingering is typically for an economic gain.
    b. The symptoms in factitious disorder are not produced intentionally, whereas they are in malingering.
    c. The symptoms in malingering are not produced intentionally, whereas they are in factitious disorder.
    d. The feigning of symptoms in factitious disorder is motivated by economic gain or to avoid some unpleasant task, whereas the motivation in malingering is to assume the sick role.

Ans: d
Page: 184
Obj: 9
Type: C

58. The chief difference between somatoform disorders and factitious disorders is whether the condition is
    a. a way of avoiding responsibility or not.
    b. iatrogenic or not.
    c. produced by the doctor's treatment or not.
    d. self-inflicted or not.

Ans: b
Page: 184
Obj: 9
Type: A

59. Wanda fakes her pain complaints because she is hoping to get a large monetary award from an insurance company. Roberta experiences fever and pain because she has injected herself with bacteria. Wanda's behavior illustrates _____; Roberta's behavior illustrates _____.
    a. malingering; somatoform disorder
    b. malingering; factitious disorder
    c. factitious disorder; malingering
    d. factitious disorder; somatoform disorder

Ans: c
Page: 184
Obj: 9
Type: A

60. In the movie *Ferris Bueler's Day Off*, Ferris deliberately induces his own headaches and stomach pains so that he could avoid going to school. Aside from his irresponsibility, Ferris would *best* be diagnosed as having
    a. conduct disorder.
    b. impulse control disorder.
    c. a factitious disorder.
    d. hypochondriasis.

Ans: d
Page: 184
Obj: 9
Type: C

61. Suppose you are the director of a mental health clinic in a neighborhood where many immigrants from India, China, and Korea live. You could expect that clients coming from these Asian backgrounds would
    a. feel that anyone with a somatoform disorder is morally weak.
    b. have almost no somatoform disorders.
    c. believe that any somatic complaints they have come from emotional stress.
    d. believe that physical problems produce emotional problems.

Ans: b
Page: 184
Obj: 9
Type: F

62. The difference between a psychosomatic and a somatopsychic view of physical symptoms is *most* likely to be emphasized by psychologists who support the _____ perspective.
    a. psychodynamic
    b. multicultural
    c. biogenic
    d. humanistic

Ans: b
Page: 184
Obj: 10
Type: A

63. Bethany has spent the past ten years in and out of hospitals. She suffers from numerous physical complaints including severe hip, joint, leg, and head pain, and frequent bouts of diarrhea and constipation, and often reports general numbing sensations. Although numerous doctors and extensive tests revealed no physical problems, Bethany still reports vague symptoms of physical problems. Bethany's problems would best fit a diagnosis of
    a. premenstrual syndrome (PMS).
    b. somatization disorder.
    c. hypochondriasis.
    d. body dysmorphic disorder.

Ans: a
Page: 184
Obj: 10
Type: C

64. A person who continually shops around for a doctor to diagnose the cause of multiple bodily symptoms that have no physical basis is *most* likely to be demonstrating the disorder called
    a. somatization disorder.
    b. malingering.
    c. conversion disorder.
    d. body dysmorphic disorder.

Ans: c
Page: 184
Obj: 10
Type: A

65. Marge has gone to doctors with more than twenty different somatic complaints in the past year and has had surgery four times. She has few anxiety or depressive symptoms, but doctors never satisfy her when they say, "There's nothing wrong with you physically." What is *unusual* about this patient?
    a. People with somatization disorder rarely shop around for doctors.
    b. Somatization disorders usually show only one physical complaint.
    c. Somatization disorder often includes depression and anxiety.
    d. Somatization disorder often involves two personalities.

Ans: c
Page: 186
Obj: 10
Type: F

66. Which statement about somatization disorder is *accurate*?
    a. It is a form of dissociative disorder.
    b. It is rarely associated with anxiety, depression, or other psychiatric disorders.
    c. It is relatively rare, having a prevalence of 2 percent.
    d. It is much more prevalent among men than among women.

Ans: a
Page: 186
Obj: 10
Type: F

67. Which is a recent change in the use of the term *somatization disorder*?
   a. It used to be grouped together with conversion disorder.
   b. It used to be rare but has recently become common.
   c. It used to be called hypochondriasis.
   d. It used to be much more common among men than among women.

Ans: c
Page: 186
Obj: 10
Type: F

68. Research on sex differences in somatization disorder shows that
   a. it is one of the most common disorders in older women and men but is extremely rare among younger women and men.
   b. although men are far more likely to be diagnosed with the disorder, women sometimes show a variation of it.
   c. although it is rarely diagnosed in men, about one-third of men with unexplained physical complaints meet the diagnostic criteria.
   d. in the United States, it is common in men, while in Asia, it is far more common in women.

Ans: d
Page: 184
Obj: 10
Type: A

69. Monica complains of chest and head pains, amnesia, nausea, and sexual problems. She goes from doctor to doctor, but none can find a physical cause for her complaints. Stephen suddenly became blind one day shortly after his boss put him under great psychological stress. There is no physiological explanation for his blindness. Monica *best* illustrates _____; Stephen best illustrates _____.
   a. conversion disorder; factitious disorder
   b. somatization disorder; hypochondriasis
   c. hypochondriasis; factitious disorder
   d. somatization disorder; conversion disorder

Ans: d
Page: 186
Obj: 10
Type: A

70. Amelia's parents were from India and continued to follow the traditions of that country. Her parents had selected her husband for her, and she was to be married in two weeks. One morning, however, Amelia woke up paralyzed, and she had no use of her legs. A thorough medical examination could find nothing physically wrong that would account for Amelia's paralysis. Amelia would *most likely* be diagnosed with
   a. hypochondriasis.
   b. factitious disorder.
   c. malingering.
   d. conversion disorder.

Ans: a
Page: 186
Obj: 10
Type: C

71. Which person's symptoms are the *most* obvious sign of a possible conversion disorder?
   a. Joan, who says her legs have been paralyzed for six months but who shows no muscle atrophy
   b. Keith, who goes from doctor to doctor complaining of pains and symptoms in many different parts of his body
   c. Lilly, who constantly thinks about the size of her ears and wants plastic surgery to reconstruct them
   d. Wes, who has had backaches that have gone on longer than his doctor thinks is reasonable

Ans: d
Page: 186
Obj: 10
Type: A

72. As Will approached the witness stand, he stopped and clutched his throat. He had to leave the courtroom because he was unable to speak. His condition might be diagnosed as
   a. panic disorder.
   b. social phobia.
   c. agoraphobia.
   d. conversion disorder.

Ans: b
Page: 186
Obj: 10
Type: F

73. Paralysis, anesthesia, and prickling or tingling sensations are common complaints in
   a. hypochondriasis.
   b. conversion disorder.
   c. dissociative pain disorder.
   d. somatization disorder.

Ans: a
Page: 188
Obj: 10
Type: F

74. Glove anesthesia makes the diagnosis of _____ disorder easy because it does not correspond to the distribution of nerve pathways.
   a. conversion
   b. body dysmorphic
   c. somatization
   d. psychogenic pain

Ans: b
Page: 186
Obj: 10
Type: A

75. Yassir has been under great stress at work. He tells his doctor that he cannot feel his hand from his wrist to his fingertips. He says it is as though all the feeling in the nerves was cut off at the wrist. The doctor, knowing how nerves are distributed, will probably see Yassir as having
   a. pain disorder.
   b. conversion disorder.
   c. factitious disorder by proxy.
   d. hypochondriasis.

Ans: c
Page: 185
Obj: 9
Type: A

76. Sharon has caused diarrhea in her three-year-old daughter by feeding her spoiled milk and rotten eggs. When the child is repeatedly hospitalized, Sharon acts like a very worried and caring mother. Since Sharon gets no obvious reward for her behavior, the appropriate diagnosis is
   a. somatoform disorder in the child.
   b. somatoform disorder in Sharon.
   c. factitious disorder by proxy.
   d. malingering.

Ans: c
Page: 188
Obj: 10
Type: F

77. Which statement about diagnosing conversion disorder is *accurate*?
   a. Conversion disorder is often confused with hypochondriasis.
   b. It is rarely difficult to distinguish actual physical disorders from conversion reactions.
   c. Because people can simulate symptoms of conversion, it is hard to distinguish it from faking.
   d. The most effective way to diagnose conversion disorder is through the patient's self-report of symptoms.

Ans: c
Page: 188
Obj: 10
Type: F

78. Pain is to _____ as paralysis and absence of pain are to _____.
   a. conversion disorder; somatoform pain disorder
   b. conversion disorder; hypochondriasis
   c. somatoform pain disorder; conversion disorder
   d. somatoform pain disorder; hypochondriasis

Ans: d
Page: 188
Obj: 10
Type: A

79. Barbara was in a car accident and experienced neck pain immediately afterward. Doctors say that any injury to her neck healed within two weeks of the accident. Nine months later, Barbara begins to visit her doctor weekly, saying the pain is still unbearable and she needs stronger pain medication. What is a reasonable diagnosis?
   a. Somatization disorder
   b. Depersonalization disorder
   c. Hypochondriasis
   d. Pain disorder

Ans: c
Page: 189
Obj: 10
Type: F

80. "Persistent preoccupation with one's health despite consistent medical evaluations showing no organic problems" is a definition of
   a. conversion disorder.
   b. dissociative disorders.
   c. hypochondriasis.
   d. somatoform disorders.

Ans: d
Page: 189
Obj: 10
Type: A

81. Mrs. Klinger has a ten-year history of fearing a heart attack, although no doctor has found anything wrong with her heart. She frequently calls emergency services and lies in bed most days worrying that she will have a coronary. Mrs. Klinger suffers from
   a. somatoform pain disorder.
   b. conversion disorder.
   c. dissociative amnesia.
   d. hypochondriasis.

Ans: a
Page: 189
Obj: 10
Type: A

82. Mr. Able is diagnosed with hypochondriasis, while Mr. Baker is diagnosed with somatization disorder. How will their symptoms be different?
   a. Mr. Able will fear he has an undetected fatal illness; Mr. Baker will have many vague physical complaints.
   b. Mr. Able will have complaints about his body; Mr. Baker will not.
   c. Mr. Able will not have any physical complaints; Mr. Baker will fear that he has cancer or a form of heart disease.
   d. Mr. Able will claim that he cannot see or walk; Mr. Baker will fear that he has an undetected fatal illness.

Ans: b
Page: 189
Obj: 10
Type: A

83. Suppose we interviewed fifty people with hypochondriasis. Which of the following quotes do you expect we would hear *most* often?
   a. "My doctor is very accurate with her diagnoses."
   b. "I can notice even the slightest changes in my body."
   c. "I know that even when I am sick, nothing terrible is going to happen."
   d. "I know I have some kind of illness, but I haven't been to see a doctor in years."

Ans: b
Page: 190
Obj: 10
Type: A

84. Ron is totally preoccupied with the shape of his nose. Although no one else thinks so, he thinks it is ugly and has had plastic surgery four times to fix it. Ron suffers from
   a. conversion disorder.
   b. body dysmorphic disorder.
   c. dissociative fugue.
   d. somatization disorder.

Ans: a
Page: 190
Obj: 10
Type: C

85. Which statement about body dysmorphic disorder (BDD) is *accurate*?
   a. The disorder may be under-diagnosed because many people with the disorder are too embarrassed to talk about it.
   b. The disorder is diagnosed when psychological distress actuallycreates a disfiguring bodily defect.
   c. Those who suffer from the disorder voluntarily disfigure themselves to get attention and care from others.
   d. Unlike others with somatoform disorders, those with BDD rarely seek medical attention.

Ans: c
Page: 193
Obj: 11
Type: A

86. A psychologist discusses a patient with hypochondriasis this way: "She focuses on her health so that she can be protected from the anxiety her underlying conflicts causes. Then, when she is shown attention and sympathy, her dependency needs are met." This psychologist
   a. probably agrees with the behavioral perspective.
   b. takes a diathesis-stress approach to hypochondriasis.
   c. is discussing primary and secondary gain.
   d. probably rejects the psychoanalytic perspective.

Ans: d
Page: 193
Obj: 11
Type: F

87. Reinforcement of illness behaviors and parental modeling of how to act sick are both etiological factors in the _____ theory of conversion disorder.
   a. biogenic
   b. family systems
   c. psychodynamic
   d. behavioral

Ans: d
Page: 192
Obj: 11
Type: C

88. A psychologist says that somatoform disorders are caused by biological predispositions to being highly sensitive to weak bodily sensations and reacting with alarm, coupled with stressors the person feels cannot be handled adequately. This causal model is an example of the _____ view.
   a. psychodynamic
   b. biological
   c. socio-cultural
   d. diathesis-stress

Ans: b
Page: 194
Obj: 11
Type: F

89. If the socio-cultural perspective concerning the cause of conversion disorder is accurate, as
   a. the economy improves, the rate of this disorder should go down.
   b. opportunities for women increase, the rate of this disorder should decrease.
   c. the economy improves, the rate of this disorder should increase.
   d. opportunities for women increase, the rate of this disorder should increase also.

Ans: d
Page: 194
Obj: 11
Type: A

90. Dr. Todd says, "Anna O. was not a victim of intrapsychic conflicts. She was an ambitious, intelligent woman who felt great guilt when she resented having to care for her sick father. She went on to become a feminist leader." These remarks
   a. support the psychodynamic explanation for somatoform disorders.
   b. support the biological perspective on somatoform disorders.
   c. reject the behavioral explanation for dissociative disorders.
   d. support a socio-cultural explanation for somatoform disorders.

Ans: a
Page: 194
Obj: 11
Type: F

91. Evidence supporting the biological perspective on hypochondriac patients includes
   a. research showing they are more sensitive than others to bodily sensations.
   b. twin studies showing they have neurotransmitter imbalances.
   c. data showing they have lower arousal levels than others.
   d. case studies indicating they are more intelligent than others.

Ans: a
Page: 195
Obj: 11
Type: F

92. The biological perspective on somatoform disorders emphasizes which difference in these patients?
   a. They may experience internal sensations more acutely.
   b. They have experienced more stress in early childhood.
   c. They are unable to learn from punishment.
   d. They are exposed to parents who model how to act sick.

Ans: d
Page: 195
Obj: 12
Type: C

93. Traditional psychoanalysts and modern hypnotherapists agree that effective treatment of somatoform disorders should include
   a. explaining the role of the nervous system in the perception of pain.
   b. reinforcement for adaptive behavior.
   c. punishing "sick role" behaviors.
   d. reliving feelings associated with repressed traumas.

Ans: b
Page: 195
Obj: 12
Type: F

94. Psychodynamic theorists have argued that involuntary self-hypnosis
   a. is desirable in people who have dissociative disorders but not somatoform disorders.
   b. occurs in both dissociative and somatoform disorders.
   c. is not relevant to somatoform disorders.
   d. is a treatment far superior to psychoanalytic therapy.

Ans: c
Page: 195
Obj: 12
Type: A

95. A psychologist tells the spouse of a hypochondriac, "If he says he's going to have a heart attack, you should say, 'I don't respond to such talk.'" What kind of psychologist would say such a thing?
   a. A sadistic one
   b. A psychoanalyst
   c. A behavior therapist
   d. A hypnotherapist

Ans: a
Page: 195
Obj: 12
Type: A

96. Dr. King says, "The best treatment for somatoform pain disorder and hypochondriasis is extinguishing complaints by ignoring them and providing reinforcement when the individual talks about issues other than his or her body." Dr. King probably holds a _____ perspective on the disorders.
   a. behavioral
   b. biogenic
   c. family systems
   d. psychodynamic

Ans: b
Page: 196
Obj: 12
Type: A

97. A therapist who read the results of Salkovskis and Warwick's (1986) clinical research on behavioral treatment of chronic pain would find out that she could get both long-term results and patients who expressed greater satisfaction if she
   a. taught them self-hypnosis and visualization methods.
   b. emphasized cognitive changes.
   c. combined exposure therapy and response prevention.
   d. altered the reinforcement patterns of the patients' spouses.

Ans: d
Page: 196
Obj: 12
Type: F

98. In the future, behavioral therapy for somatoform disorders will probably stress
   a. changing rewards, hypnotherapy, and family relations.
   b. hypnotherapy, relaxation training, and drug therapy.
   c. hypnotherapy, drug therapy, and changing cognitions.
   d. changing rewards, changing cognitions, and relaxation training.

Ans: a
Page: 196
Obj: 12
Type: A

99. A therapist says to a father with somatoform pain disorder, "Your complaints about aches and pains get you attention from your children and free you from adult responsibilities." The therapist's remarks reflect a _____ perspective.
   a. family systems
   b. socio-cultural
   c. medical
   d. psychodynamic

Ans: b
Page: 196
Obj: 12
Type: A

100. Joan Martin has been diagnosed with somatization disorder. Research suggests that in the Martin family,
   a. other family members will tend to ignore or punish Joan for her symptoms.
   b. females tend to have somatization disorder; males tend to be antisocial personalities or alcoholics.
   c. females tend to have obsessive-compulsive disorder; males tend to be hypochondriacs.
   d. virtually no one else will have a preoccupation with bodily sensations or complaints.

ESSAY QUESTIONS

1. What form does the dissociation take in depersonalization disorder, dissociative amnesia, and dissociative identity disorder? What are the major differences in the symptoms and prospects for recovery in these three disorders?

2. Describe and distinguish the psychodynamic, behavioral, and iatrogenic explanations for dissociative identity disorder. What are the points of overlap among these explanations?

3. Describe the features of somatoform disorders, factitious disorders, and malingering, delineating how the three can be differentiated from one another.

SAMPLE ANSWERS

1. People who have depersonalization disorder feel that they or the world has become unreal. These feelings cause significant impairment in their ability to work and get along with other people. Altered perceptions are also likely, such as thinking that one's body is distorted. The dissociation is in the individual's sense of self and relationship to the outside world; normal consciousness about what is real or dream and how we look or feel is lost. Memory loss is the fundamental symptom of dissociative amnesia. Whether it is recall of whole events (localized) or portions of them (selective), the individual deals with a stressful experience by splitting off his or her memory of it. In dissociative identity disorder, there is a more complete splitting off of memories. Not only does the person have no recollection of traumatic events in the past, but different personalities come to inhabit the body at different times, and only those personalities have access to event-related memories. Therefore, the dissociation, as the name implies, is more than about mere recall; it is

about identity. In all cases, there is a form of splitting off of portions of consciousness in these disorders, but depersonalization and amnesia are more likely to be time- and stress-limited conditions than is dissociative identity disorder. Once the precipitating stressor is over and the person can return to normal means of coping, depersonalization and amnesia typically spontaneously remit. The person with dissociative identity disorder, however, has developed a well-established coping mechanism and may harbor deep-seated conflicts that do not allow for easy resolution. Furthermore, it can be argued that dissociative identity disorder can be quite adaptive, allowing the person to function in parts better than might occur in an integrated whole. Treatment outcomes for dissociative identity disorder are generally poorer than for the other two dissociative disorders.

2. The person with dissociative identity disorder is unable to remember in some personalities the horrifying events that other personalities witnessed and remember. This dissociation is seen by psychoanalysts as an extreme form of repression. The components of personality (id, ego, and superego) exist in such intense conflict that, to preserve the person, they are split off into separate personalities. The intensity of the conflict is believed to be an outgrowth of traumatic stressful events in childhood, usually physical and sexual abuse. If a child has the capacity to daydream or otherwise dissociate certain memories, he or she can use this to cope with overwhelming anxiety by creating separate personalities. In other words, children who can hypnotize themselves to wall off the pain of traumatic events may develop dissociative identity disorder. Behaviorists argue that dissociation is a way of avoiding stress, too, but they emphasize the rewards that exist for symptoms. All of us, they say, engage in different actions and adopt different attitudes and emotions depending on the situational circumstances we face. The person with dissociative identity disorder does this to the extreme, selectively attending to social stimuli and switching from one role to another. Those who say that dissociative identity disorder is iatrogenic (therapist produced) note that the symptoms of the disorder have been influenced by descriptions in books and movies. Therapists, believing that childhood abuse underlies the disorder, will encourage clients to "uncover" memories of such abuse and thereby generate proof of the disorder. During hypnosis, a state of increased suggestibility, the likelihood of this process is magnified. Further, people with dissociative identity disorder are more suggestible than others.

   The three approaches all see the development of dissociative identity disorder as a coping response. Psychoanalysts and behaviorists see the separation of personalities as serving the purpose of avoiding stressful experiences. One can also see iatrogenic dissociation as a means of coping: It avoids a subtle dispute with the therapist, elicits sympathy and encouragement from the therapist, and provides the client with an explanation for his or her difficulties.

3. *Somatoform disorders* involve physical symptoms for which, based on current knowledge of physical functioning, there is no adequate explanation. Somatoform disorders are considered unintentional because persons with these disorders are not deliberately faking their physical symptoms. *Factitious disorders* also involve the presence of physical symptoms for which there is no apparent medical cause, but the symptoms are produced intentionally or faked. The motivation for the feigning of physical symptoms is the desire to assume the "sick role." *Malingering* is a third disorder involving physical symptoms. In malingering, the physical symptoms are also faked, but the motivation is for external incentives, such as economic gain or the avoidance of work or legal responsibilities.

CHAPTER 7
Psychological Factors Affecting Medical Conditions

LEARNING OBJECTIVES

1. Describe the sudden death syndrome and the factors related to it. Discuss how culture shock can lead to sudden death among Hmong immigrants. (pp. 199-200; Mental Health & Society)

2. List the DSM-IV-TR criteria for diagnosis of psychological factors affecting medical conditions. Explain the rationale for changes in terminology from "psychosomatic" to "psychophysiological." (pp. 200-201)

3. Discuss the three models for understanding stress, including Selye's general adaptation syndrome, the life change model, and Lazarus's transaction model. (pp. 201-205)

4. Discuss the research linking emotional states to vulnerability to infection. Discuss the evidence for and against the claim that stress influences the development of Acquired Immune Deficiency Syndrome (AIDS). (pp. 206-208)

5. Describe the components of the immune system and evidence that stress decreases its functioning. (pp. 208-209)

6. Describe the mediating effects of control and hardiness on stress. (pp.209-211)

7. Discuss the evidence linking personality, mood, and cancer. (pp. 211-213; Mental Health & Society)

8. Describe the relationship between stress and coronary heart disease and the influence of the Type A personality on CHD. (pp. 213-216; Critical Thinking)

9. Describe the relationship between stress and essential hypertension, and the ethnic and social factors associated with it. (pp. 216-219)

10. Describe the nature of migraine, tension, and cluster headaches. (pp. 219-221)

11. Describe asthma and the psychological factors related to it. (pp. 221-223)

12. Discuss the psychodynamic and biological perspectives on psychophysiological disorders, including the somatic weakness, autonomic response specificity, and the general adaptation hypotheses. (pp. 223-224)

13. Discuss the behavioral perspective on psychophysiological disorders, including the influence of classical conditioning and operant conditioning. Describe how sociocultural factors influence coronary heart disease. (pp. 225-226)

14. Define behavioral medicine and describe various interventions for psychophysiological disorders, including medical, relaxation training, biofeedback, and cognitive-behavior therapy. (pp. 226-228)

MULTIPLE–CHOICE QUESTIONS

Ans: c
Page: 199
Obj: 1
Type: C

1. Jason woke up feeling fine but was dead by the end of the day. Under exceptional stress, his cardiac blood vessels were normal. His death may be said to illustrate
   a. ventricular fibrillation.
   b. psychosomatic heart disease.
   c. sudden death syndrome.
   d. acute bradycardia.

Ans: d
Page: 199
Obj: 1
Type: A

2. Dr. Michaels, a heart specialist, says, "It is the leading cause of death in the industrial world and kills about 500,000 Americans each year. It is related to coronary heart disease but also occurs in people with normal hearts and cardiac blood vessels. We know stress plays at least some role in its existence." What is it?
   a. Psychosomatic disorder
   b. Arrhythmia
   c. General adaptation syndrome
   d. Sudden death syndrome

Ans: c
Page: 200
Obj: 2
Type: C

3. Thirty years ago, a psychiatrist might have considered peptic ulcer and essential hypertension to be _____, but today the term that is used is _____.
   a. psychosomatic illness; conversion disorder
   b. psychophysiological disorder; neurosis
   c. psychosomatic illness; psychophysiological disorder
   d. neurosis; psychosis

Ans: b
Page: 200
Obj: 1
Type: F

4. When some Laotian immigrants (the Hmong) went to sleep in good health but died in their sleep after screaming and making frantic movements, their deaths were often attributed to
   a. Type A death.
   b. sudden death syndrome.
   c. anxiety disorders.
   d. conversion disorder.

Ans: a
Page: 200
Obj: 2
Type: F

5. To emphasize the fact that any physical disorder can have a psychological basis, the term *psychosomatic* was changed to
   a. psychophysiological.
   b. somatoform.
   c. somatopsychic.
   d. biopsychosocial.

Ans: d
Page: 200
Obj: 2
Type: C

6. Sandi is diagnosed as having two conditions: migraine headaches and hypertension. A mental health professional should consider her as suffering from
   a. a psychophysiological disorder (migraine) and a physical condition (hypertension).
   b. two physical conditions that normally have little to do with psychological factors.
   c. a psychophysiological disorder (hypertension) and a conversion disorder (migraine).
   d. two psychophysiological disorders.

Ans: c
Page: 200
Obj: 2
Type: C

7. What is the primary difference between somatoform and psychophysiological disorders?
    a. Psychophysiological disorder is the current DSM-IV diagnostic category for what used to be called somatoform disorders.
    b. In somatoform disorders there is actual disease or tissue damage, and there is none in psychophysiological disorders.
    c. In psychophysiological disorders there is actual disease or tissue damage, and there is none in somatoform disorders.
    d. Psychophysiological disorders are all "in the mind," while in somatoform disorders psychological factors are believed to play a role in the exacerbation of a real disease.

Ans: c
Page: 200
Obj: 2
Type: A

8. Which of the following is an example of a psychophysiological disorder?
    a. Carla, who complains of a loss of feeling but shows no signs of a medical condition to account for it
    b. Wendy, who was diagnosed with a conversion disorder
    c. Brenda, whose medical condition began several days after a stressful life event
    d. Hallie, whose medical condition is genetic

Ans: b
Page: 201
Obj: 2
Type: C

9. Unlike conversion disorders, psychophysiological disorders
    a. are so subjective that they cannot be studied with systematic research.
    b. produce actual tissue damage.
    c. are unrelated to psychological conflicts or personality styles.
    d. are all in the patient's imagination.

Ans: d
Page: 201
Obj: 2
Type: C

10. Which of the following is *not* a DSM-IV criterion for diagnosing a medical condition affected by psychological factors?
    a. The onset of the medical condition is related to psychological factors.
    b. The psychological factors constitute an additional health risk factor.
    c. Psychological factors interfere with treating the condition.
    d. The medical condition causes feelings of depression or anxiety.

Ans: d
Page: 200
Obj: 1
Type: A

11. Imagine that you are a physician and your patient is a Hmong immigrant who has just arrived in the United States. The patient, through a translator, tells you that spirits come into his room while he sleeps and make it hard for him to breathe. He wakes up screaming. Considering reports from other Hmong immigrants, you should
    a. reassure the patient that there is nothing to worry about and that symptoms will disappear on their own.
    b. assume the patient suffers from a psychotic mental condition.
    c. treat the person for conversion disorder.
    d. be concerned that the patient's psychological stress will lead to sudden death.

Ans: a
Page: 201
Obj: 3
Type: C

12. Which statement concerning stressors and stress is *accurate*?
    a. Stressors are external events; stress is an internal reaction to such events.
    b. Stress is a chronic condition; stressors are only temporary.
    c. Stressors are internal reactions such as increased heartbeat; stress is an external condition.
    d. *Stress* and *stressor* are two different words that have the same meaning.

Ans: c
Page: 202
Obj: 3
Type: A

13. Which of the following pairings *accurately* illustrates a type of stressor?
    a. Biological stressor—warfare or excessive noise
    b. Social stressor—threats to self-esteem or one's belief system
    c. Social stressor—crowding or economic pressures
    d. Psychological stressor—fatigue or malnutrition

Ans: c
Page: 202
Obj: 3
Type: A

14. Dr. Wellman explains a patient's ulcer this way: "After an immediate alarm response to an external threat, the patient's body mobilized itself to resist. However, after months of prolonged resistance, the tissue simply broke down." Dr. Wellman's analysis reflects the _____ model.
    a. transactional
    b. operant conditioning
    c. general adaptation
    d. life change

Ans: a
Page: 202
Obj: 3
Type: A

15. On one particularly stressful day, Darren learns that his girlfriend is leaving him, his mother was robbed, and the IRS is auditing him. His body reacts with an increased heart rate and a loss of muscle tone. According to the general adaptation syndrome, Darren is experiencing
    a. the alarm stage.
    b. exhaustion.
    c. decompensation.
    d. the resistance stage.

Ans: d
Page: 202
Obj: 3
Type: F

16. In the general adaptation syndrome, the body automatically responds to threats
    a. by depressing the sympathetic nervous system.
    b. by decompensating.
    c. in a way that is entirely dependent on the personality of the individual.
    d. in three stages: alarm, resistance, and exhaustion.

Ans: b
Page: 202
Obj: 3
Type: A

17. Leo took care of his wife for several years after she suffered a stroke. The stress on him was overwhelming. Shortly after she died, he developed a serious illness. This fact illustrates
    a. De La Fuente's concept of decompensation.
    b. the exhaustion stage of the general adaptation syndrome.
    c. the transaction model of psychophysiological disorders.
    d. Selye's concept of alarm-resistance.

Ans: b
Page: 202
Obj: 3
Type: C

18. According to the general adaptation model, the period when the body is mobilized to defend itself and the symptoms of illness tend to disappear is considered a time of
    a. alarm.
    b. resistance.
    c. exhaustion.
    d. decompensation.

Ans: d
Page: 202
Obj: 3
Type: F

19. Continuing research on stress suggests that
    a. is stress is sustained, after a while the body learns to adapt.
    b. biological stressors can cause physiological damage, but psychological and social stressors do not.
    c. there is very little relationship between stress and health.
    d. stress affects the immune system, heart function, hormone levels, the nervous system, and metabolic rates.

Ans: d
Page: 202
Obj: 3
Type: A

20. Bodily "wear and tear" resulting from stress can contribute to all of the following *except*
    a. baldness.
    b. hybertension.
    c. heart attacks.
    d. the common cold.

Ans: a
Page: 203
Obj: 3
Type: A

21. Gina became sick shortly after she was fired from her job. Bess became sick after her car had a flat tire, her cat developed fleas, and she lost her keys. The fact that both women became ill supports the _____ model of stress and illness.
    a. life change
    b. general adaptation
    c. psychodynamic
    d. transaction

Ans: a
Page: 203
Obj: 3
Type: C

22. Is the life change model similar to the general adaptation model?
    a. No, it focuses on the frequency and characteristics of the stressors.
    b. Yes, it assumes that stressors have an impact only if they are of crisis proportions.
    c. No, it emphasizes the personality characteristics of the person experiencing stress.
    d. Yes, it involves a three-stage process.

Ans: d
Page: 203
Obj: 3
Type: A

23. Bill just got married and is about to go on his honeymoon. According to the life change model,
    a. Bill will be scoring very low on the Social Readjustment Rating Scale.
    b. Bill will be at very low risk for health problems because he has just experienced a positive life event.
    c. Bill will not register, since the life change model only addresses negative stressors, not positive stressors.
    d. Bill may still experience the effects of stress, although marriage is considered a positive life event.

Ans: c
Page: 203
Obj: 3
Type: F

24. Which model of stress and illness is *most* likely to add up the number of stressors a person has experienced in order to predict his or her chances of becoming ill?
    a. De La Fuente's crisis decomposition model
    b. Selye's general adaptation model
    c. Holmes and Rahe's life change model
    d. Lazarus's transaction model

Ans: a
Page: 204
Obj: 3
Type: C

25. Geoffrey takes the Social Readjustment Rating Scale and scores 225 over the past year. What does this indicate?
    a. According to the life change model, Geoffrey has a strong likelihood of becoming ill.
    b. According to the decompensation model, Geoffrey should have a significantly impaired immune system.
    c. According to the life change model, Geoffrey is unlikely to develop any form of illness.
    d. According to the general adaptation syndrome, Geoffrey is in the alarm stage.

Ans: d
Page: 204
Obj: 3
Type: F

26. Researchers have asked American and Chinese samples to rate the stressfulness of life events. The results show that
a. there is no overlap in the perceptions of the two cultures.
b. relationship loss is stressful to Americans but not to Chinese.
c. negative events are stressful to Americans but not to Chinese.
d. death of a spouse is the greatest stressor in both cultures.

Ans: d
Page: 203
Obj: 3
Type: A

27. Suppose you were in charge of the health center at your college or university. Based on research and the life change model of psychophysiological disorders, your expectations would be that
a. the most frequent patients would be students with the Type B personality style.
b. the most seriously ill students would have experienced stressors totaling around 50 LCUs (on the Social Readjustment Rating Scale).
c. you would be busiest when students were just getting back to campus after Christmas or summer vacation.
d. most of your students would have just experienced undesirable rather than desirable life events.

Ans: c
Page: 205
Obj: 3
Type: C

28. The _____ model of stress emphasizes the number of stressors one experiences; the _____ model of stress focuses on how we think and cope with stressors.
a. general adaptation; transaction
b. transaction; life change
c. life change; transaction
d. transaction; general adaptation

Ans: c
Page: 205
Obj: 3
Type: C

29. Ted says, "The impact of stressors can be reduced or increased depending on how they are interpreted." Ted's thoughts reflect the _____ model.
a. general adaptation syndrome
b. psychodynamic
c. transaction
d. life change

Ans: a
Page: 205
Obj: 3
Type: A

30. Stacey and Tracey are both diagnosed with skin cancer. Stacey reads about the disease, sees it as a challenge, and quickly develops a treatment plan with her doctor. Tracey is so overwhelmed with fear that she avoids the doctor and makes no plans. The differences in these women illustrate
a. Lazarus's transaction model.
b. the general adaptation syndrome.
c. the life change model.
d. the socio-cultural component of psychophysiological disorders.

Ans: b
Page: 206
Obj: 4
Type: F

31. Research on emotional states and herpes infections indicates that
a. although anxiety causes infections, depression does not.
b. anxiety appears to cause an outbreak of infections.
c. negative emotions are related to infections, but whether they are causal is unclear.
d. emotional states are the result of infections, not the cause.

Ans: a
Page: 206
Obj: 4
Type: A

32. Who is *most* likely to be susceptible to physical illness?
    a. John, who has a lot of stress in his life and refuses to go to the doctor even though he suspects that he may have prostate cancer
    b. Jake, who worries about the chemotherapy treatments he is receiving for testicular cancer
    c. Pablo, who although he has a relatively stress-free life, anticipates having a very difficult time passing the bar exam
    d. Terry, who although diagnosed with HIV, has strong social support, has a positive view of himself, and shows strong self-efficacy regarding his ability to control the disease

Ans: d
Page: 206
Obj: 4
Type: C

33. Which statement *accurately* describes the relationship between stress and health?
    a. Stress reactions increase vulnerability to disease because the immune system is strengthened.
    b. Stress reactions directly cause infections in the body.
    c. Stress reactions occur after the immune system's strength has been decreased by other factors.
    d. Stress reactions decrease the immune system's strength and thereby increase vulnerability to disease.

Ans: d
Page: 207
Obj: 4
Type: A

34. Kelly thinks that people with HIV show the fastest deterioration in immune functioning when they have few sources of emotional support and tend to become depressed. What has research shown us about the *accuracy* of Kelly's thinking?
    a. She is accurate about the role of depression but not about support.
    b. She is wrong about both support and depression: Neither affects immune functioning.
    c. She is accurate about support but not about depression.
    d. The research concerning the effects of depression and stress on the immune system are contradictory and therefore inconclusive.

Ans: c
Page: 207
Obj: 4
Type: A

35. Ezra was extremely skeptical when he heard Professor Ng describe a relationship between stress and the immune system. As Professor Ng told the class, though, researchers have found that all of the following are related to changes in the immune system except
    a. behavior.
    b. cognitions.
    c. education.
    d. social support.

Ans: d
Page: 208
Obj: 5
Type: A

36. Ron goes into the hospital for tests, which show that his corticosteroid levels are very high, his endorphins are up, and his lymphocytes are down. This might indicate that
    a. his immune system is strengthened against a stressor.
    b. he is an anxious person who gets migraine headaches.
    c. he is decompensating.
    d. his immune system is weakened.

Ans: b
Page: 208
Obj: 5
Type: F

37. High levels of T-cells, B-cells, and phagocytes indicate
    a. a person with HIV.
    b. a person with a strong immune system.
    c. a person with a weak immune system.
    d. a person with few neurohormones.

Ans: b
Page: 209
Obj: 5
Type: A

38. Bonnie, who has been married twenty-one years, just found out that her husband wants a divorce. Considering research on people dealing with similar stressors, we can expect that this incident has caused
    a. her immune system to grow in strength.
    b. a reduction in NK cells and lymphocytes.
    c. a resistance stage of adaptation, which will be followed by an alarm reaction.
    d. her corticosteroid levels to drop markedly.

Ans: c
Page: 208
Obj: 5
Type: F

39. Which system in the human body defends against microscopic invaders that produce infections?
    a. The endocrine system
    b. The hormonal system
    c. The immune system
    d. The central nervous system

Ans: d
Page: 209
Obj: 6
Type: C

40. Mrs. Fujimori has been caring for her husband who has lung cancer. She herself has become unusually susceptible to infections. One explanation is that the stress has weakened her immune system. Another is that she has
    a. a hardy personality.
    b. a Type A personality.
    c. many other emotionally supportive relationships.
    d. been neglecting her nutrition and sleep needs.

Ans: a
Page: 209
Obj: 6
Type: F

41. Langer and Rodin's research study in nursing homes demonstrated that greater responsibility and control
    a. are associated with lower death rates among patients.
    b. burden the patients and actually lower their number of NK cells.
    c. increase the elderly's sense of incompetence.
    d. increase stress levels.

Ans: b
Page: 209
Obj: 6
Type: A

42. A friend of yours is taking care of an elderly aunt. The friend wants advice on how best to provide the care so that the aunt is both happy and healthy. Based on research, you should suggest that
    a. the aunt's activity level be increased beyond the range she thinks she is capable of.
    b. your friend allow the aunt to make as many decisions as she can.
    c. your friend reduce to a minimum all decisions the aunt must make.
    d. the aunt be protected from all visitors and changes in her daily schedule.

Ans: c
Page: 210
Obj: 6
Type: A

43. Harry works in a noisy manufacturing plant. According to research, his epinephrine levels and sense of anxiety will be higher if he
    a. can remain relaxed in the situation.
    b. cannot hear the noise clearly.
    c. believes he cannot control the noise.
    d. believes he has a way of controlling the noise.

Ans: d
Page: 210
Obj: 6
Type: A

44. Dr. Frank is doing research on cancer. Rats are injected with cancer cells and then given either no electric shocks or shocks in two conditions: having control over stopping the shocks or having no control. What results should Dr. Frank expect?
    a. The sickest groups should be those getting shocks.
    b. The sickest group should be the "control shock" condition.
    c. The sickest group should be the "no shock" controls.
    d. The sickest group should be the "no control shock" condition.

Ans: b
Page: 210
Obj: 6
Type: F

45. According to Maddi and Kobasa, hardiness is a personality trait that is characterized by
   a. a willingness to let others control one's destiny.
   b. an openness to change or challenge.
   c. the need to compete against others.
   d. the ability to relax when others cannot.

Ans: b
Page: 210
Obj: 6
Type: A

46. Jill has a sense of control over her own life; she enjoys the challenge of change and is open to it. She rarely gets sick. Jill is an example of the
   a. classic migraine headache sufferer.
   b. hardy personality.
   c. Type A personality.
   d. Type B personality.

Ans: c
Page: 210
Obj: 7
Type: A

47. Based on research concerning control, personality, and stress-related illness, which person would be *least* likely to experience a weakened immune system?
   a. Joe, who feels that his manager controls his work life
   b. Jennifer, who feels little involvement with or commitment to her job
   c. Jason, who is always open to new work experiences
   d. Rochelle, who wants her job to remain the same forever

Ans: a
Page: 211
Obj: 7
Type: F

48. Which statement below is an *accurate* reflection of what is known about psychological factors, immune function, and disease?
   a. Psychological factors affect immune function but may account for only a small increase in disease occurrence.
   b. Only extreme, long-term stressors affect immune function and illness.
   c. Even significant differences in psychological outlook—extreme pessimism versus extreme optimism—have little effect on immune function.
   d. Even small changes in immune function due to improved outlook greatly reduce the chances of becoming sick.

Ans: a
Page: 211
Obj: 7
Type: A

49. All of the following individuals have the same type of cancer and are currently at the same state of health, receiving the same type of treatment, at the same facility. Who is most likely to live longest?
   a. Abby, who has high self-efficacy and is unrealistically optimistic.
   b. Bernie, who has high self-efficacy and a realistic acceptance of his condition.
   c. Carl, who has low self-efficacy, but is nonetheless optimistic.
   d. Doug, who has low self-efficacy and is pessimistic about his outcome.

Ans: c
Page: 211
Obj: 7
Type: F

50. What is the *most* widely held opinion concerning the effect of mood and attitude on cancer treatment?
   a. It is clear that mood and attitude have no impact on the course of cancer.
   b. Mood and attitude influence the course of cancer only in females, not in males.
   c. Research so far is unable to show conclusively that mood and attitude affect cancer treatment.
   d. It is clear that a positive mood stops cancers in most people.

Ans: b
Page: 212
Obj: 7
Type: F

51. Which personality and mood characteristics have been *most* related to cancer?
   a. Type A personality and a sense of being in control
   b. Anger expression, depression, and hopelessness
   c. Free-floating anxiety and the hardy personality
   d. Type A personality and the hardy personality

Ans: b
Page: 212
Obj: 7
Type: F

52. Norman Cousins is credited with suggesting that _____ increases immune functioning.
    a. exercise
    b. humor
    c. self-efficacy
    d. perception of control

Ans: b
Page: 212
Obj: 7
Type: F

53. A prospective study of personality and death from cancer shows that
    a. higher scores on the neuroticism scale are related to lower rates of cancer deaths.
    b. people with high depression scores (measured by the MMPI) are more likely to die of cancer.
    c. the greater the number of life stresses, the greater the number of cancer deaths among those who are hardy.
    d. as control over situations increases, cancer deaths decrease.

Ans: c
Page: 212
Obj: 7
Type: C

54. A researcher interested in resolving the issue of whether emotional states play a causal role in cancer must answer which of the following questions?
    a. Is Type A personality a consistent trait?
    b. Are people at risk for cancer also at risk for coronary heart disease?
    c. Does knowledge that one has cancer cause changes in emotional states, or vice versa?
    d. Do we have enough retrospective data to make an unambiguous conclusion?

Ans: d
Page: 214
Obj: 8
Type: F

55. It leads to the death of about 400,000 Americans each year, although its incidence has diminished in recent years because people are exercising more and smoking less. It is also related to hypertension and high cholesterol levels. It is
    a. migraine headache.
    b. tachycardia.
    c. asthma.
    d. coronary heart disease.

Ans: c
Page: 214
Obj: 8
Type: C

56. Based on prospective research concerning personality and coronary heart disease, which group of people would be *most* likely to die of sudden cardiac arrest?
    a. Type B personalities.
    b. Hardy personalities.
    c. People who are frequently depressed.
    d. People who are married.

Ans: d
Page: 215
Obj: 8
Type: F

57. Women with high job stress or who see themselves as having a poor relationship with their boss have been found to have higher fibrogen levels. This may contribute to
    a. cancer of the breast.
    b. fatal asthma attacks.
    c. classic migraine headaches.
    d. coronary heart disease.

Ans: a
Page: 215
Obj: 8
Type: A

58. Jeff is always working on six projects at the same time. He is easily angered and constantly competitive. His physician is worried that he will develop _____ because his personality matches the _____ profile.
   a. coronary heart disease; Type A
   b. hypertension; hardiness
   c. coronary heart disease; Type B
   d. somatization disorder; Type A

Ans: b
Page: 215
Obj: 8
Type: C

59. Which of the following sayings *best* describes the Type A individual?
   a. "Don't worry, be happy."
   b. "Do it fast and right, or get out of my way."
   c. "When I say no, I feel guilty."
   d. "Slow and steady wins the race."

Ans: d
Page: 216
Obj: 8
Type: A

60. Recent research has reexamined the relationship between Type A personality and coronary heart disease. This research suggests which one of the following men is at highest risk?
   a. Tom, who works at several jobs simultaneously
   b. Mike, who is highly competitive in all tasks
   c. Ken, who likes to get things done at high speed
   d. Paul, who is constantly irritable or hostile

Ans: b
Page: 216
Obj: 8
Type: C

61. Which person is *most* likely to have coronary heart disease?
   a. John, a Type B with low levels of cholesterol
   b. Wayne, a hostile Type A with high levels of cholesterol
   c. Tim, a Type B with high triglycerides
   d. Carter, a Type A with low hostility and low blood pressure

Ans: c
Page: 217
Obj: 9
Type: F

62. Essential hypertension means that a person
   a. is anxious or hostile most of the time.
   b. has heart disease because of blocked arteries.
   c. has blood pressure of 140 over 90 or higher
   d. is subject to muscle spasms that have no physical basis.

Ans: d
Page: 217
Obj: 9
Type: A

63. Mr. Johnson says, "Essential hypertension is blood pressure of 140 over 90 or higher. It affects nearly 28 percent of the U.S. population and has a clear biological cause in the majority of cases." Which portion of this statement is *inaccurate*?
   a. It is inaccurate to say that essential hypertension involves blood pressure.
   b. It is inaccurate to say that hypertension is defined as pressure of 140 over 90 or higher.
   c. It is inaccurate to say that essential hypertension affects nearly 28 percent of Americans.
   d. It is inaccurate to say that essential hypertension has a clear biological cause in a majority of cases.

Ans: c
Page: 218
Obj: 9
Type: F

64. Reduction of stress through relaxation appears to
   a. make no difference in the blood pressure of those with essential hypertension.
   b. increase arteriosclerosis in those with essential hypertension.
   c. significantly decrease blood pressure.
   d. increase blood pressure in those with essential hypertension.

Ans: b
Page: 218
Obj: 9
Type: F

65. Blood pressure tends to be temporarily higher when people
    a. are Type B personalities.
    b. are angry or anxious.
    c. are depressed and guilt-ridden.
    d. talk about their anger after cooling down.

Ans: d
Page: 218
Obj: 9
Type: A

66. Jessica and George work for an obnoxious boss who often aims humiliating remarks at his employees. Neither worker can respond in anger for fear of losing her or his job. Based on the results of a study by Lai and Linden (1992) concerning gender, emotional expression, and blood pressure, which person is likely to have problems with high blood pressure?
    a. Jessica
    b. George and Jessica equally
    c. Neither; only when anger is expressed does high blood pressure occur.
    d. George

Ans: a
Page: 218
Obj: 9
Type: F

67. Recent research on high blood pressure and job stress indicates that
    a. having a high-status job and a belief that success requires hard work are related to high blood pressure in all groups but white males.
    b. having a high-status job but not a belief that success requires hard work is associated with high blood pressure in all groups.
    c. African Americans have high blood pressure regardless of their job stress.
    d. high blood pressure is unrelated to job stress when people have the belief that success requires hard work.

Ans: c
Page: 218
Obj: 9
Type: A

68. Physicians often do routine screening of their patients to identify those with high blood pressure. Which town would probably identify the *most* individuals through such screenings?
    a. West City, with an Asian-majority population
    b. East City, with a White-majority population
    c. South City, with an African American–majority population
    d. North City, with an equal frequency of Asians, Whites, and African Americans

Ans: c
Page: 218
Obj: 9
Type: F

69. Racial differences in rates of _____ seem to be influenced by the availability of _____.
    a. asthma; healthy diet
    b. coronary heart disease; fibrogen
    c. essential hypertension; psychosocial resources
    d. migraine and other headaches; psychosocial resources

Ans: b
Page: 219
Obj: 10
Type: A

70. Dr. Kazinsky says, "Headaches are among the most common psychophysiological complaints. It is clear that there are three different forms of headache, each with its own cause. Headache pain can range from dull to excruciating, but in all cases stress plays a role." What portion of this statement is *inaccurate*?
    a. It is inaccurate to say that headache is among the most common complaints.
    b. It is inaccurate to say that each headache has its own cause.
    c. It is inaccurate to say that pain can range from dull to excruciating.
    d. It is inaccurate to say that stress plays a role in all headaches.

Ans: a
Page: 219
Obj: 10
Type: F

71. Current research suggests that when it comes to headaches,
    a. it is hard to distinguish among the different kinds.
    b. the pain that is experienced is a form of conversion disorder.
    c. stress plays little role in the initiation of headaches.
    d. there are specific causes for each kind of headache.

Ans: a
Page: 220
Obj: 10
Type: A

72. Tanya experiences pulsating, intense pain in her head. Prior to these attacks, her vision is distorted or she feels numbness in her fingers. The headaches are caused by excessive dilation of blood vessels. Tanya can be diagnosed with
    a. classic migraine headache.
    b. cluster headache.
    c. common tension headache.
    d. common migraine headache.

Ans: a
Page: 221
Obj: 10
Type: C

73. Lori describes her headache as a throbbing pain that is only on the left side and makes her feel nauseous. Lori is experiencing what type of headache?
    a. migraine
    b. tension
    c. lateral
    d. cluster

Ans: b
Page: 221
Obj: 10
Type: F

74. _____ headaches once were believed to be caused by contractions of the muscles in the head and neck, but research now shows that many sufferers do not have any unusual muscle contractions.
    a. Migraine
    b. Tension
    c. Classic
    d. Cluster

Ans: a
Page: 221
Obj: 10
Type: A

75. Otto complains of excruciatingly painful headaches that are centered near one eye. His eye tears, and his nose is blocked when the headache occurs. What kind of headache is Otto probably suffering from?
    a. Cluster
    b. Duodenal
    c. Classic migraine
    d. Tension

Ans: b
Page: 221
Obj: 11
Type: A

76. Murray is a child with allergies who has respiratory attacks that make breathing very difficult. These attacks often occur at night and when his parents have had a fight. Murray is probably suffering from
    a. angina pectoris.
    b. asthma.
    c. essential hypertension.
    d. posttraumatic stress disorder.

Ans: d
Page: 222
Obj: 11
Type: F

77. Asthma-related deaths in children are *most* associated with
    a. unconscious defense mechanisms.
    b. coronary heart disease in parents.
    c. an inability to express anxiety or depression in parents.
    d. family dysfunction and poor self-care.

Ans: c
Page: 223
Obj: 12
Type: F

78. According to the _____ perspective, each form of psychophysiological disorder is caused by a particular conflict.
    a. somatic weakness
    b. operant conditioning
    c. psychodynamic
    d. social learning

Ans: c
Page: 223
Obj: 12
Type: F

79. One problem with Alexander's (1950) psychodynamic theory of psychophysiological disorders is that
    a. he never linked specific unconscious needs to specific disorders.
    b. he left out the most common forms of psychophysiological disorders.
    c. there is no experimental support for his ideas.
    d. his ideas gave no direction to treat the disorders.

Ans: d
Page: 224
Obj: 12
Type: F

80. When stress leads to a physiological disorder in the body system that is the "weakest link," this supports the
    a. classical conditioning hypothesis of generalization.
    b. psychodynamic hypothesis of stimulus specificity.
    c. autonomic response specificity theory.
    d. somatic weakness hypothesis.

Ans: b
Page: 224
Obj: 12
Type: A

81. Jerry and Terry are college students. When Jerry has exams or important social occasions to worry about, he develops a skin rash. When Terry has the same stressors, he has stomach pains. The differences in psychophysiological disorders support the _____ hypothesis.
    a. psychodynamic
    b. autonomic response specificity
    c. general adaptation
    d. biofeedback

Ans: c
Page: 224
Obj: 12
Type: A

82. Autonomic response specificity is *best* described by which of these statements?
    a. "When people show a sick child attention and sympathy, they only teach that child the benefits of being ill."
    b. "I had a bad case of acne as an adolescent, so even in middle age, when I'm under stress, my face breaks out."
    c. "Ever since I was a toddler, whenever people got angry or upset, I would get a headache."
    d. "Anyone who suppresses emotions is going to suffer from ulcers sooner or later."

Ans: d
Page: 224
Obj: 12
Type: A

83. Dr. DiNapoli says, "Prolonged stress exhausts the body's capacity to resist disease. Regardless of a person's history, there are diseases of adaptation such as hypertension that produce life-threatening illness." Dr. DiNapoli's ideas support the _____ perspective on medical conditions.
    a. psychodynamic
    b. classical conditioning
    c. autonomic response specificity
    d. general adaptation

Ans: b
Page: 224
Obj: 12
Type: F

84. The general adaptation model sees the causes of disease in
    a. the conditioning history of the individual.
    b. the duration and intensity of stressors faced.
    c. the unique personality of the individual.
    d. unconscious impulses and conflicts.

Ans: d
Page: 224
Obj: 12
Type: C

85. As an infant, Henry had many problems with indigestion and diarrhea. As an adult, he has been subjected to prolonged, significant stressors. Recently, he has developed a gastric ulcer. What is an explanation for Henry's psychophysiological disorder?
   a. General adaptation syndrome alone
   b. Type A personality
   c. Somatic weakness hypothesis alone
   d. Both general adaptation and somatic weakness hypotheses

Ans: d
Page: 225
Obj: 13
Type: F

86. The _____ position suggests that certain situations are paired with physical reactions and thereby cause what we see as a psychophysiological disorder.
   a. psychodynamic
   b. general adaptation syndrome
   c. operant conditioning
   d. classical conditioning

Ans: b
Page: 225
Obj: 13
Type: A

87. Greg studies in the library only during the last panicky days of the semester before finals. Whenever he walks into the library, his heart rate increases, his stomach feels queasy, and his palms sweat. These physiological reactions illustrate the _____ approach to psychophysiological disorders.
   a. somatic weakness
   b. classical conditioning
   c. sociocultural
   d. general adaptation

Ans: c
Page: 225
Obj: 13
Type: C

88. Classical conditioning seems *best* able to explain which aspect of psychophysiological disorders?
   a. Why physiological reactions occur in the first place
   b. Why the accumulation of life stressors leads to tissue damage
   c. Why a physiological disorder continues or grows more severe
   d. Why a particular portion of the body is affected by a stressor

Ans: a
Page: 225
Obj: 13
Type: F

89. Suppose research finds that adults with asthma had parents who tended to keep them home from school when they complained of a stomachache as children. This would support the _____ theory of psychophysiological disorders.
   a. operant conditioning
   b. life change
   c. psychodynamic
   d. general adaptation syndrome

Ans: d
Page: 225
Obj: 13
Type: A

90. Bethany, age eight, develops coughing attacks on school days but never on weekends. Her parents usually provide sympathy and attention when she has an attack. If her parents saw a counselor who supported an operant conditioning viewpoint, they would probably get which piece of advice?
   a. "Ask Bethany to describe her feelings when she has an attack."
   b. "Remember that your child's health is more important than going to school."
   c. "Discover whether something happening at school is symbolic of an underlying conflict that threatens Bethany but of which she is unaware."
   d. "Reward Bethany for going to school but do not show sympathy or let her stay home when she has attacks."

Ans: a
Page: 225
Obj: 13
Type: F

91. The rate of coronary heart disease is five times greater in Japanese-Americans who become acculturated than in those who retain their traditional values. This fact supports a(n) _____ view of psychophysiological disorders.
    a. socio-cultural
    b. operant conditioning
    c. genetic
    d. autonomic response specificity

Ans: d
Page: 225
Obj: 13
Type: C

92. Suppose we discover that Cubans who have lived in the United States for several generations and have adopted American lifestyles are more likely to develop ulcers and coronary heart disease than Cubans who have maintained their traditional ways of life. This would support the _____ explanation for psychophysiological disorders.
    a. behavioral
    b. biological
    c. cognitive
    d. socio-cultural

Ans: c
Page: 226
Obj: 14
Type: C

93. Dr. Pak investigates the social, psychological, and lifestyle influences on health and illness. She tends to use the research from a number of disciplines to develop stress and anxiety management programs. Dr. Pak's work *best* illustrates
    a. the biological model of illness.
    b. a purely psychodynamic approach to illness.
    c. behavioral medicine.
    d. a sociocultural approach to illness.

Ans: b
Page: 226
Obj: 14
Type: F

94. Efforts to combine medical and psychological treatments have proved to be
    a. unsuccessful unless extensive psychoanalysis is used.
    b. successful and more than a passing fad.
    c. successful, but only because they seem to be a fad.
    d. largely unsuccessful for psychophysiological disorders.

Ans: a
Page: 226
Obj: 14
Type: A

95. Marquis is receiving relaxation training for his headache problems. Which of the following *best* illustrates what he should do?
    a. Clench certain muscle groups and then release them.
    b. Monitor his headache pain with a daily logbook.
    c. Concentrate on tones played over a set of headphones so that he can lower the tones.
    d. Change his way of thinking about the pain of a headache.

Ans: d
Page: 226
Obj: 14
Type: F

96. In relaxation training, subjects
    a. develop the ability to put themselves into a trance state.
    b. relax all their muscles at once.
    c. imagine situations that are calm and pleasant.
    d. eventually learn to relax without tensing their muscles.

Ans: b
Page: 226
Obj: 14
Type: A

97. Henry is treated for hypertension by using an operant conditioning procedure in which information about small decreases in his blood pressure serves as reinforcement. What treatment is Henry getting?
    a. Cognitive coping theory
    b. Biofeedback
    c. Autonomic response generalization
    d. Jacobson's progressive relaxation training

Ans: d
Page: 227
Obj: 14
Type: A

98. A workplace stress management program includes self-instructional training and teaches workers to think differently about the sources of their job stresses. They learn that their reactions to stress can increase or decrease their risk of illness. This program illustrates _____ interventions.
   a. biofeedback
   b. general adaptation
   c. classical conditioning
   d. cognitive-behavioral

Ans: d
Page: 227
Obj: 14
Type: A

99. Deidra's husband has left her after she was diagnosed with breast cancer. She sees the world as unfair and she is depressed. Her therapist suggests she join a group that helps members find validation and meaning in their life experience. The therapist is suggesting what approach?
   a. psychodynamic.
   b. behavioral.
   c. socio-cultural.
   d. social-cognitive processing.

Ans: c
Page: 228
Obj: 14
Type: F

100. Cognitive strategies to improve coping skills and to manage stress
   a. have been effective in improving physiological functioning, but not psychological distress in HIV seropositive men.
   b. have been effective in improving psychological distress, but not physiological functioning in HIV seropositive men.
   c. have been effective in improving both psychological distress and physiological functioning in HIV seropositive men.
   d. have not been effective in improving psychological distress or physiological functioning in HIV seropositive men.

ESSAY QUESTIONS

1. The greater the number, intensity, and duration of stressors, the higher the chances a person will develop a serious medical condition. However, some individuals withstand such periods without becoming ill, while others become ill after experiencing relatively few stressors. What concepts in psychology help explain these differences in response to stressors?

2. List and describe three different factors that moderate individuals' stress responses.

3. Compare and contrast the psychodynamic, operant conditioning, and cognitive-behavioral approaches to the treatment of psychophysiological disorders.

SAMPLE ANSWERS

1. The life change model suggests that for large populations, the greater the number, intensity, and duration of stressors, the higher the risk of developing a disease or other medical condition. Comparing two individuals who are exposed to the same set of stressors, we cannot predict who will get sick. First, the meaning of the stressful events may be different: One person may see the loss of his or her job, for instance, as a challenge, while another may see it as a catastrophe. The transaction model proposes that the way we think about events influences our arousal level and, in

turn, our susceptibility to disease. Kobasa's hardy personality concept extends this idea. If a person senses control over events, is committed to or finds meaning in life activities, and is open to change (seeing it as a challenge rather than a threat), this personality style may protect the person from stress-related illness. Another factor is the degree of social support the person receives during the stressful period. Research shows that those who have emotional supports are less likely to fall ill than those without supports, even if both experience the same life events. Somatic weakness also helps explain individual responses to stressful events, since prior bouts with illness may leave a particular organ vulnerable. Similarly, we cannot easily know the quality of the individual's immune system at the time the stressful events occur, making the same level of stress lead to illness in a person with a compromised immune system but not affecting another person with a full-strength immune system. Finally, some individuals respond to stressful events with poor health practices (drinking or eating too much, sleeping or exercising too little), so the same stressful period might produce illness in one person but not another.

2. Factors that influence one's physiological response to a stressor are one's use of coping responses; one's cognitive appraisal of the stressor, especially perceived control; personality characteristics such as hardiness; one's social support; and whether one's coping responses are adaptive (e.g., relaxation) or maladaptive (e.g., drinking). One's *cognitive appraisal* of a stressor also influences one's response to the stressor. An event that is unexpected or unpredictable, for example, may be particularly stressful for an individual because the individual has had no time to prepare for it cognitively. *Perceived control* is also important. A negative event that is perceived as controllable is likely to be less stressful than one that is perceived as uncontrollable. Perception of control over the environment seems to reduce stress effects. *Hardiness*, a personality trait characterized by openness to change, commitment, and a sense of personal control, appears to protect individuals against stress-related illness. Finally, *social support* moderates the impact of a stressor. Research suggests that social support may provide a buffer or protection against the health-damaging effects of stress.

3. The psychodynamic approach to psychophysiological disorders would examine the underlying conflicts and needs of the individual. It is believed that symptoms have symbolic relationships to family members, so that asthma sufferers might have fears of separation and unresolved dependency on mother. There is no experimental support for such ideas. Still, treatment would try to bring to consciousness causes of the illness that the individual was unaware of. Similarly, a cognitive-behavioral therapist would want the person to become aware of his or her thoughts and change them so that he or she could reduce the emotional reactions causing illness. The operant conditioning approach would focus on the rewards and punishments that exist in the person's environment for illness behaviors. Rather than examining unconscious or conscious thoughts, the operant therapist would advise family members to reward healthy behavior and extinguish illness complaints. Finally, biofeedback approaches, which are essentially operant in nature, would train people with stress-related illnesses to control their blood pressure, muscle tension, or other internal process so that illness would become less likely.

CHAPTER 8
Personality Disorders and Impulse Control Disorders

LEARNING OBJECTIVES

1. Discuss the general characteristics of personality disorders, the factors involved in considering a personality pattern a disorder, how they are diagnosed in the DSM-IV, and why they are difficult to diagnose. (pp. 231–233)

2. Discuss the prevalence and gender distribution of personality disorders and possible reasons for gender differences. (pp. 231–232; Critical Thinking)

3. Discuss the causal considerations for personality disorders, including the five-factor model and its relevance. Explain why we know little about treating personality disorders. (pp. 232–235; Mental Health & Society)

4. Describe the three clusters of personality disorders. (p. 235; Figure 8.1)

5. Describe and differentiate among the characteristics of paranoid, schizoid, and schizotypal personality disorders. Discuss how schizoid and schizotypal personality disorders are differentiated from schizophrenia. (pp. 235-239)

6. Describe and differentiate among the characteristics of histrionic, narcissistic, antisocial, and borderline personality disorders. (pp. 239-243)

7. Describe and differentiate among the characteristics of avoidant, dependent, and obsessive-compulsive personality disorders. (pp. 243-245)

8. Describe the characteristics and incidence of antisocial personality disorder and how it is differentiated from criminal behavior. Explain why it is a difficult population to study. (pp. 245-248)

9. Describe and discuss the etiological theories of antisocial personality disorders, including psychodynamic, family and socialization, and genetic theories. (pp. 248-251)

10. Discuss the relationship between central nervous system and autonomic nervous system abnormalities and antisocial personality disorder. Discuss the role of fearlessness, lack of anxiety, under-arousal, learning deficits, and thrill-seeking in the disorder. (pp. 251-255; Mental Health & Soceity)

11. Describe treatments for antisocial personality and their success. (pp. 255-256)

12. Define impulse control disorders. Describe and differentiate among the following impulse control disorders: intermittent explosive disorder, kleptomania, pathological gambling, pyromania, and trichotillomania. (pp. 256-261)

13. Discuss how impulse control disorders overlap with other conditions. Describe the two explanatory "camps" for these disorders. Review the treatments for impulse control disorders and their success. (pp. 261-262)

MULTIPLE–CHOICE QUESTIONS

Ans: c
Page: 231
Obj: 1
Type: F

1. Which group of disorders is characterized by inflexible and maladaptive behavior patterns that lead to personal difficulties, subjective distress, or problems in functioning?
   a. Impulse control disorders
   b. Anxiety disorders
   c. Personality disorders
   d. Somatoform disorders

Ans: d
Page: 231
Obj: 1
Type: A

2. Dr. Salizar says, "People with these disorders function well enough so that they may not need therapy and they rarely seek help themselves. However, their patterns of behavior are longstanding and are so rigid that they greatly impair their social functioning or cause subjective distress." Dr. Salizar is *best* describing
   a. anxiety disorders.
   b. impulse control disorders.
   c. somatoform disorders.
   d. personality disorders.

Ans: b
Page: 231
Obj: 1
Type: A

3. Elsa's friends have described her as being "close-minded." She has very set ideas and is not open to discussing other viewpoints. This close-mindedness permeates everything she does and is quite annoying to others. Nonetheless, Elsa seems to have friends and does fine at work. Should Elsa be diagnosed with a personality disorder?
   a. No; although Elsa's close-mindedness is likely causing her significant personal distress, it also must cause problems in interpersonal relationships to be diagnosed as a personality disorder.
   b. No; although her close-mindedness may be excessive, it does not appear to have caused Elsa substantial problems in interpersonal, occupational, or other areas of her life.
   c. Yes; Elsa's personality trait of close-mindedness appears to be extreme and is applied indiscriminately.
   d. Yes; Elsa has a characteristic attitude, belief, and behavioral reaction that permeates the way she thinks about herself and her world.

Ans: c
Page: 232
Obj: 1
Type: F

4. Women are more likely than men to be diagnosed with borderline, histrionic, and dependent personality disorders, while men are more likely than women to be diagnosed with antisocial, paranoid, and obsessive-compulsive personality disorders. Which of the following is not generally considered to be a reason for these differences?
   a. gender bias.
   b. biological factors.
   c. disconfirmatory bias.
   d. social factors.

Ans: b
Page: 232
Obj: 1
Type: A

5. Dr. Tran says, "Personality disorders have their onset after age eighteen and rarely lead to psychiatric hospitalization on their own. They are recorded on Axis II of the DSM-IV-TR and represent extreme forms of normal personality traits." What portion of this statement is *inaccurate*?
   a. It is inaccurate to say that they represent extreme forms of normal traits.
   b. It is inaccurate to say that their onset is after age eighteen.
   c. It is inaccurate to say that they rarely lead to hospitalization on their own.
   d. It is inaccurate to say that they are recorded on Axis II.

Ans: d
Page: 232
Obj: 1
Type: A

6. Felix has been diagnosed with major depression. His psychologist has noted that he also demonstrates inflexible and maladaptive traits that impair his interpersonal functioning. Which of the following statements concerning Felix is *accurate*?
   a. Felix will probably be assigned Axis I and Axis III diagnoses.
   b. Felix will probably be assigned Axis I and Axis IV diagnoses.
   c. Felix will probably be assigned Axis II and Axis IV diagnoses.
   d. Felix will probably be assigned Axis I and Axis II diagnoses.

Ans: b
Page: 232
Obj: 1
Type: F

7. Axis II diagnoses in DSM-IV-TR represent
   a. temporary disruptions in the ability to function normally.
   b. inflexible and maladaptive traits and styles.
   c. disorders that begin in childhood or adolescence.
   d. medical conditions.

Ans: d
Page: 233
Obj: 1
Type: F

8. Which statement about the diagnosis of personality disorders is *accurate*?
   a. It is relatively easy to diagnose personality disorders because the symptoms are unlike those of other disorders.
   b. Personality disorder symptoms usually develop in early to middle adulthood.
   c. Personality disorder symptoms are usually so severe that people with this disorder require hospitalization.
   d. It is often difficult to diagnose personality disorders because the symptoms are similar to those of other disorders.

Ans: b
Page: 233
Obj: 1
Type: C

9. Which of the following is *not* a reason to dispute a DSM-IV-TR diagnosis of personality disorders?
   a. People can have more than one personality disorder.
   b. Some of these disorders are believed to be psychotic conditions that do not involve hallucinations or delusions.
   c. They are seen as stable patterns of behavior, but many see personality as unstable across situations.
   d. Their symptoms overlap with those of other psychological conditions.

Ans: d
Page: 232
Obj: 2
Type: A

10. Lisa, Lynda, and Lana have been diagnosed with personality disorders. Bill, Bart, and Bud also have been diagnosed with personality disorders. Probabilities suggest that
    a. the men have borderline and avoidant forms of the disorders.
    b. the men have histrionic and dependent forms of the disorders.
    c. the women have paranoid and obsessive-compulsive forms of the disorders.
    d. the men have antisocial and obsessive-compulsive forms of the disorders.

Ans: a
Page: 233
Obj: 1
Type: C

11. Dr. Drake has diagnosed a person with a personality disorder using the DSM-IV-TR criteria. We can assume that
    a. the diagnosis is based on a number of traits that have characterized long-term functioning.
    b. the diagnosis made was incremental; that is, the individual was rated as having mild to severe forms of a disorder.
    c. the diagnosed person's symptoms began after the age of eighteen.
    d. symptoms affect other people but not necessarily the individual or his or her social and occupational functioning.

Ans: b
Page: 233
Obj: 1
Type: C

12. Consider an adult whose pattern of personality traits is quite inflexible and has been stable since adolescence. The person's behavior does not reflect another disorder and causes neither subjective distress nor impairments in social functioning. Can the person be diagnosed with a personality disorder?
    a. Yes, the pattern of traits must simply begin in adolescence.
    b. No, there must be distress or functioning impairment.
    c. No, the personality pattern must reflect another disorder.
    d. Yes, the pattern of traits must simply be inflexible and stable.

Ans: c
Page: 233
Obj: 1
Type: F

13. The creation of a new personality disorder would require
    a. only one thing: that the behavior pattern is an extreme version of a personality trait.
    b. that the behavior pattern has come to the attention of researchers only recently.
    c. that the behavior pattern causes subjective distress or impairment in social or occupational functioning.
    d. agreement among all cultures that the personality pattern is abnormal.

Ans: a
Page: 233
Obj: 3
Type: C

14. Which of the following characteristics of personality disorders is *not* typical?
    a. Personality disorders are usually produced by traumatic experiences.
    b. Personality disorders cause marked impairment and distress.
    c. The patterns begin to appear in later childhood and adolescence.
    d. People with personality disorders are less likely to respond positively to therapy.

Ans: b
Page: 233
Obj: 3
Type: A

15. Patrick sees personality disorders in terms of extreme forms of introversion, conscientiousness, and agreeableness. Patrick's thinking is similar to
    a. the DSM-IV category system for personality disorders.
    b. the five-factor model of personality.
    c. the behavioral approach to personality.
    d. the psychodynamic approach to personality.

Ans: c
Page: 233
Obj: 3
Type: F

16. Which of the following is *not* a component of the five-factor model of personality?
    a. Openness to experience
    b. Agreeableness
    c. Intelligence
    d. Neuroticism

Ans: b
Page: 233
Obj: 3
Type: F

17. Research by Tellegen and colleagues (1988) on the inheritance of personality traits shows that
    a. heredity predicts personality but only in situations where twins are reared in the same family environment.
    b. heredity is important and that living in the same family environment is not strongly related to personality similarity.
    c. heredity is unimportant and that living in the same family environment is strongly related to personality similarity.
    d. heredity predicts personality but not personality disorders.

Ans: a
Page: 235
Obj: 3
Type: A

18. Dr. Clark is looking for research information on the treatment of all personality disorders. It is likely that she will find
    a. information on only a limited range of the disorders.
    b. less on antisocial personality disorder than on other disorders.
    c. a great deal of information that shows the effectiveness of medication.
    d. a great deal of information on all the disorders but using only one or two treatment techniques.

Ans: b
Page: 235
Obj: 4
Type: F

19. Murray is diagnosed with one of the personality disorders. Which of the following behavior clusters is *not* likely to characterize Murray because it is not one of the categories of personality disorder?
    a. He is emotional and dramatic, often acting erratically.
    b. He shows impulsive actions that results in tension release.
    c. He is anxious, fearful, and unable to make decisions for himself.
    d. He engages in odd or eccentric behaviors.

Ans: c
Page: 235
Obj: 4
Type: F

20. Which of the following is *not* one of the three clusters the DSM-IV lists for personality disorders?
    a. Anxious or fearful behaviors
    b. Odd or eccentric behaviors
    c. Aggressive or uncontrolled behaviors
    d. Dramatic, emotional, or erratic behaviors

Ans: a
Page: 235
Obj: 5
Type: A

21. "My neighbor is suspicious of everyone, always holds grudges, and is hypersensitive to any criticism. Lacking in emotions and trusting no one, he never changes his mind. His wife says he has always been this way." What personality disorder does this *best* illustrate?
    a. Paranoid
    b. Schizoid
    c. Borderline
    d. Dependent

Ans: c
Page: 235
Obj: 5
Type: A

22. A psychologist is interviewing a refugee to this country who is unfamiliar with the majority culture here. In his former country, this person was spied on by the government and was the victim of robberies and assaults. Which personality disorder must the psychologist be *most* cautious about diagnosing?
    a. Borderline
    b. Obsessive-compulsive
    c. Paranoid
    d. Schizotypal

Ans: c
Page: 235
Obj: 5
Type: A

23. Martin is constantly accusing his wife of having affairs, although there is no cause for his suspiciousness. He is an aloof and cool husband who shares none of his secrets with others. Martin's behavior illustrates the _____ personality disorder.
    a. passive-aggressive
    b. schizoid
    c. paranoid
    d. narcissistic

Ans: a
Page: 238
Obj: 5
Type: C

24. Which of the following quotes *best* captures the essential feature of the schizoid personality disorder?
    a. "I want to be alone."
    b. "There's a sucker born every minute."
    c. "I'm a wild and crazy guy."
    d. "If I'm not the greatest, I must rank in the top two."

Ans: c
Page: 238
Obj: 5
Type: A

25. Albert, who is twenty-five, lacks affection and is unwilling to participate in family activities. He has few hobbies other than building model airplanes, surfing the Internet on his computer, and reading. He has been withdrawn—but not depressed—since childhood, not really wanting to be in a relationship with anyone. He has no "strange" ideas nor does he engage in "strange" behavior. Albert best illustrates which personality disorder?
    a. Schizotypal
    b. Avoidant
    c. Schizoid
    d. Antisocial

Ans: d
Page: 238
Obj: 5
Type: A

26. Daniel was diagnosed with schizoid personality disorder; Douglas was diagnosed with schizotypal personality disorder. We can expect that
    a. Daniel has extreme mood fluctuations but Douglas does not.
    b. Daniel showed symptoms at an earlier age than Douglas.
    c. Daniel has odd thoughts but Douglas does not.
    d. Daniel prefers to be alone but Douglas does not.

Ans: b
Page: 238
Obj: 5
Type: C

27. Which of the following statements is *most likely* to be endorsed by an individual diagnosed with schizotypal personality disorder?
    a. "I have sometimes had the feeling that I was designed for greatness and that it is just a matter of time before others realize my superiority."
    b. "I have sometimes had the feeling that my body is decaying inside of me."
    c. "I have sometimes had the feeling that others are spying on me and are out to get me."
    d. "I have sometimes had the feeling that my body is my greatest attribute and should be shown off to the fullest extent."

Ans: b
Page: 238
Obj: 5
Type: C

28. One way to differentiate the schizoid from the schizotypal personality disorder is on the basis of thoughts, because the
    a. schizoid is more likely to have delusions and hallucinations.
    b. schizotypal is more likely to have odd thoughts.
    c. schizotypal is more likely to be obsessed with perfectionism and details.
    d. schizoid is more likely to think that others are out to get him or her.

Ans: b
Page: 238
Obj: 5
Type: A

29. Diana feels that her life is becoming unreal. She isn't sure, but she thinks she can make other people get sick just by thinking about it. When she speaks, she drifts off the subject but never becomes incoherent. When in public, she thinks others are avoiding her, but she doesn't know why. Her thoughts have not interfered with her ability to work. Diana's behavior illustrates the _____ personality disorder.
    a. obsessive-compulsive
    b. schizotypal
    c. borderline
    d. avoidant

Ans: d
Page: 239
Obj: 5
Type: F

30. Vagueness, digressions, and odd ideas are key symptoms in
    a. schizoid personality disorder.
    b. antisocial personality disorder.
    c. obsessive-compulsive personality disorder.
    d. schizotypal personality disorder.

Ans: a
Page: 239
Obj: 5
Type: F

31. Research shows the strongest genetic relationship between schizophrenia and
    _____ personality disorder.
    a. schizotypal
    b. schizoid
    c. borderline
    d. avoidant

Ans: c
Page: 239
Obj: 5
Type: A

32. Shawn is diagnosed with schizotypal personality disorder. Research would
    suggest that his family
    a. is characterized by men with antisocial personality disorder.
    b. abused him when he was a child.
    c. includes some people with schizophrenia.
    d. engaged in substance abuse and comes from the lower socioeconomic
       classes.

Ans: b
Page: 239
Obj: 6
Type: A

33. People are often attracted to Christine because she is flamboyant and
    emotionally very expressive. She rarely, however, develops any long-term
    relationships, because people experience her as shallow and self-centered.
    What personality disorder would Christine *most likely* be diagnosed with?
    a. Narcissistic
    b. Histrionic
    c. Schizoid
    d. Antisocial

Ans: a
Page: 239
Obj: 6
Type: F

34. The _____ personality disorder is characterized by self-dramatization,
    attention-seeking behaviors, and exaggerated emotional expression.
    a. histrionic
    b. narcissistic
    c. schizoid
    d. borderline

Ans: b
Page: 239
Obj: 6
Type: A

35. Deena was diagnosed with histrionic personality disorder. She is attention-
    seeking and egocentric. She displays little emotion but is charming. What part
    of Deena's personality profile is *unusual*?
    a. It is unusual for histrionic personalities to be charming.
    b. It is unusual for histrionic personalities to display little emotion.
    c. It is unusual for histrionic personalities to be attention-seekers.
    d. It is unusual for histrionic personalities to be egocentric.

Ans: d
Page: 240
Obj: 6
Type: A

36. A man is described as lacking in empathy, exaggerated in his own sense of
    self-importance, and constantly overestimating his talents and power over
    others. This description best reflects the _____ personality disorder.
    a. borderline
    b. obsessive-compulsive
    c. histrionic
    d. narcissistic

Ans: a
Page: 240
Obj: 6
Type: A

37. Dr. Abdul says, "My client has feelings of inferiority that must be denied. Therefore, he devalues others and thinks himself superior to everyone else. Our therapy sessions are monologues where he recounts his successes and everyone else's stupidity. And yet if I interrupt even once, he takes great offense." Dr. Abdul's client is probably diagnosed with _____ personality disorder.
   a. narcissistic
   b. obsessive-compulsive
   c. histrionic
   d. borderline

Ans: b
Page: 241
Obj: 6
Type: F

38. The key feature of borderline personality disorder is
   a. shifts from normal to psychotic functioning.
   b. severe fluctuations in mood, self-image, and unstable interpersonal relationships.
   c. a tendency to have paranoid delusions that are identical to those of schizophrenics.
   d. demanding uncritical acceptance by authorities but needing criticism from family members.

Ans: c
Page: 241
Obj: 6
Type: A

39. Dr. Williamson says, "The central feature of this personality disorder is extreme changes in mood leading to stormy interpersonal relationships. Chronic feelings of emptiness and boredom may lead to suicidal gestures. Women are three times more likely to be diagnosed than men." The disorder being described is
   a. narcissistic personality disorder.
   b. histrionic personality disorder.
   c. borderline personality disorder.
   d. antisocial personality disorder.

Ans: a
Page: 241
Obj: 6
Type: A

40. Dr. Claven says this about individuals with borderline personality disorder: "These are very impulsive, erratic individuals. They often feel empty and suicidal. Their problems put the disorder midway between neurotic and psychotic disturbances, and the problems start in adolescence or earlier." What portion of the statement is *inaccurate*?
   a. It is incorrect to say that borderlines are between neurotic and psychotic.
   b. It is incorrect to say that borderline characteristics start in adolescence.
   c. It is incorrect to say that borderlines are impulsive or erratic.
   d. It is incorrect to say that borderlines feel empty or suicidal.

Ans: d
Page: 241
Obj: 6
Type: F

41. Object splitting and faulty self-identity are two of the explanations for _____ personality disorder.
   a. obsessive-compulsive
   b. antisocial
   c. avoidant
   d. borderline

Ans: c
Page: 241
Obj: 6
Type: A

42. Charlene's parents have been concerned about her for quite some time. After her recent suicide attempt, they decided to seek professional help. They report the following behaviors to a psychologist: Charlene often goes into uncontrollable rages for no apparent reason. Furthermore, when she becomes depressed and angry, she often cuts on her arms with a dinner knife. She has a hard time making up her mind about things. One minute she is set on pursuing a career in advertising, and the next she is looking into studying music. What is the *most likely* diagnosis for Charlene?
    a. Schizotypal personality disorder
    b. Dependent personality disorder
    c. Borderline personality disorder
    d. Avoidant personality disorder

Ans: b
Page: 242
Obj: 6
Type: F

43. According to Beck, a cognitive explanation for borderline personality disorder should emphasize
    a. the object splitting that occurred in the person's childhood.
    b. the person's beliefs that the world is dangerous and he or she is powerless and unacceptable.
    c. the person's inability to label emotions accurately.
    d. two factors: autonomic arousal and imitation of models whose emotions were poorly controlled.

Ans: d
Page: 243
Obj: 7
Type: C

44. "They crave attention but are hypersensitive to potential rejection. They fantasize about relationships but live the loner's life." Which personality disorder is being described?
    a. Borderline personality disorder
    b. Antisocial personality disorder
    c. Narcissistic personality disorder
    d. Avoidant personality disorder

Ans: c
Page: 243
Obj: 7
Type: A

45. Carol spends most of her time at home with her parents. She wants to join the other students at school functions, but she is afraid she will do something inappropriate, resulting in embarrassment and rejection. Carol *most likely* would be diagnosed with which personality disorder?
    a. Dependent
    b. Obsessive-compulsive
    c. Avoidant
    d. Schizoid

Ans: a
Page: 244
Obj: 7
Type: A

46. A patient who is submissive, unable to make decisions, and in need of constant reassurance from others would be diagnosed with
    a. dependent personality disorder.
    b. avoidant personality disorder.
    c. passive-aggressive personality disorder.
    d. antisocial personality disorder.

Ans: c
Page: 244
Obj: 7
Type: A

47. Linda is thirty years old but avoids responsibility and has no opinions of her own. Her husband makes all the decisions in the family. Linda seems very tolerant but is actually extremely low in self-confidence. A reasonable diagnosis for Linda is
    a. narcissistic personality disorder.
    b. avoidant personality disorder.
    c. dependent personality disorder.
    d. obsessive-compulsive personality disorder.

Ans: b
Page: 243
Obj: 7
Type: A

48. Esther and Emily both lack self-confidence. Esther is fearful of criticism, so she keeps apart from others. Emily is unwilling to assume responsibility, so she stays in relationships with men who control her life. If these women have personality disorders, Esther's is _____, while Emily's is _____.
   a. narcissistic; borderline
   b. avoidant; dependent
   c. avoidant; borderline
   d. narcissistic; dependent

Ans: a
Page: 245
Obj: 7
Type: A

49. Janice complains that her husband, Arnie, is a workaholic. Arnie is so focused on productivity at work that he rarely has time for her or the children. Furthermore, she knows that he has missed important deadlines recently and cannot understand how this is possible, given the number of hours he works. When Arnie is at home, he is demanding and controlling and angry at Janice if things are not done to his specifications. With what personality disorder would Arnie *most likely* be diagnosed?
   a. Obsessive-compulsive
   b. Antisocial
   c. Schizoid
   d. Narcissistic

Ans: b
Page: 246
Obj: 8
Type: A

50. George's life is centered around how he can become rich quick. He regularly develops new schemes for conning people. For example, he has made false claims to insurance companies, has received money for baggage that was not really lost, and recently has begun to shoplift. When asked about his behavior, George's response is, "The insurance companies, airlines, and stores can all afford it. They rip you off every chance they get, so now it is my turn." With what personality disorder would George *most likely* be diagnosed?
   a. Schizoid
   b. Antisocial
   c. Narcissistic
   d. Obsessive-compulsive

Ans: a
Page: 246
Obj: 8
Type: A

51. Chuck has no life plan; he simply lives from minute to minute. He can charm and manipulate others with skill. Although he has often been punished for lying and exploiting others, he neither learns from the experience nor experiences anxiety or guilt. Using Cleckley's checklist, the *best* diagnosis is that Chuck has _____ personality disorder.
   a. antisocial
   b. borderline
   c. obsessive-compulsive
   d. intermittent explosive

Ans: c
Page: 246
Obj: 8
Type: F

52. Which personality disorder has been labeled "moral insanity," "psychopathic personality," and "sociopathic personality"?
   a. Histrionic
   b. Obsessive-compulsive
   c. Antisocial
   d. Borderline

Ans: a
Page: 246
Obj: 8
Type: A

53. Carl is diagnosed as having antisocial personality disorder. He tends to be loyal to his friends but exploits others. He is witty and articulate and lies with great skill. What aspect of Carl's case is *unusual* for an antisocial personality?
    a. Antisocial personalities are rarely loyal to anyone.
    b. Antisocial personalities tend to withdraw from people, not exploit them.
    c. Antisocial personalities tend to be women.
    d. Antisocial personalities are rarely witty and articulate.

Ans: b
Page: 247
Obj: 8
Type: C

54. Unlike Cleckley's list of symptoms that characterize antisocial personality disorder, the criteria used in the DSM-IV-TR
    a emphasize how the person thinks.
    b. emphasize the person's actions.
    c. suggest that the person is borderline psychotic.
    d. suggest that the disorder is similar to avoidant personality disorder.

Ans: d
Page: 247
Obj: 8
Type: A

55. A mental health center is planning a prevention program to reduce the number of people with antisocial personality disorder. Which population should they target?
    a. Latinos from rural areas
    b. Females under the age of eighteen
    c. Shy people with low self-esteem
    d. Poor, urban males

Ans: b
Page: 247
Obj: 8
Type: A

56. Dr. Wills says, "This man has been convicted of crimes since he was sixteen. He never seems to learn his lesson when he is sent to prison. Obviously, he is an antisocial personality." What is *wrong* with Dr. Wills's statement?
    a. Antisocial personalities rarely begin a life of crime at such an early age.
    b. There must be a lack of interpersonal ties and a lack of guilt for a diagnosis of antisocial personality.
    c. Antisocial personalities rarely commit crimes.
    d. There must be a high level of anxiety and low self-confidence for a diagnosis of antisocial personality.

Ans: b
Page: 248
Obj: 8
Type: C

57. A psychologist who knows both Rollin and Jerry considers Rollin a primary psychopath and Jerry a secondary psychopath. What probably distinguishes them is that
    a. Rollin has bizarre ideas and feels compulsions; Jerry does not.
    b. Rollin lacks guilt over his antisocial acts; Jerry feels guilt.
    c. Rollin has always been a psychopath; Jerry had other personality disorders first.
    d. Rollin acts impulsively; Jerry plans his antisocial actions.

Ans: d
Page: 248
Obj: 8
Type: A

58. A senior psychology major wants to do a research project on people with antisocial personality disorder who currently are in treatment. She asks you if it will be easy to find subjects. Your advice should be:
    a. "It will be hard because antisocial is the rarest form of personality disorder."
    b. "It will be hard because all antisocial personalities are in prison."
    c. "It will be easy because antisocial personalities are willing research subjects and are commonly in treatment."
    d. "It will be hard because antisocial personalities rarely seek treatment and will not be sincere subjects."

Ans: c
Page: 248
Obj: 8
Type: F

59. The results of Widom's research in which psychopaths were recruited through a newspaper ad showed that the "ad" subjects
a. had few personality traits in common with criminal psychopaths.
b. tended to have a lower level of education than criminal psychopaths.
c. tended to exhibit personality characteristics similar to those of criminal psychopaths.
d. had a more violent past than criminal psychopaths.

Ans: a
Page: 248
Obj: 8
Type: F

60. A research psychologist wanted to study people with a particular personality disorder. She placed advertisements in newspapers that asked, "Are you adventurous? Do you lead an exciting, impulsive life? If you are the kind of person who'd do almost anything for a dare, send your name. . . ." The researcher was interested in people with _____ personality disorder.
a. antisocial
b. narcissistic
c. borderline
d. intermittent explosive

Ans: a
Page: 249
Obj: 9
Type: F

61. The psychodynamic interpretation of antisocial personality suggests that
a. superego development in childhood was faulty.
b. identification with the opposite-sex parent was especially strong.
c. id impulses are stronger in psychopaths than in non-psychopaths.
d. oral fixation occurred.

Ans: b
Page: 249
Obj: 9
Type: A

62. A psychiatrist says, "People with antisocial personality disorder fail to learn from past experience despite the criticism of parents and others. They may promise to improve, but there is no sincerity in the words; they continue to break the rules of society." If the psychiatrist is a psychoanalyst, his or her explanation will probably be
a. over-identification with parents who were strict disciplinarians.
b. a lack of superego development.
c. a cognitive inability to take another person's point of view.
d. the excessive use of projection and fantasy as defenses.

Ans: c
Page: 249
Obj: 9
Type: A

63. "The antisocial personality fails to learn ethical behavior because of a combination of parental rejection and modeling." This statement reflects the _____ orientation.
a. genetic
b. psychoanalytic
c. family and socialization
d. central nervous system abnormality

Ans: b
Page: 249
Obj: 9
Type: A

64. A social service agency manager who read Loeber's (1990) review of research on the predictors of antisocial behavior in children would learn that she should put most of her energies into _____ in order to stop delinquency.
a. giving children more freedom
b. improving the quality of parental supervision
c. increasing the socioeconomic status of parents
d. reducing parents' emphasis on superego development

Ans: d
Page: 249
Obj: 9
Type: F

65. Inconsistent reinforcement from parents and lack of feedback for behaviors that contradict social norms are family and socialization explanations for _____ personality disorder.
   a. dependent
   b. histrionic
   c. schizoid
   d. antisocial

Ans: a
Page: 249
Obj: 9
Type: C

66. Robins' (1966) research on children who were seen in a child guidance center and who, thirty years later, showed antisocial tendencies found that
   a. antisocial behavior in childhood was a predictor of antisocial personality in adults.
   b. no one could predict who would become an antisocial personality and who would not.
   c. being a gang member was the best predictor of being an adult with antisocial personality.
   d. these individuals had schizophrenic parents.

Ans: b
Page: 249
Obj: 9
Type: C

67. Dr. Cirello is treating a 25-year-old man diagnosed with antisocial personality disorder. When Dr. Cirello investigates the man's family history, she is likely to learn that
   a. his parents consistently reinforced him for being submissive.
   b. the father was aggressive and unfeeling.
   c. the mother had a serious mental condition.
   d. both parents were shy and depressed.

Ans: c
Page: 250
Obj: 9
Type: A

68. A psychologist says, "We know that genetics is the cause of antisocial personality disorder because the concordance rates for MZ twins is higher than that for DZ twins." Why is this statement *inaccurate*?
   a. Concordance rates for twins do not provide information about the genetic cause of disorders.
   b. No one has done twins studies on antisocial personality.
   c. MZ twins probably influence one another more than DZ twins.
   d. DZ twins show higher concordance rates than MZ twins.

Ans: d
Page: 250
Obj: 9
Type: C

69. Research investigating the rate of antisocial personality in adoptees with psychopathic biological parents suggests that genetic factors
   a. play almost no role at all in the disorder.
   b. are important only when the antisocial personality occurs in women.
   c. are important in a small minority of cases.
   d. play a significant role in the disorder.

Ans: b
Page: 251
Obj: 9
Type: F

70. Which of the following is *not* a reason we should be cautious in concluding that antisocial personality disorder is inherited?
   a. Evidence for genetic influence does not prevent environmental factors from being causal influences.
   b. Many studies fail to distinguish criminals from antisocial personalities.
   c. No studies to date have separated the influence of environment from that of genetics.
   d. It is not clear what is being transmitted genetically.

Ans: a
Page: 251
Obj: 10
Type: F

71. The theory that antisocial personality is related to central nervous system abnormalities is *best* supported by the fact that a large
   a. minority of psychopaths have abnormal EEGs.
   b. minority of psychopaths have an extra X chromosome.
   c. majority of psychopaths have brain damage.
   d. minority of psychopaths have too many hormones.

Ans: c
Page: 251
Obj: 10
Type: A

72. Raymond has been diagnosed with antisocial personality disorder. He has been asked by gang members to break into a jewelry store to steal valuables. Since the store is wired with silent alarms, Raymond knows that if he is caught, he will be put in jail for a long time. Raymond will most likely
   a. tell his fellow gang members that he will not commit the robbery.
   b. begin secreting more serotonin as he anticipates the burglary.
   c. experience an increased heart rate, respiration rate, and electrodermal activity as he anticipates the burglary.
   d. experience some psychophysiological arousal but not as much arousal as a person not diagnosed with antisocial personality disorder.

Ans: b
Page: 251
Obj: 10
Type: A

73. Dr. Jackson believes that antisocial personalities act as they do because they experience too little anxiety when being punished and too little emotional arousal under normal circumstances. Dr. Jackson's ideas mirror _____ theory.
   a. psychodynamic
   b. autonomic nervous system
   c. cognitive
   d. central nervous system

Ans: a
Page: 251
Obj: 10
Type: F

74. "Low arousal leads to the thrill-seeking we see in antisocial personality disorder." This statement *best* reflects the _____ explanation of the disorder.
   a. autonomic nervous system abnormality
   b. genetic
   c. central nervous system abnormality
   d. family and socialization

Ans: a
Page: 252
Obj: 10
Type: A

75. Research using the Activities Preference Questionnaire, which pairs a series of frightening or embarrassing situations with situations that are merely onerous, suggests that
   a. psychopaths are difficult children.
   b. children from warm, loving families who are encouraged to channel their fearlessness into socially approved activities may be less likely to become psychopaths.
   c. children who become heroes as adults are generally less charming than children who later become psychopaths.
   d. children who become heroes as adults are more likely to demonstrate pro-social behavior than children who become psychopaths.

Ans: b
Page: 252
Obj: 10
Type: F

76. Some would call Rambo a fictional military hero. According to Lykken's research, he would share the same characteristics as
    a. people who are cautious and fearful of stress.
    b. children from warm, loving families who are encouraged to channel their fearlessness into socially approved activities may be less likely to become psychopaths.
    c. children who become heroes as adults are generally less charming than children who later become psychopaths.
    d. children who become heroes as adults are more likely to demonstrate prosocial behavior than children who become psychopaths.

Ans: c
Page: 252
Obj: 10
Type: C

77. If Lykken is right about the role of fearlessness, we should find that
    a. both psychopaths and heroes are fearful.
    b. psychopaths are fearless, but heroes are fearful.
    c. both psychopaths and heroes are fearless.
    d. psychopaths are fearful, but heroes are fearless.

Ans: b
Page: 252
Obj: 10
Type: A

78. Jerry is diagnosed with APD. If the deficient emotional arousal explanation for the disorder is correct, we can predict that Jerry
    a. shows extremely fast physiological reactions to novel stimuli.
    b. has too little arousal under normal conditions.
    c. experiences more arousal than the normal person.
    d. has some form of damage in his frontal lobes.

Ans: c
Page: 253
Obj: 10
Type: A

79. The director of a summer camp for adolescents who uses Farley's research on thrill-seeking will probably find that the most artistic and adventurous campers will be _____, and the most violent and disobedient campers will be _____.
    a. borderline personalities; antisocial personalities
    b. Little T's; Big T's
    c. Big T's; Big T's
    d. antisocial personalities; narcissistic personalities

Ans: d
Page: 254
Obj: 10
Type: F

80. Psychopaths have some interesting difficulties in tasks that involve avoidance of punishment. Which statement is *accurate* based on research?
    a. When punishment occurs at the same time as lowered arousal, psychopaths learn best.
    b. When the probability of punishment is highly uncertain, psychopaths learn best.
    c. When the punishment involves pain or verbal feedback, psychopaths learn best.
    d. When the punishment involves loss of money, psychopaths learn best.

Ans: b
Page: 254
Obj: 10
Type: A

81. The director of a prison wants to improve the ability of antisocial personality prisoners to learn from their experience. Using research results, the director might
    a. use feelings of guilt and shame as the main methods of punishment.
    b. punish wrongdoers by taking money away from them.
    c. inject prisoners with depressants to reduce their arousal levels.
    d. keep the prisoners guessing about whether they will be punished if they do something wrong.

Ans: a
Page: 255
Obj: 10
Type: F

82. Patrick, Cuthbert, and Lang (1994) suggest that antisocial personality disorder is a cognitive problem. More specifically, they claim that there is
   a. a weak association between mental images of fear stimuli and physiological responses.
   b. an excessive amount of negative self-talk in the psychopath.
   c. an unusually strong association between anxiety-provoking stimuli and long-term memory.
   d. a deficit in the ability to express feelings of fear.

Ans: b
Page: 255
Obj: 11
Type: F

83. Various medications have been used to treat antisocial personality disorder. What can we say about their effectiveness?
   a. No type of drug has had any positive effect in reducing antisocial behavior.
   b. Tranquilizing drugs have had some positive effect in a few cases.
   c. Stimulant drugs have been quite helpful in most cases.
   d. Although drugs are quite helpful, antisocial personalities tend to become addicted to them.

Ans: d
Page: 255
Obj: 11
Type: F

84. Because antisocial personalities exhibit _____ anxiety, traditional treatment approaches, which require the cooperation of the client, have been very _____.
   a. low levels of; effective
   b. high levels of; effective
   c. high levels of; ineffective
   d. low levels of; ineffective

Ans: c
Page: 255
Obj: 11
Type: C

85. Gus has been diagnosed with antisocial personality disorder and is in treatment. His therapist supports Beck's cognitive approach to therapy. We can guess that Gus's therapist
   a. rewards and punishes Gus's behavior immediately and consistently.
   b. provides a physically and mentally stimulating environment so that Gus's thrill-seeking is redirected into something constructive.
   c. will attempt to get Gus to think less about himself and more about developing a sense of responsibility.
   d. will use guilt and shame to stop Gus from thinking about the world and himself in an irrational manner.

Ans: a
Page: 255
Obj: 11
Type: A

86. The director of a new treatment facility for delinquent youths is thinking about using behavior modification as the chief method of changing behavior. Your advice to the new director might be
   a. "This form of treatment will be effective, but maintaining behavior change requires help from peers and family."
   b. "Behavior modification relies too much on rapport-building and cognitive factors to be successful."
   c. "Use behavior modification only if you can suppress the delinquent person's tendency to seek thrills."
   d. "Behavior modification is much less effective than therapies where there is less control."

Ans: c
Page: 256
Obj: 11
Type: A

87. Which of the following statements is *most* likely to come from a person who treats antisocial personalities with a cognitive approach?
    a. "Treatment works only if you broaden the base of intervention to include the person's family and friends."
    b. "Punishment of inappropriate behavior and reward for appropriate behavior is the only way to treat these people."
    c. "I must build rapport and help the client see that developing personal responsibility is more important than self-interest."
    d. "Since over-arousal in the brain is the cause, tranquilizing drugs are the best treatment."

Ans: d
Page: 256
Obj: 12
Type: F

88. Individuals with impulse control disorders have three characteristics in common. Which of the following is *not* one of them?
    a. They feel excitement or release after engaging in the act they cannot resist doing.
    b. They fail to resist an impulse they know is wrong or harmful.
    c. They experience tension before they commit the act they cannot resist doing.
    d. They have continuously had problems with their impulses since childhood.

Ans: c
Page: 256
Obj: 12
Type: C

89. "These disorders are characterized by a failure to resist temptation and a sense of excitement or release after giving in to the temptation." The disorders being described are
    a. dissociative disorders.
    b. personality disorders.
    c. impulse control disorders.
    d. anxiety disorders.

Ans: d
Page: 256
Obj: 12
Type: A

90. Jerry is normally polite and controlled, but if he gets a wrong-number telephone call, he completely loses control. After shrieking at the caller, he may rip the phone out of the wall and hurl it across the room. Afterward, he is filled with guilt and shame. Which impulse control disorder does Jerry illustrate?
    a. Pyromania
    b. Antisocial personality disorder
    c. Kleptomania
    d. Intermittent explosive disorder

Ans: a
Page: 256
Obj: 12
Type: A

91. Tariq has episodes where he loses control of his aggressive impulses and assaults others. Sabira cannot resist impulses to steal things, even though she does not use or want them. Tariq *best* illustrates _____; Sabira *best* illustrates _____.
    a. intermittent explosive disorder; kleptomania
    b. intermittent explosive disorder; obsessive-compulsive disorder
    c. pyromania; trichotillomania
    d. kleptomania; trichotillomania

150 *Chapter 8*

Ans: d
Page: 257
Obj: 12
Type: F

92. Which statement about pathological gambling is *inaccurate*?
    a. There is usually no childhood history of antisocial behavior in pathological gamblers.
    b. Pathological gambling afflicts about 1 to 3 percent of adults and is more common in men than in women.
    c. Pathological gamblers feel tension or restlessness when they cannot gamble.
    d. Unlike antisocial personalities, pathological gamblers never engage in illegal activities.

Ans: c
Page: 259
Obj: 12
Type: A

93. Leshaun is diagnosed with pyromania. He began setting fires as an adult and gets intense pleasure from watching buildings burn. He has never set a fire to get revenge or for financial gain. What is *unusual* about Leshaun's case?
    a. It is unusual for a person with pyromania not to be motivated by revenge or financial gain.
    b. It is unusual for a man to have pyromania.
    c. It is unusual for pyromania to start in adulthood.
    d. It is unusual for a person with pyromania to get pleasure from watching a building burn.

Ans: b
Page: 260
Obj: 12
Type: F

94. One result of kleptomania is that sufferers wind up in jail; one result of trichotillomania is that sufferers wind up
    a. being obese.
    b. being bald.
    c. in debt.
    d. in institutions for the retarded.

Ans: a
Page: 260
Obj: 12
Type: A

95. Which of the following impulse control disorders typically causes harm only to the person who suffers from the disorder?
    a. Trichotillomania
    b. Intermittent explosive disorder
    c. Pyromania
    d. Kleptomania

Ans: a
Page: 261
Obj: 13
Type: C

96. Which statement is the *most* accurate concerning our knowledge of the cause of impulse control disorders?
    a. Not much is actually known about the causes.
    b. The cause is a genetic vulnerability that interacts with socio-cultural factors.
    c. It is clear that the environment plays a more important role than genetics.
    d. It is clear that genetics plays a more important role than the environment.

Ans: d
Page: 257
Obj: 13
Type: A

97. Antoine thinks constantly about betting and winning. He repeatedly gambles even when he would rather not. These characteristics of pathological gambling make it quite similar to
    a. somatoform disorders.
    b. personality disorders.
    c. sexual disorders.
    d. obsessive-compulsive disorder.

Ans: c
Page: 262
Obj: 13
Type: A

98. Dr. Nardone says this about a pathological gambler: "Her first win was a big one, but reinforcements came very irregularly after that. On top of that, her father was a big-time gambler." Dr. Nardone's explanation suggests that he holds a _____ view of impulse control disorders.
    a. cognitive
    b. biological
    c. behavioral
    d. psychodynamic

Ans: b
Page: 262
Obj: 13
Type: A

99. "There are two explanatory 'camps' for these disorders: one that suggests that problems range along a continuum from problem-free to troubled, the other that you either have a disorder or you don't. All agree that these disorders concern an inability to resist temptation, but no one thinks there is a common specific cause." These statements describe
    a. obsessive-compulsive disorders.
    b. impulse control disorders.
    c. personality disorders.
    d. antisocial disorders.

Ans: a
Page: 262
Obj: 13
Type: F

100. In Booth's (1988) review of treatment for impulse control disorders, he finds that, in many of these disorders, there is moderate success using
    a. behavioral and cognitive-behavioral methods.
    b. dream interpretation and token economies.
    c. medication as the main method.
    d. psychoanalytic methods.

ESSAY QUESTIONS

1. List the three clusters of personality disorders, providing a description of the key characteristics of each cluster and an example of a specific personality disorder from each cluster.

2. Evaluate the evidence that antisocial personality disorder stems from physiological abnormalities.

3. Describe how antisocial personality and impulse control disorders might be treated in much the same ways.

SAMPLE ANSWERS

1. The three clusters of personality disorders are as follows:

Cluster A—The eccentric or odd personality disorders. These disorders are all characterized by an eccentric or odd manner of relating to others. An example is paranoid personality disorder. Paranoid personality disorder is characterized by pervasive suspiciousness. Individuals with this disorder often believe that others are deliberately demeaning or threatening them. They constantly expect to be harmed or exploited. They doubt the loyalty or faithfulness of friends and lovers. These individuals are also typically secretive and reluctantly share personal information with others for fear of such information being used against them at a later time. Individuals with paranoid personality disorder are also quite sensitive to perceived slights, respond angrily, and hold grudges. Often individuals with this diagnosis are viewed as hostile, stubborn, needing to control situations, and preoccupied with power—their own need for it and jealousy of those who have it.

Cluster B—The dramatic/erratic personality disorders. These disorders are all characterized by an exhibition of dramatic behaviors. An example is histrionic personality disorder. Histrionic personality disorder is characterized by overemotional, attention-seeking behaviors. Often the attention-seeking takes the form of seductiveness or flamboyant patterns of dress and emotional expression. Individuals diagnosed with histrionic personality disorder often seem excitable, overreactive, and highly suggestible. In addition, the histrionic individual appears emotionally shallow, changeable, and self-centered.

Cluster C—The anxious/fearful personality disorders. These disorders are all characterized by anxiety, and the specific symptomatic behaviors are viewed as efforts to cope with such anxieties. An example is the avoidant personality disorder. The major feature of avoidant personality disorder is social discomfort—timidity and fear of negative social evaluation. An individual with avoidant personality disorder wants to enjoy the presence of others but is afraid of their reactions. Specifically, an individual with avoidant personality disorder fears criticism and disapproval and thus often avoids jobs and activities that involve major interpersonal interactions. Furthermore, the individual is reluctant to risk engaging in any behavior that might result in embarrassment.

2. There is some evidence that antisocial personality disorder may be an inherited problem since identical twins have higher concordance ratios than fraternal twins. However, identical twins shape one another's behavior more than fraternals and so are likely to act in more similar ways. Adoption studies, which separate the influence of genetics and environment, show that antisocial personality disorder is more common among boys whose fathers were antisocial than among controls, even when the boys were not raised in the presence of their fathers. What exactly is inherited is more difficult to determine. Some evidence suggests that antisocial personalities have abnormal EEGs, rather like normal young children. Surveys reveal that between 31 and 58 percent of people with antisocial personality have slow-wave theta activity, but many people with abnormal EEGs act normally, while a majority of those with antisocial personality have normal EEGs. A more promising and consistent hypothesis is that antisocial personalities have abnormally low autonomic arousal, which explains both their inability to learn from experience and their tendency to be thrill-seekers. Because they are underaroused under normal circumstances, they are easily bored. Desiring stimulation, they engage in the impulsive, antisocial behaviors that foster arousal. Eysenck has shown that psychopaths learn more slowly and tire in learning more quickly than nonpsychopaths. Lykken and Farley emphasize the fearlessness and thrill-seeking characteristics of antisocial personalities, which they see as stemming from lower autonomic reactivity in situations where nonpsychopaths become fearful and frightened. Hare has found that antisocial personalities require more intense stimuli to develop cardiac, gavanic, and respiratory signs of stress than do nonpsychopaths. Finally, Patrick, Cuthbert, and Lang (1994) propose a cognitive-emotional deficit in psychopaths. They believe that people with the disorder cannot develop associations between images or words in memory having to do with fearful stimuli and physiological responses to them. Even when psychopaths report being fearful, they seem not to be able to produce physiological signs of fear. Combined, the evidence seems strong that psychopaths are less reactive autonomically, although it is still unclear why.

3. Both antisocial personality disorder and impulse control disorders involve problems in delaying gratification. In both cases, people cannot resist impulses to perform actions that either harm others or harm themselves. For both disorders, therapists might restructure the environment so that reinforcement for delaying gratification occurs consistently and punishment also occurs consistently when individuals fail to resist temptation. There is probably a cognitive component to both disorders, too. McCormick and Taber (1988) believe that impulse control disorders involve cognitive styles that must be changed. In a study of gamblers in treatment, they found that attributional style (how the causes of negative experiences are seen) was related to relapse after treatment. Teaching changes in thinking patterns as well as behavioral skills may be useful in both antisocial personality disorder and impulse control disorders. However, antisocial personality disorder represents a particular motivational problem in that people with it rarely see themselves in need of change. In both disorders, it may be necessary for friends and family members to be

involved, since the individuals may have developed too ingrained a pattern of behavior to change without support.

CHAPTER 9
Substance-Related Disorders

LEARNING OBJECTIVES

1. Distinguish substance-related disorders from substance-use cognitive disorders, substance abuse from substance dependence, and define the terms *tolerance, withdrawal,* and *intoxication.* Discuss the overlap in criteria for dependence and abuse. (pp. 265-68; Figures 9.1-9.3)

2. Describe the nature and scope of substance use and describe the types and prevalence of substance-use disorders in the United States. (p. 268)

3. Categorize the psychoactive drugs according to their properties (sedative, stimulant, or hallucinogenic). (pp. 268-291; Table 9.1)

4. Discuss the nature and magnitude of drinking problems in the United States and the short- and long-term physiological and psychological effects of alcohol. (pp. 270-273; Mental Health & Society)

5. Describe the effects of narcotics, barbiturates, and benzodiazepines. Define polysubstance use and explain why it causes special problems. (pp. 273-276; Mental Health & Soceity)

6. Describe and discuss the problems of stimulant-use disorders, including amphetamines, caffeine, nicotine, cocaine, and crack. Evaluate the controversy concerning nicotine addiction and its treatment. (pp. 276-278)

7. Describe and discuss the problems of hallucinogen-use disorders, including marijuana, LSD, phencyclidine (PCP), and "other substance-use disorders." Evaluate evidence concerning marijuana's harmful effects. (pp. 278-281)

8. Describe the two general types of etiological theories of substance-related disorders. Describe and evaluate the evidence for specific genes and risk factors related to alcoholism and other forms of substance dependence. (pp. 281-283)

9. Describe and discuss the various explanations for alcoholism and other substance-related disorders, including psychodynamic, personality, and sociocultural explanations. Evaluate research evidence on the relation between drug use and maladjustment. (pp. 283-285; Critical Thinking)

10. Describe and discuss behavioral explanations for alcohol abuse and dependence, including the anxiety-reduction hypothesis, learned expectations, and cognitive influences. (pp. 285-287)

11. Discuss explanations for relapse among alcoholics and people who are dependent on other substances. Describe and distinguish opponent process, two-factor, and automatic processing theories of the addiction process. (pp. 287-290)

12. Describe the nature and effectiveness of alcohol and drug treatment programs, including self-help groups, pharmacological approaches to substance-use treatment, and controlled-drinking. (pp. 290-292)

13. Describe and compare the cognitive and behavioral approaches to treating substance-related disorders, including aversion therapy, covert sensitization, rapid smoking, nicotine fading,

relaxation and social learning methods, and cognitive-change treatments. (pp. 292-296; Mental Health & Society)

14. Discuss what is meant by multi-modal treatment. Describe and evaluate the evidence concerning treatment effectiveness for alcohol, smoking cessation, and other substance-related disorders. (pp. 296-298)

MULTIPLE–CHOICE QUESTIONS

Ans: b
Page: 265
Obj: 2
Type: F

1. Which statement is an *accurate* summary concerning drug use?
   a. Only in recent years have people used chemicals to change their moods or levels of consciousness.
   b. Throughout history, people have used chemicals to change their moods and levels of consciousness.
   c. All the chemicals used today to change people's moods are illegal.
   d. The only reason people put substances into their bodies is to cure their illnesses.

Ans: c
Page: 265
Obj: 2
Type: A

2. Suppose the World Health Organization looked at statistics for drug use in countries all over the world. If they reviewed drug use in the United States, they would find that
   a. unlike other countries, Americans are more likely to be smokers than drinkers.
   b. we are among the least permissive drug-using societies.
   c. the vast majority of Americans have used psychoactive substances.
   d. the drugs most often used are illegal ones.

Ans: d
Page: 265
Obj: 1
Type: F

3. Which of the following is an *accurate* definition of substance-related disorder?
   a. The use of psychoactive substances that produces intoxication, delirium, and other cognitive disorders.
   b. The use of psychoactive substances that makes an individual dangerous to others in society.
   c. Criminal activities that are the consequence of supporting a drug habit.
   d. The use of psychoactive substances causing social, occupational, or physical problems and may result in abuse or tolerance, and may affect the central nervous system.

Ans: b
Page: 265
Obj: 2
Type: C

4. Gordon is sixteen and a "typical" adolescent user of marijuana. Based on longitudinal research on youth drug use, we can guess that
   a. the next drug he will use is alcohol.
   b. he has already used alcohol and cigarettes.
   c. he will stop using drugs shortly.
   d. the next drug he will use is tobacco.

Ans: c
Page: 266
Obj: 1
Type: A

5. Sally has a dual diagnosis. This means she
   a. is addicted to two different psychoactive substances.
   b. has both an Axis I and an Axis II diagnosis.
   c. has an Axis I or Asis II diagnosis plus a drug related disorder.
   d. has two Axis I diagnoses.

Ans: c
Page: 266
Obj: 1
Type: C

6. Bess has been using Valium for two years even though it impairs her work performance and jeopardizes her safety because she often drives while intoxicated on the medication. She shows neither tolerance nor withdrawal. According to the DSM-IV, Bess's drug use illustrates
   a. substance intoxication.
   b. substance dependence.
   c. substance abuse.
   d. substance-induced disorder.

Ans: b
Page: 266
Obj: 1
Type: C

7. Jana has been diagnosed with substance abuse. Lyle has been diagnosed with substance dependence. According to the DSM-IV-TR, both of them must show
   a. withdrawal symptoms when the drug is not in the body.
   b. symptoms over a twelve-month period.
   c. another mental disorder such as depression or mania.
   d. tolerance to the drug's effects.

Ans: a
Page: 267
Obj: 1
Type: C

8. Tolerance and withdrawal are the hallmarks of substance
   a. dependence.
   b. consumption.
   c. abuse.
   d. use.

Ans: c
Page: 267
Obj: 1
Type: F

9. The body's decreased response to repeated administrations of a drug so a person must use more of the drug to obtain the same effect is called
   a. physical dependence.
   b. withdrawal.
   c. tolerance.
   d. addiction.

Ans: d
Page: 267
Obj: 1
Type: F

10. In the absence of a particular chemical, a person sweats, vomits, and has pains and tremors. This person is experiencing
   a. psychological dependence.
   b. tolerance.
   c. addiction.
   d. withdrawal.

Ans: b
Page: 267
Obj: 1
Type: A

11. Stewart is a musician and often takes "speed" before his performances to help give him an "edge." Recently he has found that when he hasn't had a performance for several days and thus has not taken the "speed," he begins to feel fatigued and dragged out. Stewart is
   a. demonstrating an addiction.
   b. demonstrating symptoms of withdrawal.
   c. demonstrating psychological dependence.
   d. demonstrating tolerance.

Ans: d
Page: 267
Obj: 2
Type: F

12. Which statement about diagnosing substance-related disorders is *accurate*?
   a. If a person shows signs of withdrawal or tolerance, a diagnosis of substance-induced intoxication is automatically made.
   b. Substance-related disorders are diagnosed only when there is intentional drug use.
   c. A person who meets the criteria for abuse and dependence is diagnosed as having only a substance-related form of abuse.
   d. The distinction between dependence and abuse can differentially predict treatment outcome.

Ans: a
Page: 268
Obj: 2
Type: F

13. Substance-related disorders are most prevalent among Americans who are
    a. youths and young adults.
    b. over age forty-five.
    c. between the ages of thirty-five and forty-five.
    d. in their early teens.

Ans: c
Page: 268
Obj: 2
Type: A

14. Chance, a jazz guitarist, is demonstrating a typical pattern in the progression from drug experimentation to abuse. He has already started to plan his daily activities around opportunities to use drugs and his drug use is increasing. We would expect Chance to exhibit
    a. heightened performance when playing his guitar.
    b. constant fatigue.
    c. self-destructiveness, risk taking, and poor functioning.
    d. criminal behavior to sustain his drug habit.

Ans: a
Page: 268
Obj: 2
Type: F

15. The Epidemiological Catchment Area study surveyed Americans and found that
    a. adult lifetime prevalence for drug abuse and dependence (excluding alcohol and cigarettes) is about 6 percent.
    b. adult lifetime prevalence for drug abuse and dependence (excluding alcohol and cigarettes) is almost 26 percent.
    c. the drug, excluding alcohol and cigarettes, that is most often abused is cocaine/crack.
    d. the drug, excluding alcohol and cigarettes, that is most often abused is heroin.

Ans: d
Page: 268
Obj: 2
Type: A

16. A drug treatment center director, using the results of the Epidemiological Catchment Area study, would expect most of his or her clients to be
    a. older African American males.
    b. older, white females.
    c. younger white females.
    d. younger white males.

Ans: b
Page: 269
Obj: 2
Type: F

17. Lifetime prevalence rates for drug abuse and dependence are
    a. about equal for African Americans, Hispanics, and Whites.
    b. higher for Whites than for African Americans and Hispanics.
    c. higher for Hispanics than for Whites and African Americans.
    d. higher for African Americans than for Whites and Hispanics.

Ans: c
Page: 268
Obj: 3
Type: C

18. Which of the following is *not* one of the categories of substances that cause substance-related disorders?
    a. Depressants
    b. Stimulants
    c. Hormones
    d. Hallucinogens

Ans: b
Page: 276
Obj: 3
Type: C

19. Sally is dependent on a drug that energizes her central nervous system and produces euphoria. It is likely that the drug is a form of
    a. depressant.
    b. stimulant.
    c. hallucinogen.
    d. painkiller.

Ans: a
Page: 268
Obj: 3
Type: C

20. Because the drug Kelly takes makes him feel calm, relaxed, and more sociable, we can guess that the drug is a form of
    a. depressant.
    b. stimulant.
    c. amphetamine.
    d. LSD.

Ans: d
Page: 270
Obj: 4
Type: C

21. If you examined the medical records of a large group of people with alcoholism, you would probably find two general ways in which their drinking problems were exhibited. They would be
    a. drinking to reduce stress and avoid responsibility.
    b. morning drinking and evening drinking.
    c. binge drinking and drinking in response to mental disorder.
    d. daily use and binge drinking.

Ans: a
Page: 270
Obj: 4
Type: F

22. Which statement about alcohol consumption in the United States is *accurate*?
    a. Only about 10 percent of drinkers consume half of all the alcohol consumed.
    b. The heaviest drinking group is in the age range forty to forty-nine.
    c. About 60 percent of all adults are considered heavy drinkers.
    d. Roughly 90 percent of all adults are drinkers.

Ans: d
Page: 271
Obj: 4
Type: F

23. Which statement about alcohol consumption and culture is *accurate*?
    a. In general, Asian cultures drink more than European and North American cultures.
    b. The level of consumption is roughly the same around the world.
    c. Unlike the rest of the world, in the United States women consume less than men.
    d. Drinking alcohol is less common in some Asian countries than in Europe and the United States.

Ans: d
Page: 273
Obj: 4
Type: A

24. Gerald is an alcoholic who has lost his job due to his drinking problem. He is supported by his wife and his disability payments. If Gerald's life expectancy is typical of other alcoholics, we would expect his life to be shortened by about
    a. one to two years.
    b. three to five years.
    c. six to nine years.
    d. ten to twelve years.

Ans: a
Page: 273
Obj: 4
Type: C

25. A man with a blood alcohol concentration of 0.50 percent is seen at a hospital. We can guess that this man is
    a. unconscious or dead.
    b. not an alcoholic.
    c. having trouble walking a straight line.
    d. feeling happy and uninhibited.

Ans: d
Page: 272
Obj: 3
Type: C

26. Frequently when alcohol is initially ingested, individuals report feeling "wild and excited." These feelings result because
    a. the absorption of alcohol is quite slow, allowing one's expectancies to control behavior initially.
    b. alcohol is a stimulant.
    c. alcohol inhibits the functioning of the parasympathetic nervous system, thus allowing the sympathetic nervous system free reign.
    d. alcohol depresses the inhibitory controls in the brain.

Ans: a
Page: 272
Obj: 3
Type: A

27. Dr. Applebaum says, "Contrary to popular belief, this substance actually functions to inhibit the central nervous system. At low doses it appears to cause disinhibition because the inhibitory centers of the brain are those first depressed. At high doses, this drug can cause unconsciousness and even death." What drug is Dr. Applebaum referring to?
    a. Alcohol
    b. Cocaine
    c. Nicotine
    d. Cannabis

Ans: c
Page: 272
Obj: 4
Type: C

28. Juan is feeling the short-term negative effects of heavy, prolonged drinking. These effects probably include
    a. extreme hyperactivity and delusions of persecution.
    b. having flashbacks and hallucinating.
    c. impaired sexual performance and hangover.
    d. brain damage and cirrhosis of the liver.

Ans: b
Page: 272
Obj: 4
Type: A

29. When Barney drinks four beers with his friends, he becomes lively and even verbally hostile. When he drinks four beers by himself, he becomes sleepy. These differences indicate that
    a. Barney is an alcoholic.
    b. the psychological effects of alcohol depend on the context of drinking.
    c. the short-term effects of alcohol are different depending on heredity and body weight.
    d. the effects of alcohol on psychological functioning are predominantly physiological.

Ans: d
Page: 273
Obj: 4
Type: C

30. Norm is an alcoholic; Norma is an alcoholic, too. Based on research evidence, it is likely that
    a. he had alcoholic parents and an unhappy childhood, while she did not.
    b. they had virtually identical family backgrounds.
    c. they both caused their children to suffer fetal alcohol syndrome.
    d. she became an alcoholic later in life than he did.

Ans: b
Page: 273
Obj: 4
Type: A

31. A doctor suggests to his patients that the light or moderate use of a certain mood-altering drug might reduce their risk of heart disease. What drug is the doctor talking about?
    a. Caffeine
    b. Alcohol
    c. Nicotine
    d. Marijuana

Ans: a
Page: 274
Obj: 4
Type: F

32. The organization called Mothers Against Drunk Driving (MADD)
    a. has pushed for tougher laws against drunk driving.
    b. was the group in the early 1900s that pushed for Prohibition.
    c. began when the governor of California was arrested for drunk driving.
    d. has argued that drinking should be made illegal.

Ans: c
Page: 273
Obj: 5
Type: F

33. Codeine, heroin, and morphine are all _____ derived from the _____.
    a. stimulants; opium plant
    b. stimulants; coca plant
    c. narcotics; opium plant
    d. hallucinogens; marijuana plant

Ans: d
Page: 273
Obj: 5
Type: A

34. City health departments are interested in reducing the number of cases of AIDS. Because AIDS can be transmitted through needle sharing, health departments are *most* probably concerned if they see an increase in _____ use.
    a. barbiturate
    b. marijuana
    c. crack cocaine
    d. heroin

Ans: a
Page: 273
Obj: 5
Type: A

35. A health class videotape says, "This drug comes from opium and is really scary because, after feeling relaxed and happy, you develop a tolerance quickly and need more. Because most people put it in their bodies with needles, there is an increased risk of getting AIDS. The withdrawal effects are awful." What drug is being described?
    a. Heroin
    b. Marijuana
    c. LSD
    d. Crack cocaine

Ans: a
Page: 274
Obj: 5
Type: F

36. Which statement about narcotics addiction is *accurate*?
    a. More males than females are addicted, and many turn to criminal activities to support their drug habit.
    b. Lifetime prevalence is about 10 percent and increases with age.
    c. Dependency rarely interferes with the dependent person's ability to maintain relationships and a career.
    d. Tolerance builds up very gradually and withdrawal effects are slight or nonexistent.

Ans: c
Page: 274
Obj: 5
Type: C

37. They are depressants that are sometimes prescribed as tranquilizers. Too high a dose may result in slurred speech, poor coordination, and sleep. It is easy to overdose on them, especially if they are taken with alcohol. What are they?
    a. Anxiolytics
    b. Benzodiazepines
    c. Barbiturates
    d. Opiates

Ans: d
Page: 274
Obj: 5
Type: A

38. Danielle's family is justifiably worried that her excessive use of a "downer" will lead to an accidental overdose and death. It further worries them that she often takes the drug with alcohol. Which drug are they probably concerned about?
    a. Phencyclidine
    b. Marijuana
    c. Amphetamine
    d. Barbiturate

Ans: d
Page: 276
Obj: 5
Type: A

39. Natalie uses cocaine, marijuana, and alcohol on a daily basis and shows tolerance. She's been doing this for almost two years now. According to the DSM-IV-TR, she meets the criteria for
    a. multiple substance–induced cognitive disorder.
    b. alcoholism but not addiction to the other two drugs.
    c. cocaine, marijuana, and alcohol abuse.
    d. polysubstance dependence.

Ans: b
Page: 276
Obj: 5
Type: A

40.　Mrs. Healy originally took this widely prescribed sedative medication to reduce anxiety and muscle tension. Now, however, she cannot deal with stress without using it, and she has developed a tolerance to it. What drug is she probably taking?
　　a.　Antabuse
　　b.　Valium
　　c.　Phencyclidine
　　d.　Caffeine

Ans: c
Page: 276
Obj: 5
Type: F

41.　Which drug name is correctly paired with its general category of drugs?
　　a.　Morphine—benzodiazepine
　　b.　Valium—barbiturate
　　c.　Valium—benzodiazepine
　　d.　Morphine—hallucinogen

Ans: d
Page: 276
Obj: 5
Type: C

42.　Which drug does *not* belong in the same category as the others?
　　a.　Amphetamine
　　b.　Caffeine
　　c.　Nicotine
　　d.　Benzodiazepine

Ans: c
Page: 276
Obj: 6
Type: A

43.　In his younger days, Kevin was considered a "speed freak" because he injected himself with a drug. He would get delusional and hyperactive, looking just like a paranoid schizophrenic. When he almost died of an overdose, he stopped using. On what drug was Kevin once dependent?
　　a.　Barbiturate
　　b.　Heroin
　　c.　Amphetamine
　　d.　Benzodiazepine

Ans: a
Page: 276
Obj: 6
Type: C

44.　It inhibits appetite, increases alertness, and works by increasing dopamine concentrations in the brain. It easily becomes habit forming, with rapid development of tolerance. Chronic users experience paranoid delusions and brain damage. What is it?
　　a.　amphetamine
　　b.　caffeine
　　c.　barbiturate
　　d.　heroin

Ans: d
Page: 276
Obj: 6
Type: A

45.　Betty has tried to stop using a particular drug permanently, but her attempts have been unsuccessful. When she stops using, she experiences irritability and difficulty concentrating. Even though she has emphysema, a serious physical disorder, she continues to use it. Surprisingly, it is a legal drug. To which drug is Betty probably addicted?
　　a.　Caffeine
　　b.　Alcohol
　　c.　Marijuana
　　d.　Nicotine

Ans: b
Page: 276
Obj: 6
Type: A

46. Tobacco manufacturers claim that nicotine is not addictive. If you were to testify at congressional hearings on this topic, you would reply
    a. "It is true that research has not substantiated withdrawal effects, but tolerance has been well documented."
    b. "Both tolerance and withdrawal have been documented for nicotine, as well as complex and potentially fatal effects on health."
    c. "It is true that research has not substantiated tolerance effects, but withdrawal effects have been well documented."
    d. "Although nicotine does not result in physical dependence, there are many complex and potentially fatal effects on health that stem from nicotine use."

Ans: b
Page: 276
Obj: 6
Type: A

47. Dr. Mahmoud says, "The prevalence of smoking is decreasing all over the world, and it is a good thing because nicotine is a stimulant that is harmful to the body and leads to continued use despite serious physical disorders." Dr. Mahmoud's statement would be *more* accurate if she said that
    a. smokers rarely continue to use cigarettes when they have physical disorders.
    b. the prevalence of smoking is increasing in the developing parts of the world.
    c. nicotine is a depressant.
    d. nicotine is a mild hallucinogen.

Ans: b
Page: 277
Obj: 6
Type: A

48. When Russell is stressed, he takes cocaine because it slows his heart rate and makes him sleepy and hungry. He snorts the drug and is unable to stop using it. When the cocaine effects wear off, he feels depressed. What portion of Russell's substance use is *unlikely*?
    a. It is unlikely that he will feel depressed after the effects wear off.
    b. It is unlikely that cocaine slows his heart or makes him sleepy and hungry.
    c. It is unlikely that cocaine will be snorted.
    d. It is unlikely that cocaine users will become unable to stop using.

Ans: d
Page: 276
Obj: 6
Type: A

49. Imagine reading a news article from the late 1800s in which doctors describe a wonder drug that can relieve depression and reduce pain. On the next page, you see an advertisement for tonics and wines that include the drug. The drug is what we call
    a. codeine.
    b. nicotine.
    c. caffeine.
    d. cocaine.

Ans: a
Page: 278
Obj: 6
Type: A

50. Tanniqua uses a drug that heightens her insight and produces vivid sensory awareness but does not lead to tolerance. We can be sure she is *not* using
    a. cocaine.
    b. LSD.
    c. phencyclidine.
    d. marijuana.

Ans: b
Page: 278
Obj: 6
Type: A

51. Darryl, age fifteen, likes this drug because it is inexpensive, it produces an intense and immediate high, and, like cigarettes, it is smoked. Darryl is similar to about 3 percent of young adults who have used this drug during a one-year period. The drug is
    a. PCP.
    b. crack.
    c. amphetamine.
    d. powder cocaine.

Ans: d
Page: 278
Obj: 6
Type: F

52. Which statement concerning crack cocaine is *accurate*?
    a. It is snorted through the nose.
    b. It produces a slower but more pleasant euphoria than regular cocaine.
    c. It is a form of cocaine that does not produce tolerance or withdrawal.
    d. It is a more potent form of cocaine that is smoked.

Ans: a
Page: 278
Obj: 7
Type: C

53. One-third of the population of the United States has used it, but it is illegal. It is the mildest hallucinogen, and it is usually smoked. It is called
    a. marijuana.
    b. cocaine.
    c. heroin.
    d. nicotine.

Ans: c
Page: 279
Obj: 7
Type: A

54. Bernie is a heavy marijuana user who has developed lung problems. He is physically addicted to the drug and uses it to relax. What is *unusual* about Bernie's case?
    a. Most marijuana users are women.
    b. Marijuana use rarely results in lung problems.
    c. Marijuana rarely, if ever, produces physical addiction.
    d. Marijuana is used for its stimulant effects.

Ans: b
Page: 279
Obj: 7
Type: A

55. Melissa had been smoking marijuana for several hours before her mother came home. It is likely that when her mother comes home, Melissa will
    a. experience "flashbacks" when she tries to act sober.
    b. be somewhat tranquil and passive.
    c. become extremely aggressive when she tries to act sober. .
    d. be too hyperactive to alter her behavior.

Ans: a
Page: 279
Obj: 7
Type: A

56. A health teacher says, "Marijuana has some of the effects of hallucinogens, although the DSM-IV-TR does not technically consider it one. Once the drug is taken, subjective time passes slowly and memory is impaired. There are no medical uses for marijuana; it is strictly a recreational drug." The teacher's statement would be *completely* accurate if he said that
    a. marijuana is helpful in treating physical ailments.
    b. marijuana is considered a hallucinogen by everyone.
    c. the drug causes subjective time to speed up.
    d. marijuana has no impact on memory.

Ans: d
Page: 279
Obj: 7
Type: A

57. Mrs. Kowalski has cancer and glaucoma. To relieve her symptoms, she uses an illegal drug that she gets from her eighteen-year-old grandson. The drug is most likely
    a. phencyclidine.
    b. heroin.
    c. crack cocaine.
    d. marijuana.

Ans: a
Page: 279
Obj: 7
Type: C

58. Hallucinations, bad trips, and flashbacks are associated with this drug, which gained notoriety in the 1960s. What drug is being described?
   a. LSD
   b. Amphetamine
   c. Marijuana
   d. Valium

Ans: b
Page: 279
Obj: 7
Type: C

59. The only drug to imitate behavior seen in acute psychotic reactions and to produce flashbacks days or weeks after taking it is
   a. phencyclidine.
   b. LSD.
   c. heroin.
   d. crack.

Ans: c
Page: 279
Obj: 7
Type: A

60. Timothy orally ingests LSD. He experiences visual hallucinations and has developed a quick tolerance for the drug. In addition to the effects from LSD, Timothy has experienced panic attacks and delusional thinking. What part of Timothy's case is *unusual*?
   a. Visual hallucinations are rare with LSD.
   b. LSD is generally injected, not taken orally.
   c. Tolerance development is rare for LSD.
   d. Few people who use LSD exhibit panic attacks.

Ans: a
Page: 280
Obj: 7
Type: F

61. Which negative consequence of using phencyclidine is *most* likely?
   a. Uncontrolled aggression
   b. Emphysema and lung cancer
   c. Total tranquility and passivity
   d. AIDS

Ans: c
Page: 280
Obj: 7
Type: A

62. Herschel was brought to the hospital by six policemen who struggled to keep him from acting violently. He had been smoking a mixture of marijuana and a particular drug. During his first several days in the hospital, Herschel was either suspicious and violent or fearful. He staggered when he walked and slurred his words. Herschel was probably using marijuana and what drug?
   a. Barbiturate
   b. LSD
   c. Phencyclidine
   d. Heroin

Ans: c
Page: 280
Obj: 7
Type: F

63. Which pair of drugs would be included in the DSM-IV-TR category "other substance-related disorder"?
   a. Marijuana and phencyclidine
   b. Caffeine and nicotine
   c. Anabolic steroids and nitrous oxide
   d. Benzodiazepines and Valium

Ans: c
Page: 277
Obj: 7
Type: A

64. Stephanie met Sam at rave. As they were talking, Sam put a drug into Stephanie's drink when she turned her head to talk to a friend. When she woke up the next morning, she found herself in bed with Sam and learned he had raped her the night before, although she had no memory of the assault. It is most likely that the drug Sam put into Stephanie's drink was
   a. Ecstacy.
   b. MDMA.
   c. Rohypnol.
   d. LSD.

Ans: d
Page: 281
Obj: 8
Type: C

65. The most recent and complex approach to substance-related disorders
   a. keeps separate the psychological factors that begin the dependency process from the biological factors that maintain it.
   b. recognizes that biological factors play a much less important role than socio-cultural factors.
   c. emphasizes the fact that they involve biological dependence.
   d. assumes that physical and psychological factors interact throughout the development and maintenance of problems.

Ans: d
Page: 282
Obj: 8
Type: F

66. The results of Cadoret and Wesner's (1990) research on adopted children of biological parents who were alcoholics found that
   a. only the family environment of the adoptive family predicted alcoholism in the adoptees.
   b. only having an alcoholic biological parent predicted alcoholism in the adoptees.
   c. neither genetics nor family environment predicted alcoholism in the adoptees.
   d. both genetics and environmental influences increased the risk of alcoholism in the adoptees.

Ans: a
Page: 282
Obj: 8
Type: C

67. Regarding research on genetic factors and alcoholism, which of the following statements is *accurate*?
   a. The role of genetic factors seems to vary with the type of alcoholism.
   b. The manner of genetic transmission is well understood.
   c. Genetic factors appear to play a greater role in alcoholism for females than for males.
   d. Genetic factors appear to play a greater role in late-onset alcoholism than in early-onset alcoholism.

Ans: c
Page: 282
Obj: 8
Type: A

68. Your grandmother asks you, "Is alcoholism inherited?" Based on adoption and twins research, a good answer is,
   a. "No one has a good idea yet."
   b. "It definitely is; family life plays almost no role."
   c. "It depends on the kind of alcoholism."
   d. "It definitely isn't; it is all due to family influence."

Ans: c
Page: 283
Obj: 8
Type: C

69. For as long as they can remember, the Ernst family has had many alcoholic members. Mr. Ernst is an alcoholic. Research suggests that if his son has a biological risk factor for alcoholism, it is
   a. a low score on the quantitative trait loci (QTL) for aggressiveness.
   b. extreme sensitivity to small doses of alcohol.
   c. abnormal central nervous system functioning.
   d. low personal regard for academic achievement.

Ans: d
Page: 283
Obj: 9
Type: C

70. Dr. Berg, a psychoanalyst, says about the cause of alcoholism,
   a. "The question of whether you will become an alcoholic is settled at conception; it's all based on genetics."
   b. "If your family has a history of the disorder, you will probably develop it at an early age."
   c. "Heavy drinking is something you learn by seeing your parents drink heavily."
   d. "Traumas in early infancy can produce oral needs that only the symbolic bottle of booze can satisfy."

Ans: a
Page: 283
Obj: 9
Type: F

71. Nathan (1988) concluded that only two personality characteristics are associated with alcohol problems:
    a. depression and antisocial behavior.
    b. depression and repression.
    c. sexuality and aggression.
    d. repression and hostility.

Ans: a
Page: 284
Obj: 9
Type: F

72. Shedler and Block (1990) did a longitudinal study evaluating the psychological adjustment of adolescents and their drug use. Their results suggest that
    a. both abstainers and heavy users have worse adjustment than those who have experimented with drugs.
    b. even heavy drug use has little relationship to adjustment.
    c. the best adjusted adolescents are those who have never used drugs.
    d. moderate use of drugs causes an improvement in one's adjustment.

Ans: c
Page: 285
Obj: 9
Type: C

73. What is the relationship between alcohol consumption and the rate of alcoholism in various countries?
    a. As consumption goes up, the rate of alcoholism goes up, too.
    b. As consumption goes up, the rate of alcoholism first goes up, then goes down.
    c. There is no consistent relationship between the two.
    d. As consumption goes up, the rate of alcoholism goes down.

Ans: b
Page: 285
Obj: 9
Type: A

74. Town A's population is largely Irish-American, Town B's is largely American Indian, and Town C's is largely Hispanic and Asian. Which town(s) is/are likely to have high rates of alcoholism?
    a. Town A
    b. Town A and Town B
    c. Town C
    d. Town B and Town C

Ans: d
Page: 285
Obj: 10
Type: C

75. According to early behavioral explanations of alcohol abuse,
    a. the disorder was seen as a disease of moral weakness.
    b. expectancies were believed to be the chief factor in the disorder.
    c. certain personalities were assumed to be prone to heavy drinking.
    d. alcohol temporarily reduces tension and drinking was learned.

Ans: b
Page: 286
Obj: 10
Type: F

76. The results of the Martlatt et al. (1973) study that used alcoholics as subjects and manipulated whether they thought they were drinking alcohol or tonic indicate that
    a. a subject's expectations concerning alcohol have little effect on the amount drunk.
    b. alcoholism is not simply a disease in which a person loses control over drinking.
    c. physiological factors are more important than psychological factors in the maintenance of the disorder.
    d. alcoholism is a disease in which one drink makes a drunk.

Ans: a
Page: 286
Obj: 10
Type: A

77. Based on research concerning expectations, what would happen if an alcoholic was served one alcoholic drink at a party but thereafter was given Virgin Marys (tomato juice without liquor) while being told they were Bloody Marys (tomato juice and vodka)?
   a. The alcoholic would drink many of the Virgin Marys.
   b. The alcoholic would have one drink and then stop.
   c. The alcoholic would become angry when the drink failed to produce relaxation.
   d. The alcoholic would become drunk on the one drink, then sober up.

Ans: b
Page: 287
Obj: 10
Type: A

78. According to research by Carney et al. (2000) to test tension-reduction models for drinking. who would be most likely to increase alcohol consumption?
   a. Ira, whose boss threatened to fire him today.
   b. Irving, whose girlfriend broke up with him today.
   c. Irwin, whose daughter graduated from high school today.
   d. Ian, whose secretary quit without giving notice today.

Ans: d
Page: 288
Obj: 11
Type: A

79. Dr. Parker has a client named Jessica who is in treatment for alcoholism. Jessica calls Dr. Parker and is very upset because she had a drink last night at a party. Dr. Parker responds, "Your behavior should be seen as a temporary setback that can be overcome. You can master your problem and regain self-control." What form of treatment is reflected in Dr. Parker's comments to Jessica?
   a. A recovery program based on the unitary disease model
   b. Structural-strategic therapy
   c. Alcoholics Anonymous program
   d. Relapse prevention training

Ans: a
Page: 288
Obj: 11
Type: F

80. Risk of relapse following drug treatment is *highest* in which situation?
   a. Within the first three months of treatment completion
   b. When one is feeling very positive emotional states
   c. When one is unable to distract oneself from stressful situations
   d. Several years after treatment has ended

Ans: b
Page: 288
Obj: 11
Type: C

81. Donna is beginning an alcohol rehabilitation program and asks you for advice on how she can avoid relapse. One piece of useful advice would be to tell her
   a. to avoid situations in which she feels "too good" because such situations present a high risk for relapse.
   b. to attribute relapse to factors over which she has control.
   c. to think of one drink as a complete failure so that she develops a strong attitude against relapse.
   d. to avoid expressing her abstinence violation effect (AVE).

Ans: c
Page: 288
Obj: 11
Type: A

82. Melanie and Melvin completed alcoholism treatment last month. They both went to parties last week and had several drinks. Melanie maintained her confidence in staying sober and has not had another drink. Melvin felt guilty and lost hope after the party, and he has not been sober since. What does this illustrate?
   a. Melvin put himself in a high-risk situation; Melanie didn't.
   b. Melvin is a real alcoholic; Melanie is actually a social drinker.
   c. Melvin fell victim to the abstinence violation effect; Melanie didn't.
   d. Melvin has familial alcoholism; Melanie has non-familial alcoholism.

168 *Chapter 9*

Ans: a
Page: 288
Obj: 11
Type: C

83. Marlon is physically dependent on heroin. If he stops using the drug, he may
    a. experience withdrawal no more agonizing than a bad case of the flu.
    b. go right back to using again because of the bodily need for the drug.
    c. have a potentially deadly withdrawal unless supervised by a doctor.
    d. find that Antabuse makes the withdrawal symptoms much easier to take.

Ans: a
Page: 289
Obj: 11
Type: C

84. When Jacquie first used cocaine, it gave her a great feeling of euphoria. But as
    she became a chronic user, her motivation for taking the drug changed: All
    she wanted was to relieve her withdrawal discomfort and maintain her drug-
    related friendships. This change in motivation illustrates
    a. opponent-process theory.
    b. Tiffany's concept of automatic processes.
    c. Marlatt's concept of abstinence violation.
    d. learned expectancy theory.

Ans: c
Page: 290
Obj: 11
Type: A

85. Cassie is addicted to Valium. Her therapist wants to treat her withdrawal
    symptoms but is also convinced she must be taught that Valium was a
    positively reinforcing substance for her. Cassie must develop skills not only in
    avoiding Valium but in coping with general life situations. The therapist's
    approach mirrors the _____ theory of substance-related disorder.
    a. biological
    b. automatic processes
    c. two-factor
    d. psychodynamic

Ans: b
Page: 290
Obj: 11
Type: C

86. Which statement *accurately* reflects our knowledge of the causes of drug use?
    a. One personality style—the antisocial personality—is the basis for all drug
       use.
    b. Physical addiction and the need to avoid withdrawal are insufficient
       explanations for continued narcotics use.
    c. All drug users have one thing in common: a genetic predisposition to use
       drugs.
    d. People start using drugs because they are forbidden; if drugs were legal,
       people would stop using them.

Ans: c
Page: 290
Obj: 11
Type: C

87. Which of the following *best* illustrates what Wise (1988) means by a drug
    acting as a negative reinforcer?
    a. Monica continues to take Valium even though it no longer helps her get to
       sleep.
    b. Whenever James comes to work drunk, he is yelled at by his boss.
    c. Lester snorts cocaine to avoid thinking about his empty life.
    d. The more Oscar injects heroin, the less he thinks he is capable of earning a
       living.

Ans: a
Page: 290
Obj: 12
Type: C

88. Dr. Arnold says to an alcoholic client, "The first step in treatment is getting all
    of that alcohol out of your body. You may go through withdrawal, but it is a
    necessary step for treatment." Dr. Arnold is talking about
    a. detoxification.
    b. using aversive conditioning.
    c. the value of Alcoholics Anonymous.
    d. relapse prevention treatment.

Ans: b
Page: 291
Obj: 12
Type: F

89. Fellowship, spiritual awareness, and public self-revelations are all important ingredients in the treatment called
a. detoxification.
b. Alcoholics Anonymous.
c. systematic desensitization.
d. multi-modal therapy.

Ans: b
Page: 291
Obj: 12
Type: F

90. Research on the Alcoholics Anonymous program
a. suggests that it is superior to individual psychotherapy.
b. is limited; the available research has methodological limitations because AA does not open itself to scientific evaluation.
c. suggests that it is superior to hospitalization.
d. suggests that it is superior to both individual psychotherapy and hospitalization.

Ans: b
Page: 293
Obj: 13
Type: F

91. Stanley Schachter argues that people smoke for one reason:
a. to feel more competent and alert.
b. to avoid symptoms of nicotine withdrawal.
c. to provide them with something to do with their hands.
d. to resolve unconscious conflicts about oral dependency.

Ans: a
Page: 294
Obj: 13
Type: A

92. A company wants to reduce its health care costs by finding an effective way to help smokers quit permanently. Research suggests that the *best* method is
a. providing nicotine patches and behavioral therapy.
b. an inpatient program that uses family therapy.
c. a combination of methadone and systematic desensitization.
d. punishing employees if they smoke in or near the company premises.

Ans: d
Page: 292
Obj: 12
Type: A

93. Which patient is getting the correct pharmacological treatment for his or her drug abuse problem?
a. Zachary, who smokes marijuana, is getting methadone.
b. Sue, who abuses cocaine, is getting Antabuse.
c. Helmut, who injects heroin, is getting a nicotine patch.
d. Ilene, who drinks heavily, is getting Naltexone.

Ans: a
Page: 292
Obj: 13
Type: C

94. Dr. Kelly says, "The kind of alcohol treatment I suggest can consist of skills training for coping with negative emotions, conditioned aversion to alcohol, and modeling that shows how you can control intake." Dr. Kelly is describing
a. behavioral approaches to alcohol treatment.
b. Alcoholics Anonymous.
c. psychodynamic approaches to alcohol treatment.
d. the need for detoxification and Antabuse in treatment.

Ans: c
Page: 293
Obj: 13
Type: A

95. Your best friend smokes cigarettes and wants the most effective method for achieving long-lasting abstinence. Based on research, good advice would be,
a. "Make up your mind to stop and just do it cold turkey."
b. "Use nicotine gum until your withdrawal symptoms are over."
c. "Gradually increase the time between the cigarettes you smoke."
d. "Use methadone because if you smoke while taking it, you'll feel sick."

Ans: d
Page: 296
Obj: 12
Type: F

96. People who suggest that alcoholics can be taught to control their drinking
   a. reject the use of behavior therapy.
   b. usually support the psychodynamic perspective on abnormal behavior.
   c. use Antabuse as the means by which they teach control.
   d. disagree with the genetic-physiological view of alcoholism.

Ans: d
Page: 296
Obj: 14
Type: A

97. Mr. Henderson is in treatment for cocaine dependence. After detoxification, he spent two weeks in an inpatient treatment facility, where he began attending Cocaine Anonymous meetings. Afterward, he went to outpatient group and individual counseling, while his family was involved in family therapy. This case illustrates
   a. a behavioral approach to cocaine treatment.
   b. a pharmacological approach to cocaine treatment.
   c. the ineffectiveness of current cocaine treatment.
   d. a multi-modal approach to cocaine treatment.

Ans: a
Page: 297
Obj: 14
Type: C

98. Information campaigns in the media and school-based efforts to reestablish norms against drug use and for abstinence are examples of
   a. prevention programs.
   b. multi-modal treatment.
   c. cognitive-behavioral treatment.
   d. psychodynamic treatment.

Ans: c
Page: 297
Obj: 14
Type: F

99. Dent and associates' (1995) evaluation of a junior high school smoking prevention program found that
   a. children will smoke regardless of the prevention program they attend.
   b. the "Just say 'no' to drugs" program is all that is needed to produce long-term reductions in drug use.
   c. resistance training and information can have a positive impact even two years after the program is completed.
   d. providing information on the negative health effects of cigarettes actually *increases* the likelihood of smoking two years after the program is completed.

Ans: c
Page: 297
Obj: 14
Type: A

100. Dr. Hong says, "Research indicates that treatment can reduce substance dependence but only modestly. Most alcoholics and smokers relapse within a year. This is especially tragic because it is impossible for individuals to recover without treatment." Dr. Hong's statement would be *accurate* if he said that
   a. most alcoholics remain abstinent for a year after treatment.
   b. most smokers stay cigarette-free for a year after treatment.
   c. some individuals recover without treatment.
   d. treatment can reduce dependence very successfully.

ESSAY QUESTIONS

1. Alcohol and narcotics are both depressants. Discuss how they have both similar and different effects on and consequences for those who are dependent.

2. Describe and evaluate the hypothesis that alcoholism is related to the drug's anxiety-reducing properties.

3. Describe the cognitive-behavioral and the anonymous peer-support approaches used in the treatment of addictions.

SAMPLE ANSWERS

1. Both alcohol and narcotics such as heroin and morphine depress the central nervous system and slow down responses. They help people feel more calm and relaxed. They may also increase their sociability and make them feel less inhibited. The initial use of both drugs can have negative effects: Most people do not like the taste of alcohol the first time, and many people who use heroin experience nausea. As use increases for both drugs, a tolerance to its effects develops, so larger doses must be taken to get the same effect. Reasons for using the drugs also change. Despite obvious negative consequences, use continues, in part, because taking the drug protects the user from uncomfortable withdrawal symptoms. The withdrawal effects in both cases can be quite severe, although some have described heroin withdrawal as no worse than having the flu. In both cases, the drugs dominate the users' lives to the detriment of relationships, careers, and self-esteem.

   There are significant differences in the effects of the two drugs. Alcohol produces hangovers, can lead to fetal alcohol syndrome (if used excessively during pregnancy), and can cause such physical conditions as cirrhosis of the liver, cancer of the mouth and throat, and heart failure. Heroin does not produce these consequences, but because it is injected, it produces puncture marks on the extremities and is associated with HIV infection as a result of sharing needles. Further, because heroin is illegal and expensive, many addicts must turn to criminal activities to support their habit.

2. To an extent, psychoanalytic explanations for alcoholism involve the anxiety reduction hypothesis. Unconscious conflicts generate anxiety and other negative emotions that intoxication allows to be expressed. But more clearly, behaviorists have emphasized alcohol's anxiety-reducing role. In a classic experiment, cats were given aversive stimuli in situations previously associated with food. The experimentally induced neurosis these cats experienced was reduced when they were given alcohol. Later research has refined this view to show that alcohol seems to reduce avoidance behaviors and therefore is reinforcing. However, more recent research calls into question the idea that all of alcohol's effects are pharmacological anxiety reduction. Marlatt, Deming, and Reid's (1973) study, in which alcoholics received either alcohol or tonic water but were, in half the cases, told they were getting the opposite, showed that expectation plays a major role. Other studies have shown alcohol to increase tension, not decrease it. For example, if a distracting activity is available, alcohol serves to reduce anxiety in people facing a stressor, but if distraction is not possible, alcohol intensifies anxious feelings. Expectations as to the social benefits of alcohol predict future use, so more than anxiety reduction is involved in alcohol abuse and dependence.

3. One approach to treating addictions is a *cognitive-behavioral approach* that focuses on relapse prevention training. This program is a combination of cognitive and behavioral skills taught to clients to help them gain self-control over their substance use. One aspect of the program is helping individuals differentiate between minor and major relapses. Individuals are taught to view minor relapses as temporary setbacks that can be overcome rather than as proof that their addiction cannot be controlled. Relapse prevention training provides skills in the interpretation of lapses and in the mastery of stressful experiences that typically have led to excessive consumption in the first place. More specifically, components of the program include teaching clients to identify high-risk situations that predispose them to lapses, helping clients identify and develop alternative activities that reduce risky situations, and providing decision-making skills to facilitate the selection of long-term goals over short-term gratification.

   A second approach to the treatment of addictions is the *"anonymous" peer-support programs*, better known as AA or twelve-step programs. Basically, AA is a fellowship of men and women who share their experiences with one another so that they can help one another solve their common problems and help others recover from their addictions. AA is a self-help organization that adheres to twelve steps: admitting to being powerless over the substance; believing that a greater power can restore one's sanity; deciding to turn one's will and life over to the care of God; making a moral inventory of one's self; admitting to God, one's self, and others the exact nature of one's wrongdoing; being ready to have God remove all defects of character; asking for God to remove one's shortcomings; making a list of all persons harmed and making amends to them; making direct amends to such people; continuing to take personal inventory and admitting when wrong; seeking through prayer and meditation to improve one's contact with God; and having a spiritual awakening as the result of the twelve steps. AA programs are the largest source of support for alcohol and drug users.

CHAPTER 10
Sexual and Gender Identity Disorders

LEARNING OBJECTIVES

1. Distinguish between sexual dysfunctions, paraphilias, and gender identity disorders. (p. 301)

2. Discuss the problems of defining "normal" sexual behavior. (pp. 302-305; Mental Health & Society)

3. Indicate the contributions of Kinsey, Masters and Johnson, Kaplan, and the Janus Report in the history of studying human sexuality. (p. 305)

4. Describe and discuss the four stages of the human sexual response cycle. (pp. 305-306)

5. Explain why homosexuality is not considered a mental disorder. (pp. 306-309)

6. Discuss the results of research on sexuality among those over age sixty. (pp. 309-311)

7. Describe and differentiate sexual desire disorders in men and women, sexual arousal disorder in men and women, and male and female orgasmic disorder. Describe and discuss the causes of sexual pain disorders. (pp. 311-318)

8. Discuss the biological causes and treatments for psychosexual dysfunctions. (pp. 318-321)

9. Discuss the psychological factors that cause, and the behavioral therapy techniques used to treat, sexual dysfunctions. (pp. 321-323)

10. Define gender identity disorders and describe their symptoms. Discuss the biological, psychodynamic, and behavioral explanations for these disorders and how gender identity disorders are treated. (pp. 323-327)

11. Define paraphilias and list the three categories of these disorders. Describe and differentiate fetishism, transvestic fetishism, exhibitionism, voyeurism, frotteurism, pedophilia, sadism, and masochism. (pp. 327-334)

12. Discuss the problems of people who were childhood victims of sexual abuse. (pp. 331-332)

13. Discuss the biological, psychodynamic, and behavioral etiological theories of paraphilia and how those theories lead to different forms of treatment. (pp. 334-336)

14. Differentiate the terms *sexual coercion, sexual aggression, rape,* and *incest.* Describe the effects of rape on victims, including the acute and long-term phases of rape trauma syndrome. Discuss what is known about the cause of rape, including the three motivational types of rapists. (pp. 336-343; Mental Health & Society)

15. Discuss the effects of media portrayals of sexual violence and socio-cultural variables. (pp. 342-343; Critical Thinking)

16. Describe and evaluate the conventional and controversial treatments provided for incest offenders and rapists. (pp. 343-344)

MULTIPLE–CHOICE QUESTIONS

Ans: a
Page: 301
Obj: 1
Type: F

1. These disorders involve a conflict between one's actual sex and one's psychological sense of being male or female. They are called
   a. gender identity disorders.
   b. sexual deviance disorders.
   c. sexual arousal disorders.
   d. paraphilias.

Ans: d
Page: 301
Obj: 1
Type: C

2. Paraphilias differ from sexual dysfunctions in that paraphilias
   a. involve problems of sexual arousal while sexual dysfunctions do not.
   b. typically are of no harm to others, only to the individual with the paraphilia.
   c. are likely to affect men and women equally, while sexual dysfunctions predominantly affect women.
   d. often involve the intentional infliction of pain.

Ans: c
Page: 301
Obj: 1
Type: C

3. Scott has sexual fantasies and engages in sexual behavior that is focused on objects and situations that are not part of the usual pattern of affectionate sexual activity. His behavior often puts him at risk for being arrested. If Scott has a sexual problem, it is in the general category of
   a. sexual dysfunctions.
   b. gender identity disorders.
   c. paraphilias.
   d. sexual personality disorders.

Ans: b
Page: 301
Obj: 1
Type: C

4. Loretta has very little desire for sexual arousal or behavior. When she does engage in sexual intercourse, she never experiences an orgasm. Loretta's problems are *most* likely in the general category of
   a. psychosexual mood disorders.
   b. sexual dysfunctions.
   c. paraphilias.
   d. gender identity disorders.

Ans: d
Page: 302
Obj: 1
Type: F

5. Compulsive Sexual Behavior (CSB), or sexual addiction
   a. Has been classified as a sexual disorder since DSM-III-R.
   b. has recently been included as a sexual disorder in DSM-IV-TR.
   c. has been broadened in DSM-IV-TR from its original name, nymphomania, to include men as well as women.
   d. is not recognized as a classification of sexual disorder in the DSM.

Ans: d
Page: 304
Obj: 1
Type: F

6. The definition of sexual disorders is
   a. unique because it does not include subjective distress.
   b. among the clearest of all forms of psychological disorders to identify.
   c. based primarily on the statistical rarity criterion.
   d. difficult because it is influenced by moral and legal judgments.

Ans: c
Page: 304
Obj: 2
Type: C

7. Which of the following *best* describes the central problem in determining whether or not a sexual practice is abnormal?
   a. The abnormal behavior usually does not threaten society, impair social or occupational functioning, or cause distress to the individual.
   b. While the laws are usually clear about what is illegal, people are often unaware of the laws.
   c. Acceptable sexual practices differ between cultures and historical times.
   d. The DSM–IV–TR only lists sexual disorders that are illegal, not ones that are merely unusual or abnormal.

Ans: b
Page: 304
Obj: 2
Type: A

8. Dr. Ruiz says, "Definitions of normal sexual behavior are quite consistent across time but differ dramatically across cultures. What is valued in some cultures is illegal in others. Comparing sexual behavior in Western and non-Western cultures is particularly difficult." What portion of this statement is *inaccurate*?
   a. Nothing in the statement is inaccurate.
   b. It is inaccurate to say that definitions are consistent across time.
   c. It is inaccurate to say that definitions differ dramatically across cultures.
   d. It is inaccurate to say that comparing Western and non-Western behavior is particularly difficult.

Ans: a
Page: 305
Obj: 3
Type: C

9. A student who wanted to read about changes in American sexual behavior from the 1950s to the 1990s would be interested in the survey research done by
   a. Kinsey and the Januses.
   b. Freud and Kinsey.
   c. Masters and Johnson.
   d. Freud and Kaplan.

Ans: b
Page: 305
Obj: 4
Type: F

10. Each of the following are stages in the human sexual response cycle *except*
    a. resolution.
    b. dyspaurenia.
    c. desire (appetitive).
    d. excitement.

Ans: c
Page: 306
Obj: 4
Type: C

11. Nancy has a sexual problem that is diagnosed as occurring during the appetitive phase of sexual response. We can guess that Nancy's problem involves
    a. an inability to experience relaxation after orgasm.
    b. difficulties during the last two stages of the response cycle.
    c. difficulties concerning thoughts or fantasies about sex.
    d. an inability to experience orgasm.

Ans: b
Page: 306
Obj: 4
Type: A

12. Shalisa has little desire for sexual activity; Kareina experiences no vaginal lubrication despite direct sexual stimulation. Which person and stage of the sexual response cycle is *correctly* paired?
    a. Shalisa—resolution; Kareina—excitement
    b. Shalisa—appetitive; Kareina—excitement
    c. Shalisa—arousal; Kareina—appetitive
    d. Shalisa—appetitive; Kareina—orgasm

Ans: a
Page: 306
Obj: 4
Type: A

13. Mr. and Mrs. Bell are concerned about their sex lives. Mr. Bell is usually unresponsive to sexual stimulation after he has an orgasm. Mrs. Bell is capable of multiple orgasms. Prior to orgasm, Mrs. Bell experiences neither vaginal lubrication nor expansion of the clitoris. What should a therapist tell the Bells?
    a. "Mrs. Bell's lack of lubrication may reflect an excitement phase problem."
    b. "Everything the Bells experience is part of the normal sexual response cycle."
    c. "Mrs. Bell's having multiple orgasms is a sign of an orgasm disorder."
    d. "Mr. Bell's unresponsiveness is a sign of an orgasm disorder."

Ans: d
Page: 308
Obj: 5
Type: F

14. Which statement about homosexuality is *accurate*?
    a. Homosexuals tend to regret being homosexual and can usually change their sexual orientation through psychotherapy.
    b. The human sexual response cycle does not apply to homosexual sex.
    c. Homosexuals show greater psychological disturbance and gender identity confusion than heterosexuals.
    d. Because of the social context, homosexual sexual concerns may differ significantly from those of heterosexuals.

Ans: a
Page: 308
Obj: 5
Type: C

15. According to the current psychological and scientific perspective, homosexuality is considered
    a. a normal variation in sexual behavior.
    b. a problem that needs to be fixed.
    c. an effort to maintain white male dominance in society.
    d. the result of poor parenting.

Ans: b
Page: 310
Obj: 6
Type: A

16. Elmer is seventy years old and views masturbation as an acceptable sexual outlet. He gets aroused looking at attractive women. According to research, Elmer
    a. was probably sexually inactive during his middle-age years.
    b. is likely to be a normal sexually active man.
    c. is statistically quite rare.
    d. will be unable to function sexually within the next two to three years.

Ans: a
Page: 310
Obj: 6
Type: F

17. The Janus Report (1993) suggests that among the elderly,
    a. sexual dysfunction is least likely among those who were sexually active at younger ages.
    b. sexual activity and enjoyment is quite low.
    c. sexual dysfunctions actually decrease in frequency.
    d. sexual activity and masturbation are seen as evil.

Ans: d
Page: 312
Obj: 7
Type: C

18. Elizabeth, married for six years, has no interest in either fantasizing or engaging in sexual activity. In fact, she does whatever she can to avoid situations where intercourse is a possibility. According to the DSM-IV-TR, Elizabeth
    a. has the rarest form of sexual dysfunction.
    b. has a normal variant of the human sexual response cycle.
    c. has a sexual arousal disorder.
    d. has a sexual desire disorder.

Ans: a
Page: 311
Obj: 7
Type: C

19. Joanne had orgasms infrequently even though she had been married happily for twelve years. She enjoyed her sex life, but asked her doctor what she would recommend. Her doctor recommended
    a. no treatment at all.
    b. psychoanalysis.
    c. sensate focus therapy.
    d. hormone treatment.

Ans: c
Page: 311
Obj: 7
Type: A

20. Natalie has no interest in sex and appears unconcerned about it. She cannot remember a time in her life when she was interested in or enjoyed engaging in sex. Her husband says they have a good marriage and does not seem to be bothered by her lack of interest in sex. Natalie
    a. has an atypical problem that is likely transient, and thus, she would receive a hypoactive sexual desire disorder diagnosis.
    b. would be diagnosed as having a sexual desire disorder.
    c. would not be diagnosed because the situation is not disturbing to Natalie or to her husband.
    d. would be diagnosed as a paraphilia.

Ans: b
Page: 315
Obj: 7
Type: A

21. A man who is unable to maintain an erection sufficient for intercourse goes to a therapist. Which of the following responses by the therapist is based on research evidence?
    a. "In only about 5 percent of cases is this problem due to a biological cause."
    b. "Medical conditions can be the cause of erection difficulties, but it is difficult to make an accurate diagnosis."
    c. "In almost every case, erection problems are due to biological causes."
    d. "A foolproof way to find out whether the problem is psychological is to use nocturnal penile tumescence."

Ans: d
Page: 316
Obj: 7
Type: C

22. Which of the following descriptions illustrates secondary erectile disorder?
    a. Bill, whose inability is caused by a physiological problem he was born with
    b. Charlie, whose inability has psychological causes
    c. Emmett, who has never had an erection sufficient for intercourse
    d. Del, who used to have adequate erections but now is unable

Ans: a
Page: 317
Obj: 7
Type: F

23. What do professionals say about the necessity for women to have orgasms during intercourse?
    a. "There is such controversy on this issue that there is little agreement on what is 'normal.'"
    b. "Normal sexuality involves an absence of orgasm in women."
    c. "No one believes that female orgasm should involve manual stimulation."
    d. "Intercourse without orgasm is abnormal and a sign of a physical defect."

Ans: b
Page: 317
Obj: 7
Type: A

24. A young woman consults with a sex therapist because she has never had an orgasm during intercourse. Before assuming that the young woman has female orgasmic disorder, the therapist should
    a. assume that the problem represents a primary disorder.
    b. find out if the woman has had experiences conducive to producing orgasmic responses.
    c. assume that she has the same physiological problems males have when they are not orgasmic.
    d. remind the woman that 80 percent of women have never achieved an orgasm by any means.

Ans: c
Page: 317
Obj: 7
Type: F

25. Research on primary inhibited female orgasm suggests that
a. neurotransmitter deficits account for the problem.
b. the problem is related to inhibited sexual desire.
c. the problem is not equivalent to primary orgasmic dysfunction in men.
d. the problem is much more widespread than previously believed.

Ans: d
Page: 318
Obj: 7
Type: A

26. Dr. Ward says, "Premature ejaculation is a relatively common sexual dysfunction in which the inability to achieve an erection leads to ejaculating reflexively. It is a source of anguish for many males." What part of the statement is *inaccurate*?
a. It is inaccurate to say that premature ejaculation involves reflexive ejaculation.
b. It is inaccurate to say that premature ejaculation causes anguish for many males.
c. It is inaccurate to say that premature ejaculation is common.
d. It is inaccurate to say that premature ejaculation involves an inability to achieve an erection.

Ans: b
Page: 318
Obj: 7
Type: C

27. Unlike _____, which can occur in both men and women, _____ is a problem for women only.
a. vaginismus; dyspareunia
b. inhibited arousal; vaginismus
c. erectile dysfunction; inhibited arousal
d. premature ejaculation; vaginismus

Ans: d
Page: 318
Obj: 7
Type: C

28. Artise suffers from a rare disorder in which the uncontrolled spasming of her vaginal muscles causes such pain that it prevents her husband from having intercourse. The disorder is
a. dyspareunia.
b. a form of inhibited orgasm.
c. a form of sexual aversion disorder.
d. vaginismus.

Ans: c
Page: 318
Type: A
Obj: 7

29. Your friend, Carolyn, just got back from her honeymoon. When you ask her how her trip was, she says that she ruined everything. When you ask her what she means, she tells you that she and her new husband could not consummate their marriage because she just got too "tight." What sexual dysfunction is Carolyn *most likely* describing?
a. Hypoactive sexual desire
b. Dyspareunia
c. Vaginismus
d. Sexual aversion disorder

Ans: a
Page: 318
Obj: 8
Type: C

30. Which statement about the cause of sexual dysfunctions is *accurate*?
a. Recent studies indicate that biological factors may play a major role in some sexual disorders.
b. Masters and Johnson tended to deemphasize the importance of psychological factors.
c. Almost all of them are primary forms of the disorders.
d. Recent studies show that biological factors only explain secondary forms of the disorders.

Ans: b
Page: 318
Obj: 8
Type: C

31. Although the relationship between hormones and sexual functioning is complex and unclear, we would expect that low levels of testosterone would be associated with
    a. paraphilias.
    b. hypoactive desire disorder.
    c. premature ejaculation.
    d. vaginismus.

Ans: d
Page: 319
Obj: 8
Type: A

32. Giovani has been treated with vascular surgery to increase blood flow to his genitals. When that did not cure his sexual dysfunction, he was given extra hormones. Now he is a candidate for implant surgery. What disorder is he most likely to suffer from?
    a. Premature ejaculation
    b. Hypoactive desire disorder
    c. Male orgasmic disorder
    d. Erectile disorder

Ans: b
Page: 319
Obj: 8
Type: F

33. Medical treatment for erectile problems includes
    a. the "squeeze technique."
    b. injections into the penis that produce erections for several hours.
    c. creams that reduce genital sensitivity.
    d. hypertensive medications.

Ans: a
Page: 321
Obj: 9
Type: F

34. Which of the following is considered a predisposing psychological factor for sexual dysfunction?
    a. A strict moral upbringing that produced anxiety about sex
    b. Anxiety when another person makes sexual overtures
    c. Pain when engaging in sexual intercourse
    d. Feeling pressured into having sex when it is not desired

Ans: b
Page: 322
Obj: 9
Type: F

35. Which of the following is *not* a psychological factor associated with female orgasmic dysfunction?
    a. Having a partner who is sexually dysfunctional
    b. Being raised in a sexually permissive home
    c. Having a crippling fear of performance failure
    d. Being ignorant about sexuality or sexual technique

Ans: c
Page: 322
Obj: 9
Type: C

36. A sex therapist counsels his clients to masturbate and use both tactile exploration and sexual imagery to increase arousal and therefore performance. The clients who hear this advice are *most* likely to have which sexual dysfunction?
    a. Sexual pain disorder
    b. Premature ejaculation
    c. Female orgasmic disorder
    d. Paraphilia

Ans: a
Page: 322
Obj: 9
Type: C

37. A therapist instructs Mrs. Weaver: "Stimulate your husband's penis until he feels ejaculation is about to happen, then stop all stimulation for a while. Continue with stimulation and then stop, repeating until he can tolerate longer periods of stimulation without ejaculating." What sexual dysfunction is being treated?
    a. Premature ejaculation
    b. Secondary erectile dysfunction
    c. Sexual aversion disorder
    d. Vaginismus

Ans: b
Page: 322
Obj: 9
Type: F

38. In general, research on the effectiveness of treatment for sexual dysfunctions shows that
   a. discussing the problem with a partner or reading books is very ineffective.
   b. relapse is a significant problem.
   c. initial reports that behavior therapy is highly successful have been confirmed.
   d. long-term outcome for vaginismus is very poor.

Ans: c
Page: 322
Obj: 9
Type: F

39. What disorder is being treated when a woman is taught to relax and then inserts increasingly large dilators until the comfortable insertion of a penis is possible?
   a. Dyspareunia
   b. Female orgasmic dysfunction
   c. Vaginismus
   d. Sexual aversion disorder

Ans: c
Page: 323
Obj: 10
Type: A

40. Jimmy is a little boy who engages in exclusively feminine play and claims he wants to grow up to be a woman. He is disgusted by his penis. Jimmy illustrates
   a. transvestism.
   b. paraphilia.
   c. childhood gender identity disorder.
   d. pedophilia.

Ans: d
Page: 324
Obj: 10
Type: C

41. Which description *best* illustrates transsexualism?
   a. Pedro is sexually attracted to other men.
   b. Carlos experiences sexual arousal only if he dresses in women's clothes.
   c. Miguel is constantly preoccupied with thoughts of castration.
   d. Luis has had poor social relationships because he has always been distressed about being a man.

Ans: b
Page: 324
Obj: 10
Type: A

42. Norman is diagnosed with specified gender identity disorder. We can confidently guess that as a child he
   a. was considered a very aggressive boy.
   b. avoided rough-and-tumble activities.
   c. was sexually attracted to other boys.
   d. cross-dressed as a way of attracting attention from others.

Ans: c
Page: 325
Obj: 10
Type: A

43. Under stress, Jerald cross-dresses. He also has persistent thoughts about castration, although he has no desire to become a person with bodily characteristics associated with women. Does Jerald have a psychological disorder?
   a. No, he is considered a homosexual.
   b. No, he shows no form of sexual disorder.
   c. Yes, he has a type of gender identity disorder.
   d. Yes, he suffers from a paraphilia.

Ans: a
Page: 325
Obj: 10
Type: C

44. The biological cause of gender identity disorders probably involves
   a. abnormal levels of sex hormones.
   b. excessive amounts of certain neurotransmitters.
   c. lack of development in certain brain structures.
   d. stress-related organ dysfunction.

Ans: d
Page: 325
Obj: 10
Type: C

45. Keith is diagnosed with transsexualism by a psychoanalyst. How is the therapist likely to explain his disorder?
    a. "You cross-dress because it allows you to experience sexual arousal."
    b. "As a child, you over-identified with your strong and independent father."
    c. "We will probably find that his mother encouraged Keith to dress up like a girl and may have punished him for being aggressive."
    d. "There must be some oedipal issues that are unresolved."

Ans: d
Page: 325
Obj: 10
Type: F

46. The fact that children in one study adopted the gender identity that their parents imposed regardless of their anatomical sex supports
    a. the psychodynamic position that gender identity disorder does not actually exist.
    b. the biological explanation for transsexualism.
    c. the idea that transsexualism is actually a form of homosexuality.
    d. the behavioral explanation of transsexualism.

Ans: b
Page: 325
Obj: 10
Type: A

47. To treat a gender identity disorder, Carl and his parents are involved in therapy. Carl is "educated" by the therapist about appropriate sex-role behavior, while his parents are taught behavioral principles to extinguish inappropriate behavior. Carl's therapy is
    a. based on psychodynamic principles.
    b. standard treatment for gender identity disorders.
    c. unlikely to be helpful in treating Carl.
    d. based on a biological viewpoint of gender identity.

Ans: c
Page: 325
Obj: 10
Type: C

48. Vitaly is diagnosed as a child with gender identity disorder. He and his parents go to a behavior therapist. Which of the following is likely to occur during treatment?
    a. He will be encouraged to act out his fantasies of being a girl.
    b. His parents will be told that a sex-change operation is the only effective treatment.
    c. He will be punished for transsexual fantasies and rewarded for masculine behavior.
    d. His parents will be instructed that the traditional male sex role is detrimental to Vitaly's mental health.

Ans: d
Page: 325
Obj: 10
Type: F

49. Which statement about treatment of transsexualism is *accurate*?
    a. Sex reassignment surgery is much easier for women who wish to be men than for men who wish to be women.
    b. Sex-change operations became possible only in the mid-1980s.
    c. The only valuable therapy is sex reassignment surgery.
    d. Behavior therapy has proved to have some positive value.

Ans: c
Page: 327
Obj: 10
Type: A

50. Brenda was a transsexual who had a sex-change operation. She now calls herself Brad. Research on the outcome of these operations suggests that
    a. she will get more negative reactions from others than if she were a man who changed to a woman.
    b. she will quickly relapse to gender identity disorder.
    c. she will be more satisfied with surgery than men who change to women.
    d. she will never feel depressed again.

Ans: b
Page: 327
Obj: 11
Type: F

51. The sexual disorders called _____ involve intense sexual urges regarding nonhuman objects, real or simulated suffering, or non-consenting others.
    a. gender identity disorders
    b. paraphilias
    c. dyspareunia
    d. psychosexual disorders

Ans: a
Page: 327
Obj: 11
Type: C

52. A man has persistent fantasies about having sex with non-consenting people. These fantasies have lasted for almost a year and cause the man severe distress. What diagnosis is appropriate and why?
    a. Mild paraphilia, because the man has not acted on his distressing fantasies
    b. No mental disorder, because unless the man acts on his fantasies, there is no form of sexual deviance
    c. Sexual dysfunction, because the man is not able to achieve sexual arousal normally
    d. Gender identity disorder, because the man has fantasies about having sex with non-consenting people

Ans: c
Page: 327
Obj: 11
Type: F

53. When an individual has a paraphilia, it *likely* occurs
    a. because of a homosexual orientation.
    b. after a stressful life event.
    c. in the presence of some other paraphilia.
    d. if he or she had one or more earlier gender identity disorders.

Ans: b
Page: 327
Obj: 11
Type: A

54. Mary has a fetish for men's clothes and has two other forms of paraphilia as well. She is distressed with her fantasies and actions. These paraphilias have lasted several years. What aspect of Mary's case is *unusual*?
    a. It is unusual for a paraphilia to last several years.
    b. It is unusual for a woman to have paraphilias.
    c. It is unusual for a person to have more than one paraphilia.
    d. It is unusual for a person with a paraphilia to be distressed.

Ans: d
Page: 327
Obj: 11
Type: C

55. Dr. Thompson says, "They are disorders in which there is a recurrent and intense sexual urge related to an object such as shoes but *not* because of cross-dressing." Dr. Thompson is describing
    a. homosexual transsexualism.
    b. transvestic fetishism.
    c. a gender identity disorder.
    d. fetishism.

Ans: b
Page: 327
Obj: 11
Type: C

56. When an object such as shoes or women's underwear is used during masturbation as the sole means of achieving sexual gratification and this practice is distressing, the diagnosis is
    a. frotteurism.
    b. fetishism.
    c. transvestic fetishism.
    d. transsexualism.

Ans: c
Page: 328
Obj: 11
Type: A

57. Wayne has neither homosexual fantasies nor an attraction to other men. He knows he is male, but he can only achieve sexual arousal by shopping for women's clothes, dressing in them, and masturbating in front of a mirror. An appropriate diagnosis for Wayne is
   a. gender identity disorder.
   b. transsexualism.
   c. transvestic fetishism.
   d. exhibitionism.

Ans: d
Page: 328
Obj: 11
Type: A

58. Brent has been diagnosed with transvestic fetishism. Although he is married, he has long wanted a sex-change operation. He must dress as a woman to be able to have intercourse with his wife. If the diagnosis is accurate, what is *unusual* about Brent's case?
   a. It is unusual for cross-dressing to be used for heterosexual sex.
   b. It is unusual for a man to have transvestic fetishism.
   c. It is unusual for a person with transvestic fetishism to be married.
   d. It is unusual for a person with transvestic fetishism to want a sex-change operation.

Ans: c
Page: 330
Obj: 11
Type: C

59. Both transsexuals and transvestites cross-dress. What factor helps differentiate the two disorders?
   a. Transsexuals develop their interest in cross-dressing at a much later age than transvestites.
   b. Only transvestites are sexually aroused by cross-dressing.
   c. Only transsexuals are unaroused by cross-dressing.
   d. Transvestites tend to be homosexuals.

Ans: a
Page: 330
Obj: 11
Type: F

60. It is a relatively common paraphilia and involves urges or fantasies about exposing one's genitals to strangers in order to cause shock in the observer. The disorder is called
   a. exhibitionism.
   b. voyeurism.
   c. fetishism.
   d. frotteurism.

Ans: c
Page: 331
Obj: 11
Type: A

61. All of these men were diagnosed with exhibitionism. Which is *typical* of men with this disorder?
   a. Wayne, who maintains complete self-control throughout his episodes of exposing himself
   b. Lars, who is sexually aroused only by pictures of women in the nude
   c. Jim, who is 24 years old and married
   d. Arnold, who is 53 years old and unmarried

Ans: a
Page: 327
Obj: 11
Type: C

62. Which of the following is *not* a paraphilia involving non-consenting others?
   a. Fetishism
   b. Voyeurism
   c. Pedophilia
   d. Frotteurism

Ans: b
Page: 331
Obj: 11
Type: F

63. Sexual gratification obtained through observing others engaging in sexual intercourse is called
   a. spectator sex.
   b. voyeurism.
   c. pedophilia.
   d. exhibitionism.

Ans: d Page: 331 Obj: 11 Type: C	64. Which paraphilia is *correctly* paired with its major symptom? a. Voyeurism—exposing one's genitals to strangers b. Exhibitionism—"peeping" at undressed strangers c. Pedophilia—obtaining sexual arousal by inflicting pain d. Frotteurism—touching and rubbing non-consenting persons
Ans: a Page: 331 Obj: 11 Type: A	65. For the past three years, Larry has repeatedly fondled his preteen stepdaughter and has sworn her to secrecy. Larry's behavior illustrates a. pedophilia. b. voyeurism. c. transvestic fetishism. d. sadomasochism.
Ans: b Page: 332 Obj: 11 Type: F	66. Which statement about pedophilia is *accurate*? a. Most pedophiles are under sixteen years of age and molest children nearly their same age. b. In most cases, one relative or friend of the family molests one child. c. Most pedophiles remain unaroused when they see hard-core pornographic films. d. Most pedophiles are highly intelligent and socially skilled.
Ans: a Page: 332 Obj: 11 Type: F	67. The *most* common pattern of child molestation is for a. females between ages eleven and thirteen to be fondled. b. strangers to molest male children. c. strangers to have sexual intercourse with children under age six. d. mothers to molest their male children.
Ans: b Page: 332 Obj: 11 Type: A	68. Norm is suspected of being a child molester. If he is a pedophile, we would expect him to show which of the following? a. Sexual arousal to slides of neutral, clothed women b. Impulsivity and discomfort in social situations c. High intelligence and right hemisphere dysfunction d. Lack of interest in hard-core pornography
Ans: c Page: 332-333 Obj: 11 Type: C	69. Pedophilia is to _____ as sadomasochism is to _____. a. pain; exposing b. children; cross-dressing c. children; pain d. exposing; children
Ans: d Page: 332 Obj: 12 Type: C	70. A therapist working with child victims of sexual abuse is likely to see symptoms that *most* closely parallel a. bipolar (manic-depressive) disorder. b. dissociative identity (multiple personality) disorder. c. paraphilias. d. posttraumatic stress disorder.
Ans: a Page: 333 Obj: 11 Type: A	71. Stefanie has intense sexually arousing fantasies of being utterly helpless while being tied up and humiliated. She is quite distressed by these fantasies. A reasonable diagnosis is a. masochism. b. that she was a victim of child sexual abuse. c. pedophilia. d. sadism.

Ans: c
Page: 333
Obj: 11
Type: F
	72. A study of 178 sadomasochists found that the majority
	    a. reported that "straight" sex is more satisfying than sadomasochistic
	       activities.
	    b. played either a dominant or a submissive role but not both.
	    c. engaged in behaviors that caused only mild pain.
	    d. reported that they seek to injure others or be injured themselves.

72. A study of 178 sadomasochists found that the majority
a. reported that "straight" sex is more satisfying than sadomasochistic activities.
b. played either a dominant or a submissive role but not both.
c. engaged in behaviors that caused only mild pain.
d. reported that they seek to injure others or be injured themselves.

Ans: c / Page: 333 / Obj: 11 / Type: F

73. Dr. Monte says about a patient, "As a child, he was often spanked on the bare buttocks by his very attractive governess. He cannot remember these incidents clearly, but as an adult he always associates pain with sexual arousal." Dr. Monte's patient probably has which disorder?
a. Voyeurism
b. Exhibitionism
c. Pedophilia
d. Sadomasochism

Ans: d / Page: 333 / Obj: 13 / Type: A

74. Dr. Kovacs says, "Psychoanalytic thinking about paraphilias suggests that unconscious conflicts are important. Biological researchers have proved that hormones and brain abnormalities are the cause. Still, behavioral treatment has generally had positive results." Which portion of this statement is *inaccurate*?
a. No part of the statement is inaccurate.
b. It is inaccurate to say that psychoanalysts emphasize unconscious conflicts.
c. It is inaccurate to say that researchers have proved hormones and brain abnormalities to be the causes of paraphilias.
d. It is inaccurate to say that behavioral treatment for paraphilias is generally positive.

Ans: c / Page: 334 / Obj: 13 / Type: A

75. A key concept in the psychodynamic explanation of paraphilias is
a. excessive superego.
b. castration anxiety.
c. inadequate id impulses.
d. the defense mechanism of projection.

Ans: b / Page: 335 / Obj: 13 / Type: F

76. Dr. Julius says to his exhibitionist patient, "Your dreams tell us that, for you, fear of castration requires that you prove to others that you still have a penis by exposing yourself. Once you acknowledge and overcome that fear, your need to exhibit will disappear." Dr. Julius holds a(n) _____ viewpoint on the disorder.
a. psychodynamic
b. cognitive-behavioral
c. operant conditioning
d. humanistic-existential

Ans: a / Page: 335 / Obj: 13 / Type: C

77. Suppose that, in a research study, slides of nude women were shown to men at the same time they held or stroked white feathers. If these stimuli were paired enough times for the feathers alone to produce an erection, this would suggest
a. that paraphilias are actually under the voluntary control of the individual.
b. that paraphilias are unrelated to "preparedness."
c. support for the biological perspective on paraphilias.
d. support for a classical conditioning theory of paraphilias.

Ans: d / Page: 335 / Obj: 13 / Type: C

Ans: b
Page: 335
Obj: 13
Type: A

78. A psychologist discussing the cause of fetishes says, "In most men, sexual arousal is associated with women's breasts, not shoes or handbags. It is possible, but very difficult, to condition men to react sexually to these neutral objects. Some object-arousal associations are harder to condition than others." The psychologist
   a. supports Masters and Johnson's treatment methods.
   b. is discussing "preparedness."
   c. is a psychoanalyst.
   d. believes that "preparedness" plays no role in paraphilias.

Ans: a
Page: 335
Obj: 13
Type: C

79. Ali is being treated for a shoe fetish. The therapist pairs electric shock with the sight and touch of shoes. The therapist also is teaching Ali to engage in appropriate social skills and how to feel sexual pleasure without resorting to shoes. The therapist probably supports a _____ approach to treatment.
   a. learning
   b. psychodynamic
   c. biogenic
   d. cognitive

Ans: d
Page: 335
Obj: 13
Type: F

80. Shame and humiliation are *most* likely to be used by behavior therapists to treat
   a. people with sexual dysfunction.
   b. masochists.
   c. people with gender identity disorders.
   d. exhibitionists.

Ans: c
Page: 335
Obj: 13
Type: A

81. Tad is an exhibitionist. His therapist has him expose himself to a preselected group of females. He is made to be fully aware of his actions and thoughts because he must talk about his penis and his fantasies in front of these women. This form of treatment is
   a. based on psychodynamic assumptions.
   b. usually considered a form of chemical castration.
   c. an example of behaviorally oriented therapy.
   d. one of the least effective forms of treatment for paraphilias.

Ans: b
Page: 336
Obj: 13
Type: F

82. The *main* problems with research on the effectiveness of behavioral treatment for paraphilias are
   a. the control groups have been too large and only one treatment technique has been used.
   b. few control groups and several treatment techniques have been used.
   c. only rapists have been studied and only one treatment technique has been used.
   d. there is no theory on which treatment is based and only large samples have been treated.

Ans: a
Page: 336
Obj: 14
Type: F

83. Which of the following is the *best* definition of *sexual coercion*?
   a. Any form of sexual pressure
   b. Rape and incest
   c. Any form of sexual aggression
   d. Sexual arousal produced by an object or non-consenting person

Ans: d
Page: 337
Obj: 14
Type: F

84. Which statement about rape in the United States is *accurate*?
    a. Although few victims report being raped, the conviction rate for the crime is about 80 percent.
    b. Most rape victims are in middle age and are attacked by strangers.
    c. As defined in the United States, rape is a sexual crime, not a violent one, and it occurs only when a stranger forces sex on an unwilling individual.
    d. Because many women do not report being raped, the actual prevalence is probably much higher than that which is reported.

Ans: b
Page: 337
Obj: 14
Type: F

85. Some experts believe that unreported rapes range from times the official numbers.
    a. 1 to 2
    b. 2 to 10
    c. 5 to 15
    d. 10 to 20

Ans: b
Page: 337
Obj: 14
Type: A

86. Maria went on a date with a guy she knew from her office. After dinner, he attacked her and forced her to have sex. Maria's experience illustrates
    a. incestuous sex.
    b. date rape.
    c. sadomasochism.
    d. violent voyeurism.

Ans: a
Page: 338
Obj: 14
Type: A

87. A group of 100 female undergraduate students are surveyed. More than half say they have been victims of sexual aggression. The men who coerced them into intercourse manipulated them by using alcohol and interpreted their protests of sexual advances as meaning, "go ahead." What aspect of this group's survey results is *unusual*?
    a. Unfortunately, nothing about these survey results is unusual.
    b. It is unusual for one-half of undergraduate females to report being victims of sexual aggression.
    c. It is unusual for men who coerce sex to use alcohol.
    d. It is unusual for men who coerce sex to interpret protests as insincere.

Ans: d
Page: 340
Obj: 14
Type: A

88. Magda is in the long-term phase of rape trauma syndrome. Which of the following symptoms is *most* likely to be seen?
    a. Severe depression
    b. Feelings of self-blame for the rape
    c. Being convinced that the rapist will return and kill her
    d. Lack of desire and fear of sex

Ans: b
Page: 340
Obj: 14
Type: F

89. In one study of sexually active rape victims, one-half reported a symptom usually seen in posttraumatic stress disorder. That symptom is
    a. promiscuous sexual behavior.
    b. flashbacks of the rape event.
    c. paranoid delusions.
    d. prolonged sleeping.

Ans: a
Page: 340
Obj: 14
Type: F

90. Rape victims seem to be *most* helped by
    a. receiving non-demanding affection and support.
    b. reliving the rape experience.
    c. forcing themselves to have sex immediately after the trauma.
    d. being left alone by others.

Ans: d
Page: 340
Obj: 14
Type: A

91. Brad has committed several rapes. He has grave concerns about his own sexual adequacy, and he needs to intimidate women through rape. Using the three categories of rapists of Groth et al. (1977), Brad illustrates the _____ rapist.
 a. fetishistic
 b. anger
 c. sadistic
 d. power

Ans: d
Page: 340
Obj: 14
Type: C

92. According to the finding of Groth et al. (1977), there are several types of rapists, based on their motivation. Which man illustrates the *most* common type?
 a. Joseph, who feels confident and comfortable with women
 b. Melvin, who derives satisfaction from torturing women
 c. Pete, who believes he is trapped in a woman's body
 d. Henry, who compensates for feeling inadequate by intimidating women

Ans: c
Page: 340-341
Obj: 14
Type: C

93. Which statement about the differences between rapists and nonrapists is *accurate*?
 a. Initial findings that nonrapists are more responsive to aggressive cues than rapists have not been confirmed.
 b. Only rapists respond sexually to aggressive cues in the absence of sexual cues.
 c. Initial findings that only sadists or rapists respond sexually to aggressive cues have not been confirmed.
 d. Only rapists are sexually aroused by portrayals of women being raped.

Ans: a
Page: 341
Obj: 15
Type: F

94. The "cultural spillover" theory of rape suggests that a culture in which there _____ will have a high rate of rape.
 a. is easy access to guns and media portrayals of violence
 b. is a strong value placed on the frequency of heterosexual sex
 c. are many African Americans and Hispanic Americans
 d. is a lack of sex-role stereotyping

Ans: b
Page: 343
Obj: 15
Type: C

95. Which remark *best* illustrates the socio-biological perspective on rape?
 a. "Rape occurs when society gives men control over women and allows them to be violent without incurring negative consequences."
 b. "Evolution has produced sex differences in the sex drive, which increases the chances that men will be motivated to assault women for sex."
 c. "Since there are marked cross-cultural differences in the likelihood of rape, social factors must play a central role in motivation to rape."
 d. "Rape is not a sex crime; it is a phenomenon that is biologically caused by hormones that incite violent behavior."

Ans: a
Page: 342
Obj: 14
Type: A

96. As an adolescent, Marla was in a brief incestuous relationship with her brother. Her sister, Rhonda, was in a long-term incestuous relationship with their father. We can expect that
 a. Rhonda was more psychologically damaged than Marla.
 b. Rhonda's incestuous relationship was more mutual than Marla's.
 c. Marla was more psychologically damaged than Rhonda.
 d. There were few negative psychological effects on either woman.

Ans: b
Page: 343
Obj: 16
Type: A

97. Colin was convicted of rape. He is receiving the most common form of behavior change technique society provides rapists:
   a. aversive behavioral treatment.
   b. imprisonment without treatment.
   c. chemical castration with Depo-Provera.
   d. psychoanalytic psychotherapy.

Ans: d
Page: 343-344
Obj: 16
Type: F

98. Behavior therapy for incest offenders and rapists stresses
   a. the need to relax when deviant stimuli are presented.
   b. our cultural bias in favor of strong and independent men.
   c. the individual's underlying needs for power and control.
   d. the extinction of sexual responses to deviant stimuli.

Ans: c
Page: 344
Obj: 16
Type: F

99. Surgical castration of sexual offenders
   a. is the most common form of treatment in the United States.
   b. uses electric shock to pair arousal with deviant stimuli.
   c. in Europe shows low rates of recidivism.
   d. works because it makes the man unable to have intercourse.

Ans: a
Page: 344
Obj: 16
Type: F

100. Chemical therapy with the hormone Depo-Provera, when used with pedophiles, is designed to
   a. reduce psychological desire.
   b. decrease the pedophile's anxiety when he sees a child.
   c. induce anxiety when the individual sees a child.
   d. make the pedophile physically incapable of having an erection.

ESSAY QUESTIONS

1. Describe the four stages of the human sexual response. Indicate how at least one form of sexual dysfunction can occur in these stages.

2. Describe and differentiate transsexualism and transvestic fetishism. What are the causes and treatments of these disorders?

3. Name and describe the characteristics of two paraphilias. Hypothesize on the origins of the paraphilias that you identify.

SAMPLE ANSWERS

1. Masters and Johnson did scientific observations of the human sexual response in the laboratory. The results of their studies and the clinical work of therapist Helen Singer Kaplan produced a four-stage model of the human sexual cycle. The appetitive stage begins the cycle and involves thoughts and desires for sexual arousal. Daydreaming about sex or more specific thoughts about individuals characterize this stage. When direct sexual stimulation occurs (although this need not involve physical touching), the excitement phase has begun. There are physiological changes in both sexes: increases in heart rate, blood pressure, and respiration rate. Blood flow to the genitals increases, causing an erection in the penis in men and engorgement of the clitoris in women. In men, the testes enlarge and elevate; in women, nipples become erect, the clitoris expands, and vaginal lubrication occurs. Sexual tension is released in the third phase, orgasm. In men, the base of the penis contracts, and semen is propelled out. Men typically are unresponsive to sexual stimulation for a time after ejaculation. In women, the outer third of the vagina contracts rhythmically. Women

are capable of have continued orgasms if stimulation is maintained. The fourth stage, resolution, has the body returning to normal levels of arousal.

The sexual dysfunction that most commonly brings couples to counseling is a lack of sexual desire, related to the first stage. Hypoactive desire disorder occurs in roughly 15 percent of men and 20 to 35 percent of women. People with this disorder have little or no interest in actual or fantasized sexual activity, although they usually have the ability to experience orgasm. Sexual aversion disorder, quite rare in men, involves avoidance of sexual intercourse. Both of these sexual desire disorders can be caused by psychological or a combination of psychological and biological factors.

Male erectile disorder is an example of a sexual dysfunction of the excitement phase. It involves an inability to attain or maintain an erection sufficient for intercourse. Clinicians estimate that as many as one-half of men experience transient erectile problems and that between 10 million and 15 million American men have this disorder. Biological causes such as medical conditions can make men vulnerable to continued erectile problems because of anxiety over performance.

An example of a sexual dysfunction in the orgasm phase is female orgasmic disorder, also called inhibited female orgasm, which affects an estimated 5 to 10 percent of women. It is characterized by persistent delay in or inability to achieve orgasm with adequate stimulation during the excitement phase. However, as the DSM-IV notes, lack of orgasm during intercourse in which there is no manual stimulation of the clitoris represents a normal variation in the female sexual response. It is not clear what exactly normal female orgasmic functioning is. One psychologist (Wakefield, 1988) argues that with enough stimulation, the prevalence of female orgasmic disorder drops to less than 1 percent of women. This disorder, like male erectile disorder, can be considered primary (the person has never been functional) or secondary (the person has past experience being functional).

There is no category of sexual dysfunctions that characterize the resolution phase.

2. Transsexualism is another term for specified gender identity disorder. People with this disorder feel that they are trapped in the wrong body, that they are psychologically the opposite sex. It is much more common in males than in females. As children, boys avoid rough-and-tumble play and engage in feminine pursuits. They dress in girls' clothes and experience significant social impairments and subjective distress. Transvestic fetishists are males who cross-dress, but for different reasons. Transvestic fetishists identify themselves as males and are typically married heterosexuals who derive sexual arousal from cross-dressing. If a male cross-dresses and experiences no arousal, he cannot be considered a transvestic fetishist. The causes of these disorders are not well understood, but gender identity is probably an outgrowth of lower testosterone levels and family environments in which oedipal conflicts are unresolved or parents encourage feminine behavior, cross-dressing, and dependence on mother. Psychoanalysts see the explanation of transvestic fetishism as a symbolic refutation of castration fears by having an erection occur in women's clothes. Behaviorists emphasize the associations that are made between masturbation and specific objects and images.

Treatment for transsexualism has involved modeling and rehearsal to increase sex-appropriate behaviors and extinguish opposite-sex behaviors. Punishment, in the form of electric shock, also has been used to stop transsexual fantasies. Treatment during childhood attempts to correct stereotypes about sex roles, boys are assigned male therapists who can be role models, and parents are taught to reinforce appropriate behaviors. For some transsexuals, sex-change operations have been successful. These require hormone therapy, a period during which the person must live as a member of the opposite gender, and surgery that removes genitalia and constructs primary and secondary sex characteristics of the opposite gender. Generally, female-to-male change is more satisfactory for the person.

Treatment for transvestic fetishism never involves sex change but uses psychotherapy and behavioral techniques to reduce the desire for and performance of cross-dressing. Behaviorists use conditioning methods to punish or extinguish cross-dressing while reinforcing appropriate sexual behaviors and developing social skills that make traditional sexual arousal more likely.

3. (Answers will vary)

a. *Fetishism*—the key feature of this paraphilia is an intense sexual urge involving a nonsexual item—commonly an inanimate extension of the body such as clothing (e.g., women's undergarments, shoes, purses) or a material of a particular texture (e.g., rubber, leather). The fetish also might be a part of the body—for example, feet. The person holds, rubs, or wears the fetish while masturbating or asks the sexual partner to wear it. The person may be unable to experience sexual arousal without the fetish.

b. *Sexual sadism*—this paraphilia is characterized by sexually arousing urges and fantasies involving acts that inflict physical or psychological suffering on another person. The person may employ the fantasies during sexual activity or actually perform the acts with a consenting partner. The sadistic acts and fantasies involve having complete control over the other person.

The origins of paraphilias are unknown but may involve learning (classical or operant conditioning) or faulty cognitive processes or they may be due to poor social skills.

CHAPTER 11
Mood Disorders

LEARNING OBJECTIVES

1. Describe the mood disorders and distinguish them from normal mood changes. Recall prevalence rates for these disorders. (pp. 347-348)

2. Describe the symptoms of depression, including the affective, cognitive, behavioral, and physiological domains. (pp. 348-351)

3. Describe the symptoms of mania. Differentiate the two levels of manic intensity. (pp. 351-352)

4. Describe and differentiate among the following mood disorders and the symptom features that may accompany these disorders: major depressive disorder, dysthymic disorder, the bipolar disorders, cyclothymic disorder, and mood disorders associated with a medical condition or substance use. (pp. 352-355)

5. Describe and differentiate course specifiers including cycling type, seasonal, postpartum, and longitudinal patterns of mood disorders. Compare unipolar and bipolar disorders. (pp. 355-356)

6. Contrast the various theories of depression, including psychodynamic, behavioral, and Lewinsohn's comprehensive view of depression. (pp. 356-360)

7. Discuss the cognitive and cognitive-learning approaches to depression. Give examples of the logical errors depressives make and the pessimistic attributions they might use. (pp. 360-365)

8. Describe various socio-cultural explanations for mood disorders, including cross-cultural differences, the role of stress, and social support in depression. (pp. 365-368; Mental Health & Society)

9. Describe what is known about sex differences and depression and the explanations for any differences. (pp. 368-369).

10. Describe the biological theories of mood disorders, including genetic and neurotransmitter theories, the role of cortisol and REM sleep in depression. (pp. 369-373)

11. Evaluate the strengths and weaknesses of the various causal theories of depression. (p. 373)

12. Indicate the kinds of biological therapies that have been used to treat depression, including medication and electroconvulsive therapy (ECT). Discuss the effectiveness of these treatments and their side effects. (pp. 373-376; Mental Health & Society; Critical Thinking)

13. Describe psychological treatments for mood disorders, including interpersonal psychotherapy and cognitive-behavioral therapy. Evaluate the effectiveness of these treatments. (pp. 376-380)

14. Describe the use of lithium and its problems in treating bipolar disorders. (pp. 380)

MULTIPLE–CHOICE QUESTIONS

Ans: c
Page: 347
Obj: 1
Type: F

1. Disturbances in emotions that cause subjective distress are considered
   _____ disorders.
   a. personality
   b. thought
   c. mood
   d. anxiety

Ans: d
Page: 347
Obj: 1
Type: F

2. A person who shows mania is
   a. usually at high risk for suicide.
   b. engaging in criminal behavior.
   c. unable to move his or her limbs.
   d. experiencing an extremely elevated mood.

Ans: a
Page: 347
Obj: 1
Type: A

3. The director of a new mental health center is developing plans to provide
   treatment for the disorder that is the most common complaint for those who
   come for mental health care. That disorder is
   a. depression.
   b. manic depression.
   c. anxiety.
   d. hyperactivity.

Ans: b
Page: 347
Obj: 1
Type: A

4. Karen has been feeling very sad and apathetic since her husband died two
   weeks ago. Although she continues to eat and sleep properly, she has had
   little desire to go to work and has decided to take a leave of absence. Karen
   has no history of missing work or of feeling so sad and apathetic. According
   to DSM-IV-TR,
   a. Karen would be diagnosed with unipolar depression.
   b. Karen would not receive a clinical diagnosis.
   c. Karen would be diagnosed with bipolar depression.
   d. Karen meets the criteria for a depressive syndrome.

Ans: c
Page: 347
Obj: 1
Type: A

5. Jill has had one episode of major depression. What is the likelihood that she
   will have another during her lifetime?
   a. 1 percent
   b. 10 percent
   c. 50 percent
   d. 90 percent

Ans: d
Page: 347
Obj: 1
Type: F

6. A recent survey of college students (Furr et al. 2001) found that over _____
   percent said they had experienced depression.
   a. ten
   b. twenty
   c. twenty-five
   d. fifty

Ans: a
Page: 347
Obj: 1
Type: A

7. Bridget is expansive and hyperactive; she is "high" but irritable. Douglas is
   withdrawn and intensely sad; he feels worthless and incapable of being
   successful. Which statement about these two people is *accurate*?
   a. Bridget illustrates mania; Douglas illustrates depression.
   b. Bridget illustrates mania; Douglas illustrates normal mood.
   c. Bridget illustrates depression; Douglas illustrates normal mood.
   d. Bridget illustrates normal mood; Douglas illustrates depression.

Ans: d
Page: 347
Obj: 1
Type: A

8. Dr. Sanders says, "Mania is a disorder that occurs about as commonly as depression. It is characterized by elevated mood and hyperactivity. It occurs in about as many men as women." Which statement by Dr. Sanders is *inaccurate*?
   a. Mania is twice as common in women as in men.
   b. When people experience mania, they slow down.
   c. Mania involves a depressed mood.
   d. Mania is far less common than depression.

Ans: c
Page: 349
Obj: 2
Type: A

9. Suppose 100 people admitted to a psychiatric hospital were all given diagnoses of mood disorder. We could expect that
   a. 70 percent were manic and 30 percent were depressed.
   b. 50 percent were depressed and 50 percent were manic.
   c. 90 percent were depressed and 10 percent were not yet depressed.
   d. 50 percent of those who were depressed were men.

Ans: a
Page: 349
Obj: 2
Type: C

10. Lucy feels worthless and extremely sad. She has had crying spells that do not stem from any particular event. Life seems uninteresting and colorless. Lucy's symptoms illustrate the
    a. affective symptoms of depression.
    b. behavioral symptoms of depression.
    c. cognitive symptoms of mania.
    d. physiological symptoms of depression.

Ans: d
Page: 349
Obj: 2
Type: C

11. The affective symptoms of depression include
    a. slowed speech and action.
    b. thoughts of suicide.
    c. an inability to sleep.
    d. intense sadness and feelings of worthlessness.

Ans: b
Page: 349
Obj: 2
Type: A

12. Luis's mother died suddenly, and he has experienced great sadness. Which statement indicates that this is clinical depression rather than normal mourning?
    a. He feels that he needs to mourn in order to adjust to his mother's death.
    b. He feels a general sense of worthlessness.
    c. He cries when he thinks of his mother.
    d. He has experienced a short, intense period of dejection and sadness.

Ans: c
Page: 352
Obj: 2
Type: A

13. Timothy has been unable to function at work for five months since the death of his mother. He feels he is worthless and is unable to talk or talk as quickly as he once did. Timothy's reaction to his mother's death
    a. indicates a bipolar disorder.
    b. can be considered within the normal limits of bereavement in most cultures.
    c. indicates a severe depression.
    d. would be considered mania in some cultures but normal bereavement in others.

Ans: d
Page: 349
Obj: 2
Type: C

14. The cognitive symptoms of depression include
    a. crying spells that do not relate to a particular event.
    b. feeling worthless.
    c. slowed movements.
    d. self-accusations of being incompetent.

Ans: a
Page: 349
Obj: 2
Type: A

15. Harold says, "I cry for hours and feel a profound sense of loss. I experience no joy, but I can still see a positive future for myself. I know I am competent; I just feel very sad all the time." If Harold is experiencing depression, he illustrates
    a. none of the cognitive signs but many of the affective ones.
    b. most of the cognitive and affective signs.
    c. most of the behavioral signs but none of the affective ones.
    d. none of the affective signs but many of the cognitive ones.

Ans: b
Page: 350
Obj: 2
Type: C

16. A psychologist describes a patient as showing the "cognitive triad of depression." Which patient is being described?
    a. Rachel, who is apathetic, anxious, and socially withdrawn
    b. Meagan, who is pessimistic about herself, the world, and the future
    c. Kate, who is crying, easily fatigued, and moves very slowly
    d. Wendy, who has physiological impairments in her nervous system, gastrointestinal system, and immune system

Ans: a
Page: 350
Obj: 2
Type: F

17. Which of the following is a behavioral symptom of depression?
    a. Slowing down all body movements and speech
    b. Becoming more and more involved with other people's problems
    c. Having trouble getting to sleep but feeling full of energy
    d. Having thoughts of suicide

Ans: b
Page: 352
Obj: 2
Type: F

18. All of the following are physical symptoms of unipolar depression *except*
    a. change in activity level.
    b. marked difficulties in concentration and decision making.
    c. loss of energy and feelings of fatigue.
    d. persistent tiredness.

Ans: d
Page: 350
Obj: 2
Type: A

19. Ralph has lost twenty pounds since he was fired from his job. He either cannot get to sleep or wakes up early and is exhausted the next day. These facts illustrate the _____ symptoms of depression.
    a. cognitive
    b. affective
    c. unconscious
    d. physiological

Ans: d
Page: 350
Obj: 2
Type: C

20. Which of the following is *not* a physiological symptom of depression?
    a. Disruption of normal menstrual cycle
    b. Lack of interest in eating and weight loss
    c. Difficulty getting to sleep or waking up early
    d. Decreased need for sleep and high arousal

Ans: b
Pages: 350
Obj: 2
Type: A

21. Professor Hecker told her class that depression is experienced around the world, with similar symptoms, and that the core symptoms are the same for children, adolescents, and adults. Which part of Professor Hecker's statement is incorrect?
    a. Depression is experienced around the world.
    b. The symptoms are similar around the world.
    c. Core symptoms are the same for children, adolescents, and adults.
    d. Her entire statement is correct.

Ans: a
Page: 351
Obj: 3
Type: F

22. Unlike depression, in mania
    a. the mood is elevated, expansive, or irritable.
    b. mood changes occur without any changes in behavior.
    c. the mood remains normal, while the cognitive and behavioral symptoms change.
    d. mood changes do not affect social or occupational functioning.

Ans: b
Page: 351
Obj: 3
Type: A

23. Which individual *best* illustrates the symptoms of mania?
    a. Jim, who has suddenly developed an aversion to sexual activity
    b. Paul, who has boundless energy and becomes angered when frustrated
    c. Alice, who is highly anxious about future events
    d. Esther, whose energy level is so low that she has become withdrawn from other people

Ans: c
Page: 351
Obj: 3
Type: F

24. Which of the following terms is *correctly* paired with its definition?
    a. Hypomania is when a person is beginning to feel depressed.
    b. Mania is when a person is "high" but totally coherent.
    c. Hypomania may involve poor judgment but not delusions.
    d. Mania is a less severe form of the disorder than hypomania.

Ans: a
Page: 352
Obj: 4
Type: A

25. For the past several weeks, Ian's thinking races from one idea to the next, and he cannot stay focused on any one idea. He feels pressure to keep on talking, feels a decreased need for sleep, and has been arrested for harassing pedestrians on the street. What diagnosis would Ian *most likely* be given?
    a. Bipolar disorder
    b. Unipolar depression
    c. Cyclothymic disorder
    d. Dysthymic disorder

Ans: d
Page: 352
Obj: 4
Type: A

26. Carrie has terrible episodes of depression. Most of the time she is depressed, but one time in the past two years she experienced a week-long episode during which her energy level increased dramatically. She developed a grandiose and irritable mood and became pleasure seeking in her behavior. What is Carrie's probable diagnosis?
    a. Cyclothymia
    b. Depression with psychotic features
    c. Major depressive episode
    d. Bipolar disorder

Ans: d
Page: 351
Obj: 3
Type: A

27. Romeo is grandiose in his thinking, incoherent in his speech, and so hyperactive he has hardly sat down in the past week. DeJuan is overactive and elated, starting projects but not completing them. However, he shows neither delusions nor incoherence in his speech. According to the DSM-IV-TR,
    a. Romeo illustrates the hypomanic state, DeJuan the manic state.
    b. Romeo and DeJuan both illustrate the manic state.
    c. Romeo and DeJuan both illustrate the hypomanic state.
    d. Romeo illustrates the manic state, DeJuan the hypomanic state.

Ans: a
Page: 352
Obj: 4
Type: F

28. In the DSM-IV-TR, the mood disorders are divided into two major subcategories:
    a. unipolar depressive disorder and bipolar disorder.
    b. Bipolar I and Bipolar II.
    c. mild and severe.
    d. major depression and dysthymic disorder.

Ans: c
Page: 352
Obj: 4
Type: C

29. Taylor is diagnosed with major depression. One thing we are sure of is   that he
   a. will never have another episode of depression after this one.
   b. has shown impairment of functioning for less than two weeks.
   e. does not alternate between depression and mania.
   d. swings from extremely low energy to very high energy.

Ans: b
Page: 352
Obj: 4
Type: A

30. Reinhart's long-term friends describe him as being chronically down, pessimistic, hopeless, withdrawn, brooding, irritable, unhappy, listless, and inactive for over three years. The most likely diagnosis for Reinhart would be
   a. seasonal affective disorder.
   b. dysthymia.
   c. psychotic depression.
   d. a major depressive episode.

Ans: c
Page: 352
Obj: 4
Type: C

31. It is possible to distinguish between major depression and dysthymia because
   a. in dysthymia the depressive mood lasts only several weeks.
   b. in major depression the depressive mood has become a persistent way of life.
   c. in major depression there is a marked deterioration from the person's previous functioning.
   d. in dysthymia once the immediate stress is over, the mood will improve.

Ans: d
Page: 352
Obj: 4
Type: A

32. Brianna has always been pessimistic. For the past three years, on most days she feels tired, guilty, and unable to concentrate. However, her eating, sleeping, and daily functioning have not been impaired. This chronic depressed state *best* illustrates
   a. depression not otherwise specified.
   b. cyclothymia.
   c. major depression.
   d. dysthymic disorder.

Ans: a
Page: 352
Obj: 4
Type: F

33. For an event to qualify as a manic episode, the DSM-IV-TR says that
   a. the state must last for one week.
   b. there must also be a depressive episode.
   c. there must be an elevated mood that does not impair functioning.
   d. the state must last for two months.

Ans: b
Page: 352
Obj: 4
Type: C

34. Ronnie has recurrent major depressive episodes that alternate with hypomania. According to the DSM-IV, Ronnie should be diagnosed with
   a. Bipolar I.
   b. Bipolar II.
   c. cyclothymia.
   d. major depressive disorder not otherwise specified.

Ans: c
Page: 352
Obj: 4
Type: C

35. The answer to one question is needed to decide whether a person should be diagnosed as Bipolar I or Bipolar II. That question is,
   a. "Have any of your close relatives ever had this problem?"
   b. "How long have you felt depressed?"
   c. "Have you ever had a manic episode?"
   d. "How many cycles of high and low mood have you experienced?"

Ans: a
Page: 354
Obj: 4
Type: A

36. Nathan has a seven-year history of mild mood swings. When he is "high," he is coherent; when he is "low," he is never suicidal or unable to function. What is the *best* diagnosis for Nathan?
   a. Cyclothymic disorder
   b. Bipolar disorder, mixed
   c. Major depressive disorder, mixed
   d. Dysthymic disorder

Ans: b
Page: 354
Obj: 4
Type: F

37. Which diagnoses *correctly* indicate prevalence from most prevalent to least?
   a. major depression, Bipolar I, cyclothymia
   b. major depression, cyclothymia, Bipolar II
   c. Bipolar I, Bipolar II, dysthymia
   d. dysthymia, cyclothymia, major depression

Ans: c
Page: 352
Obj: 4
Type: C

38. Bipolar disorder is to _____ disorder as major depression is to _____ disorder.
   a. dysthymic; cyclothymic
   b. cyclothymic; anxiety
   c. cyclothymic; dysthymic
   d. psychotic; neurotic

Ans: d
Page: 3354
Obj: 4
Type: A

39. Gertrude was diagnosed with breast cancer last year. After having a mastectomy and six weeks of chemotherapy, she is free of cancer but quite sad, withdrawn, and apathetic. According to the DSM-IV, what diagnosis is *appropriate*?
   a. Bipolar disorder associated with general medical condition
   b. Dysthymic disorder due to substance use
   c. Psychosomatic depressive disorder
   d. Mood disorder due to general medical condition

Ans: a
Page: 355
Obj: 4
Type: A

40. Suzanne was addicted to cocaine for several years. Since she has stopped using, she has been low in energy and dejected to the point of contemplating suicide. She is obviously quite distressed, and her symptoms have impaired her ability to work and interact with her family. The *correct* diagnosis is
   a. substance-induced mood disorder.
   b. major depression.
   c. mood disorder due to a general medical condition.
   d. dysthymia.

Ans: c
Page: 355
Obj: 5
Type: F

41. What information does a symptom feature provide?
   a. How long the symptoms usually last
   b. When symptoms usually manifest themselves
   c. The severity or way symptoms present themselves
   d. Whether the disorder is inherited or the product of stress

Ans: b
Page: 355
Obj: 5
Type: A

42. Mrs. Smyth is diagnosed with depression because she has lost weight, expresses excessive guilt, and is unresponsive to pleasurable things. Further, she is mute and stands in one position for hours at a time. Which symptom features should be listed with the diagnosis of depression?
   a. Rapid cycling and behavioral apathy
   b. Melancholia and catatonia
   c. Postpartum pattern and catatonia
   d. Melancholia and postpartum pattern

Ans: c
Page: 355
Obj: 5
Type: C

43. A depression that has regularly occurred in the winter for three straight years and always lifts by April would be an example of a _____ depression.
   a. cycling
   b. postpartum
   c. seasonal
   d. psychotic

Ans: b
Page: 355
Obj: 5
Type: A

44. Greta's psychiatrist advises her to buy bright lights, which are to be put on in the early morning hours of winter days to reduce her problem with depression. We can guess that Greta's problem is
   a. dysthymia due to medical condition.
   b. seasonal affective disorder.
   c. postpartum depression.
   d. rapid-cycling bipolar disorder.

Ans: c
Page: 356
Obj: 5
Type: C

45. Which of the following would suggest that an individual suffered from bipolar disorder rather than unipolar depression?
   a. The individual is a woman.
   b. The individual developed the disorder after age thirty-five.
   c. The individual benefits from lithium.
   d. The individual has no family history of the disorder.

Ans: b
Page: 357
Obj: 6
Type: C

46. According to psychoanalysts, depression stems from
   a. fixation at the anal stage of development.
   b. physical or symbolic separation.
   c. a lack of superego.
   d. a conflict between sexual urges and superego constraints.

Ans: c
Page: 357
Obj: 6
Type: C

47. Dr. DeVille thinks that depression is actually a mask for anger that has no safe way to be expressed. We can guess that Dr. DeVille supports the _____ perspective on depression.
   a. biological
   b. behavioral
   c. psychodynamic
   d. socio-cultural

Ans: d
Page: 357
Obj: 6
Type: A

48. Research by Stroebe and Stroebe (1991) suggests that what a funeral director should say about the "proper" way to grieve after the death of a spouse is,
   a. "Directly confronting the death is the best way to prevent depression."
   b. "Depression is usually caused by people directly confronting death (that is, performing grief work)."
   c. "How people deal with the death of a spouse has nothing to do with whether they become depressed."
   d. "What works for widows does not seem to work for widowers."

Ans: a
Page: 358
Obj: 6
Type: C

49. Dr. Thomasson is a psychoanalyst, and Dr. McGuire is a behaviorist. Both see separation and loss as important issues in depression, but they see them differently.
   a. Dr. McGuire sees loss in terms of a reduced chance for reinforcement.
   b. Dr. Thomasson emphasizes how sympathy for the person experiencing the loss rewards helplessness.
   c. Dr. Thomasson sees loss as changing the hormonal balance within the depressive's body.
   d. Dr. McGuire highlights the symbolic nature of loss.

Ans: b
Page: 358
Obj: 6
Type: C

50. When Bill is seriously depressed, he reduces his activity level. His wife, Doris, shows sympathy and concern and reinforces Bill's inactivity. According to behaviorists, Doris's reinforcement represents a
    a. means of classically conditioning Bill to stay depressed.
    b. form of secondary gain.
    c. way of extinguishing Bill's depressive behaviors.
    d. symbolic mothering that Bill unconsciously desires.

Ans: c
Page: 358
Obj: 6
Type: F

51. Which of the following are key concepts in the behavioral explanation of depression?
    a. Incomplete mourning and unexpressed anger
    b. Irrational thinking and poor logic
    c. Few reinforcers and poor social skills
    d. Lack of imagination and self-absorption

Ans: b
Page: 359
Obj: 6
Type: A

52. Which of the following statements *best* mirrors Lewinsohn's comprehensive view of depression?
    a. "The depressed person has a low self-concept that is made worse by poor family supports, but more important is the person's neurotransmitter imbalances."
    b. "Low rates of positive reinforcements are crucial, but prior level of stress and the person's loss of self-confidence lead to a downward spiral."
    c. "Classically conditioned depression is combined with modeling of other depressed individuals until depression becomes almost contagious."
    d. "In addition to the stressors the person suffers, we must look at the unconscious conflicts which bubble to the surface."

Ans: d
Page: 360
Obj: 6
Type: A

53. Which statement *best* illustrates Staats and Heiby's behavioral explanation of bipolar disorder?
    a. "Manic states are periods of masked anger, which, after repeated expression, so drain the person that periods of depression naturally result."
    b. "It is not a predictable state; it occurs whenever biological changes occur inside the body."
    c. "It is a result of imitating televised portrayals of happy people."
    d. "Social behaviors are rewarded and lead to higher levels of euphoria before they finally bring negative reactions and depression."

Ans: a
Page: 360
Obj: 6
Type: A

54. Bob has suffered from depression for several months. His therapist says, "Bob, you believe that anything you try will fail simply because you once applied for a job and didn't get it. Your beliefs, not events, determine how long you will stay depressed." Bob's therapist is *most likely* a proponent of
    a. cognitive theory.
    b. humanistic theory.
    c. interpersonal theory.
    d. psychodynamic theory.

Ans: b
Page: 360
Obj: 7
Type: C

55. Errors in logic, low self-esteem, and expectations of failure are all concepts central to the _____ theory of depression.
    a. biological
    b. cognitive
    c. operant
    d. psychodynamic

Ans: a Page: 361 Obj: 7 Type: C	56. Which statement *best* illustrates Beck's explanation of depression? 　a. "Depression is primarily a problem in thinking; negative schemas make one feel depressed." 　b. "When opportunities for reinforcement are reduced, people do less and are therefore more likely to become depressed." 　c. "Depressives use internal and global causal attributions for negative events rather than external and specific attributions." 　d. "Depressives see the world with little distortions; they accurately appreciate the brutality of life."
Ans: d Page: 361 Obj: 7 Type: A	57. Which situation *best* illustrates Beck's concept of overgeneralization in depressives? 　a. When it rains on the day of the picnic, the host feels he should have scheduled it for another day. 　b. Despite feeling great anger at his mother, a boy yells at himself. 　c. When a girl is complimented on her hair, she assumes that the complimenter was just showing pity for her. 　d. A man burns the toast one morning at breakfast and concludes that he is a worthless father and husband.
Ans: c Page: 361 Obj: 7 Type: F	58. What are the effects of the errors in logic, such as selected abstraction, that Beck sees as the core of depression? 　a. They make people direct their hidden anger toward people who are not actually the source of their anger. 　b. They make people believe that they have little control over the outcomes of their efforts. 　c. They lower self-esteem and lead to unrealistic expectations of failure. 　d. They cause people to explain negative events in terms of external, specific causes that are inaccurate.
Ans: b Page: 362 Obj: 7 Type: F	59. Research comparing depressives and nondepressives shows that when they have a choice of listening to tape-recorded messages, 　a. nondepressives want to hear about the difficulties others have had. 　b. depressives have no preference about whether the message is positive or negative. 　c. depressives want to hear about the successes others have had. 　d. nondepressives have no preference about whether the message is positive or negative.
Ans: c Page: 362 Obj: 7 Type: A	60. According to Seligman's perspective on depression, which person below is *most likely* to suffer depression? 　a. Karen, who attributes poor performance to bad luck and other external factors 　b. Joe, who never mourned the death of his parents 　c. Bernie, who suffered many setbacks over which he had no control 　d. Norma, who brought on many of the stresses in her own life
Ans: b Page: 362 Obj: 7 Type: C	61. A person who believes that his or her behavior has little effect on the environment and who becomes passive and depressed illustrates _____ perspective on depression. 　a. Beck's low self-esteem 　b. Seligman's learned helplessness 　c. Lewinsohn's operant 　d. Freud's psychodynamic

Ans: a
Page: 362
Obj: 7
Type: C

62. Which quote *best* illustrates what Seligman means by learned helplessness?
    a. "Nothing I do will ever improve my situation."
    b. "Everyone can dance well except me."
    c. "I can't remember anything good ever happening to me."
    d. "Many of the stresses in my life I brought on myself."

Ans: b
Page: 362
Obj: 7
Type: C

63. In therapy, a psychologist tries to convince a depressed woman that her actions *do* affect the environment and that even though uncontrollable events happened in the past, they need not happen again. This therapist is making use of principles from
    a. psychodynamic theory.
    b. learned helplessness theory.
    c. the biogenic theory of depression.
    d. the cognitive triad.

Ans: c
Page: 363
Obj: 7
Type: C

64. In its revised cognitive version, learned helplessness theory examines
    a. the reinforcement that comes from acting depressed.
    b. the genetic vulnerability of the person.
    c. whether a person's causal attributions for failure are global or specific.
    d. whether a person uses overgeneralization or other forms of poor logic.

Ans: b
Page: 363
Obj: 7
Type: A

65. All of the following people were unsuccessful in getting a job after undergoing three interviews. Which person's thinking illustrates the depressive attributional style?
    a. Esther: "I may be terrible at job interviews, but the rest of my skills are exceptionally strong."
    b. Theresa: "I am always incompetent—in job interviews and everything else."
    c. Anthony: "I didn't get a job because of a bad streak of luck, and luck is always ripe for changing."
    d. Paul: "I didn't try my hardest; if I work at it, I can get a job."

Ans: d
Page: 364
Obj: 7
Type: A

66. A critic of Seligman's revised helplessness theory (now called hopelessness theory) is *correct* in saying,
    a. "The theory puts too much emphasis on the inherited aspects of brain function."
    b. "The idea that depressives attribute failure to external factors does not get support from research."
    c. "The theory suggests that thinking and expectation play almost no role in depression, an obvious oversimplification."
    d. "Internal attributions may be associated with some forms of depression but not all of them."

Ans: b
Pages: 364
Obj: 7
Type: F

67. Lewinsohn, Joinder, & Rohde (2001) state that both Beck's and Seligman's theories propose what type of process?
    a. learning
    b. diathesis-stress
    c. psychodynamic
    d. sociocultural

Ans: c
Page: 365
Obj: 8
Type: A

68. When it comes to depression, the director of a mental health center serving an ethnically diverse population should expect
    a. higher than average numbers of people with northern European ancestry.
    b. lower than average numbers of American Indians.
    c. higher than average numbers of people with Southeast Asian ancestry.
    d. Chinese-Americans to have few somatic (bodily) complaints.

Ans: a
Page: 365
Obj: 8
Type: F

69. Individuals from _____ culture are especially likely to present bodily complaints when they are depressed.
    a. Chinese
    b. Russian
    c. American Indian
    d. mainstream European American

Ans: c
Page: 367
Obj: 8
Type: F

70. In Hammen's view, the relationship between stress and depression is that stress
    a. is the result of depression, never its cause.
    b. always causes depression.
    c. can cause depression but that coping with depression can cause further stress.
    d. produces depression only in people who are biologically vulnerable to becoming depressed.

Ans: d
Page: 367
Obj: 8
Type: A

71. Dr. Oldham says, "Stress often precedes depression. Often one severe stress causes depression when several minor stressors do not. While long-lasting, chronic stress is *not* associated with depression; stress appears to be important in relapse (reverting to depression after treatment)." What part of Dr. Oldham's statement is *incorrect*?
    a. It is incorrect to say that stress is related to relapse.
    b. It is incorrect to say that stress often precedes depression.
    c. It is incorrect to say that one severe stress is more likely to cause depression than several minor stressors.
    d. It is incorrect to say that chronic stress is not associated with depression.

Ans: a
Page: 367
Obj: 8
Type: F

72. According to Hammen and colleagues (1992), some people respond to stress with depression because
    a. they have poor adaptive skills.
    b. they have social supports who make them dependent.
    c. they see themselves as so independent that they refuse to accept help from others.
    d. they have too much norepinephrine in the frontal lobes.

Ans: d
Page: 368
Obj: 9
Type: A

73. A physician notices that twice as many female patients complain of depression as male patients. The physician's first thought is that the cause is hormonal or genetic differences in the sexes. Research
    a. has shown that only males who have a genetic vulnerability develop depression.
    b. has extensively studied this and found support for it.
    c. has proved that this is never the case.
    d. has rarely been done on this, and results are inconsistent.

Ans: c
Page: 368
Obj: 9
Type: C

74. The gender difference in depression may be more apparent than real. One factor that could explain why women *seem* to be more prone to depression is that
   a. women are socialized to be gentle and sensitive to others.
   b. women may have higher concentrations of particular hormones than men.
   c. depression in men may be given other diagnoses such as substance dependence.
   d. women's gender roles put them under such stress that they feel greater helplessness than men.

Ans: d
Page: 369
Obj: 9
Type: A

75. Imagine that there is an equal level of stress in Gerald's and Mary's lives. Ruling out biological differences, we might expect Mary to be more prone to depression if she
   a. maintains a nontraditional sex role.
   b. is employed outside the home and has no children.
   c. sees herself as controlling her life situations.
   d. tends to ruminate and amplify her depressive moods.

Ans: c
Page: 370
Obj: 10
Type: C

76. Evidence for heritability of bipolar disorders suggests that
   a. no significant evidence regarding heritability and bipolar disorders has been discovered.
   b. a gene for bipolar disorder exists on chromosome 11.
   c. there is an inherited factor, although researchers are unclear what is inherited.
   d. the concordance rate for bipolar disorder is higher for dizygotic twins than for monozygotic twins.

Ans: d
Page: 370
Obj: 10
Type: C

77. Suppose you bet $10,000 to find a person who had a mood disorder but whom you were not allowed to meet, interview, or know personally. For which person would you have a better than even chance of winning your bet?
   a. The identical twin of a person with unipolar depression
   b. A person raised in an adoptive home with depressed parents
   c. The fraternal twin of a person with unipolar depression
   d. The identical twin of a person with bipolar disorder

Ans: a
Page: 370
Obj: 10
Type: F

78. An *accurate* summary statement of current research on genetics and mood disorder is,
   a. "Heredity is especially important in bipolar disorder, but most researchers feel that many genes are involved rather than one."
   b. "Adoption studies show that the environment is more important than heredity for both the bipolar and unipolar mood disorders."
   c. "We know that a single gene is responsible for unipolar disorders, but it is not clear whether a different gene accounts for bipolar disorders."
   d. "One gene that is the blueprint for the production of catecholamines has been found to be responsible for all mood disorders."

Ans: c
Page: 370
Obj: 10
Type: F

79. Norepinephrine, serotonin, and dopamine are
   a. chemicals that block the re-uptake of neurotransmitters.
   b. drugs that reduce the symptoms of depression but not bipolar disorder.
   c. neurotransmitters that are called catecholamines.
   d. enzymes that interact with MAO-inhibitor medications to cause severe side effects.

Ans: b
Page: 370
Obj: 10
Type: F
	80. Depressed behavior, including inaction, is related to too
	   a. much norepinephrine.
	   b. little norepinephrine.
	   c. little reserpine.
	   d. much reserpine.

Ans: d
Page: 371
Obj: 10
Type: C
	81. Mrs. Watanabe is depressed. Her levels of serotonin and norepinephrine are quite low. What processes might account for this?
	   a. The amount of reserpine in her brain is deficient.
	   b. She was given cortisol when taking the dexamethasone suppression test.
	   c. She does not have enough of the enzyme monoamine oxidase.
	   d. The re-uptake of catecholamines is operating too efficiently.

Ans: c
Page: 372
Obj: 10
Type: C
	82. Doctors are not clear whether Dante is depressed or has some other disorder. In the hospital, he is given the dexamethasone suppression test. If he is depressed, the results should show
	   a. increases in the re-uptake process of his neurotransmitters.
	   b. that his level of cortisol fell more quickly than in others who get dexamethasone.
	   c. that Dante has a high level of cortisol despite being given a drug to suppress it.
	   d. that Dante's catecholamine levels fell quickly after he was given dexamethasone.

Ans: a
Pages: 373
Obj: 10
Type: A
	83. Rose, an elderly woman, suffers from depression. An evaluation at a sleep clinic is likely to find that Rose
	   a. quickly goes into REM sleep and she also has increased REM sleep.
	   b. takes a long time to enter REM sleep.
	   c. has less REM sleep than nondepressed persons.
	   d. takes a long time to enter REM sleep and also has less REM sleep than nondepressed persons.

Ans: d
Page: 372
Obj: 11
Type: C
	84. A psychologist says, "The problem with this theory is that it is difficult to test. It uses concepts such as 'symbolic loss' and 'anger turned inward' that are hard to operationalize." The psychologist is commenting on the _____ perspective on depression.
	   a. attributional
	   b. learned helplessness
	   c. cognitive
	   d. psychodynamic

Ans: b
Page: 362
Obj: 11
Type: C
	85. Although extensive research supports this theory, it explains only those depressions that follow an uncontrollable stressor. Which theory is being described?
	   a. Psychodynamic theory
	   b. Learned helplessness theory
	   c. Lewinsohn's operant theory
	   d. Beck's cognitive theory

Ans: c
Page: 373
Obj: 11
Type: C

86. The text suggests that different theories are appropriate for explaining different levels of mood disorders. Which description seems *most* reasonable?
    a. Disorders in the middle of the continuum are best explained by genetics; those at the extremes are best explained by environmental factors.
    b. For all disorders, environmental and genetic explanations are equally useful.
    c. Mild disorders are more externally caused, moderate ones are more likely caused by a combination of environment and genes, and severe disorders are more endogenous.
    d. For mild disorders, genetics is the best explanation; environmental theories are useful for severe cases.

Ans: b
Page: 374
Obj: 12
Type: F

87. Which biological treatment would be used for unipolar depression?
    a. electroconvulsive therapy.
    b. tricyclic medication.
    c. amphetamines.
    d. dexamethasone suppression.

Ans: a
Page: 374
Obj: 12
Type: C

88. Norm is told by his psychiatrist, "I'm giving you this drug to elevate your mood, but you must be sure not to eat cheeses, wines, and other foods that might have tyramine in them. The interaction between the drug and tyramine can have dangerous consequences." What drug is Norm probably taking?
    a. An MAO inhibitor
    b. Reserpine
    c. A tricyclic medication
    d. Lithium

Ans: c
Page: 374
Obj: 12
Type: F

89. Electroconvulsive therapy is generally reserved for
    a. mild depressions such as dysthymia.
    b. manic episodes that have not responded to lithium treatment.
    c. severe depressions that have not responded to drug treatment.
    d. bipolar disorder.

Ans: a
Page: 376
Obj: 12
Type: F

90. Which of the following statements regarding ECT is *accurate*?
    a. A negative side effect of ECT is some memory loss.
    b. Because of the negative side effects of ECT, it is no longer used in the United States.
    c. The effects of ECT on reducing depressive symptoms have been well understood by researchers.
    d. ECT is generally the first treatment used with severely depressed individuals.

Ans: b
Page: 375
Obj: 12
Type: A

91. The case of Norman Endler illustrates that
    a. recovery from severe depression often requires good social support.
    b. combinations of treatments can effectively treat even severe mood disorders.
    c. depression is rarely effectively treated with medication.
    d. as long as a person does not have negative thoughts, he or she is immune to bipolar disorder.

Ans: a
Page: 377
Obj: 13
Type: C

92. Carol is being treated for major depression. Her therapist emphasizes the relationships she is in and the links between current conflicts and early life experiences and traumas. Carol's therapist is using
   a. interpersonal psychotherapy.
   b. cognitive-behavioral techniques.
   c. attribution therapy.
   d. social skills training.

Ans: c
Page: 377
Obj: 13
Type: F

93. Interpersonal psychotherapy for depression is *most closely* associated with
   a. biological principles.
   b. humanistic-existential thinking.
   c. psychodynamic principles.
   d. classical conditioning principles.

Ans: d
Page: 377
Obj: 13
Type: A

94. The first step in cognitive-behavioral therapy usually requires that the client
   a. learn to relax.
   b. increase his or her activity in the world so that reinforcement is possible.
   c. replace irrational thoughts with more rational alternatives.
   d. become aware of his or her thoughts and emotions.

Ans: c
Page: 377
Obj: 13
Type: C

95. Which therapy focuses on reducing depressive symptoms by helping the client to become more actively engaged in pleasurable or productive activities and by helping him or her to challenge automatic negative thoughts?
   a. Sensate-focused therapy
   b. Psychoanalytic therapy
   c. Cognitive-behavioral therapy (CBT)
   d. Interpersonal therapy (IPT)

Ans: b
Page: 379
Obj: 13
Type: A

96. Mel has been in cognitive-behavioral therapy for about six weeks. He has become more active and is aware of his more common irrational thought processes. Most cognitive-behavioral therapists at this point would
   a. suggest he get some electroconvulsive therapy.
   b. ask that he attend a social skills training program.
   c. urge him to reduce the number of activities he is engaged in.
   d. link his current relationship conflicts to early childhood traumas.

Ans: a
Page: 380
Obj: 13
Type: A

97. An insurance company is interested in the most effective treatment for acute unipolar depression. Based on recent research, the *best* advice to the company is,
   a. "Medication, interpersonal psychotherapy, and cognitive-behavioral treatments are all equally effective."
   b. "Interpersonal psychotherapy is far more effective than either medication or cognitive-behavioral therapy."
   c. "Belief in treatment is enough—even placebo pills are as effective as psychotherapy or medication."
   d. "Only antidepressant medication is effective."

Ans: c
Page: 379
Obj: 13
Type: F

98. Which treatment of depression seems to have the *lowest* rate of relapse?
   a. Psychoanalysis
   b. Electroconvulsive therapy
   c. Cognitive
   d. Prozac

Ans: c
Page: 380
Obj: 14
Type: F

99. The medication that revolutionized the treatment of bipolar disorder is
   a. norepinephrine.
   b. the class of drugs called MAO inhibitors.
   c. lithium carbonate.
   d. serotonin.

Ans: d
Page: 380
Obj: 14
Type: C

100. Although lithium carbonate can effectively treat bipolar disorder, one problem is that
   a. it is too expensive for most patients to afford.
   b. in large doses, it can produce severe memory loss.
   c. the drug interacts with the tyramine in certain foods to produce a life-threatening side effect.
   d. many patients do not stay on the prescribed dosage.

ESSAY QUESTIONS

1. Describe the difference between unipolar and bipolar depression. Be sure to include a description of the clinical characteristics of each.

2. Compare and contrast Lewinsohn's explanation of major depression with Seligman's attribution-learned helplessness approach.

3. Evaluate the evidence for a biogenic cause for all mood disorders. How does this relate to methods of treatment?

SAMPLE ANSWERS

1. Unipolar depression involves multiple symptoms, including mood, cognitive, physical, and behavioral, that persist over time and cause impaired functioning. When depresion occurs without the extreme positive mood (called *mania*), it is called *unipolar depression*. Specific depression symptoms include feeling sad, down, or blue; a loss of enjoyment and the inability to experience pleasure; irritability; negative thinking; pessimism; hopelessness; difficulty in concentration, memory, and decision making; feeling fatigued and without energy; psychomotor retardation or agitation; increase or decrease in sleep; increase or decrease in appetite; and social withdrawal. To warrant a diagnosis of a *unipolar depressive disorder*, a person must never have had a manic or hypomanic episode. *Bipolar disorder* is much rarer than unipolar disorder and involves not only depression but also mania or hypomania. Individuals cycle between periods of elevated or depressed mood and normal mood. In many ways *mania* is the opposite of depression. It is a disorder marked by grandiose or irritable mood; increased energy, acitivty, and distractibility; and excessive engagement in pleasurable behaviors that may lead to painful consequences. *Hypomania* is a mild version of mania. To determine whether a person should be diagnosed with unipolar or bipolar disorder, the clinician must look beyond the client's present episode and get information about the client's previous history.

2. Peter Lewinsohn and his colleagues at the University of Oregon have developed a behavioral explanation for depression. This model suggests that a lack of reinforcements leads to feelings of depression. The lack of reinforcement can occur for reasons external to the person or can be an

outgrowth of reduced activity. Either way, the depressed person engages in fewer and fewer actions that can be reinforced, so a downward spiral of negative emotions and reduced activity continues. In addition, the sympathy of others may inadvertently reward the depressed person for inaction, so the depression deepens further. Depressed individuals are seen as having weak social skills—they initiate few conversations, smile less, and complain more, therefore reducing their ability to obtain reinforcement. In recent elaborations of this model, Lewinsohn has noted that prior to being depressed, individuals who experience major stresses may feel that they can no longer predict their world and, feeling they can no longer control events, become more self-critical. As self-awareness of inadequacy intensifies, the person functions less appropriately and feels less self-confident and more depressed. Therefore, in addition to strictly operant (stimulus-response-consequence) components, this model includes the cognitive and emotional elements of depression.

In Seligman's original model of depression, the lack of a contingent relationship between responses and consequences was the key factor. Animals and people who suffered uncontrollable stresses learned that they could do nothing to alter the outcomes. Depressives were seen as people who mistakenly generalized this view to other, controllable situations. Depression was seen as a form of learned helplessness. There are clear connections to Lewinsohn's more recent concepts of feeling that the world is unpredictable and that depressed individuals become passive in such a world. Seligman's modification of his theory, including attributional style, also adds a cognitive component, as Lewinsohn did. However, attributional style focuses on the misperception of causes of negative events rather than the awareness of inadequacy. Seligman and his colleagues argue that depressives are pessimists: They see the causes of negative events as due to internal factors (them!) and stable traits (rather than ones that can change with time or situation) and as affecting global rather than specific spheres of their lives.

In general, Lewinsohn and Seligman share common ground in assuming that a lack of activity and a belief in lost control are the keys to depression. However, Lewinsohn emphasizes the behavioral deficiencies of people prone to depression, while Seligman points out the attributional (cognitive) deficiencies.

3. Twins studies have made it clear that inheritance plays a role in both major depression and bipolar disorders, although more so for the latter. The average concordance rate for bipolar disorders among identical twins is 72 percent; for unipolar depression it is 40 percent. In both disorders, the concordance rate drops to 10 to 14 percent for fraternal twins. Obviously, genetic endowment is important. Findings from adoption research strengthen the argument, since researchers have found that children reared by adoptive parents who have mood disorders are no more likely to develop the disorders than the general population. Only adoptees whose biological parents have the disorders are at higher risk. What exactly is inherited is harder to determine. Abnormally low levels of neurotransmitters called catecholamines (norepinephrine, serotonin, and dopamine) or abnormally low levels of receptor sensitivity to these chemicals are often found in depressives. It is not clear whether this is a cause or a result of depression. Other biological correlates of depression may represent inherited abnormalities. These include rapid onset and greater degree of rapid eye movement (REM) sleep in depressives and abnormally high levels of the adrenal hormone cortisol, even when a drug that normally suppresses cortisol (dexamethasone) is given.

Evidence for the catecholamine hypothesis has been strengthened by the effectiveness of antidepressant drugs that either block the re-uptake of these neurotransmitters or impede their breakdown by enzymes. Electroconvulsive therapy (ECT) also has powerful, short-term effects on severe depression. It is not clear how ECT affects the brain. However, a biological cause of mood disorders does not require a biological treatment. Cognitive-behavioral and interpersonal psychotherapies have proved to be just as effective as antidepressants, and people who receive cognitive-behavioral treatments appear to be less vulnerable to relapse than those given medication.

CHAPTER 12
Suicide

LEARNING OBJECTIVES

1. Explain why suicide is a serious concern in the United States and the problems involved in studying it. (pp. 384-387)

2. Identify some of the possible reasons for suicide and discuss the relationships among hopelessness, depression, and suicide. (pp. 387-391; Table 12.2)

3. Discuss the relationship between suicide and other psychological factors, including alcohol abuse and other DSM-IV disorders. (pp. 381-392; Mental Health & Society)

4. Describe the socio-cultural factors in suicide, including egoistic, altruistic, and anomic suicide. (pp. 392-393)

5. Describe the psychodynamic and biological factors related to suicide and the different types of suicide notes. (pp. 393-394)

6. Describe and discuss research on child and adolescent suicide, including characteristics of suicidal children, family issues, and copycat suicides. (pp. 394-395)

7. Describe and discuss research on child and adolescent suicide, including characteristics of suicidal children, family issues, copycat suicides, and the elderly. (pp. 395-398)

8. Discuss suicide among special populations, including the elderly and among Asian Americans. (pp. 398-399)

9. Describe clues to suicide intent and crisis intervention efforts to prevent it. (pp. 399-402; Table 12.3)

10. Describe the methods used by workers in suicide prevention centers and the effectiveness of these efforts. (pp. 402-405; Mental Health & Society)

11. Describe how community prevention programs may help to reduce the stress of suicide on survivors, with a focus on school-based interventions. (pp. 405-406)

12. Discuss the moral, ethical, and legal implications of the right to suicide. Clarify your own position on the legality of doctor-assisted suicide. (pp. 406-409; Critical Thinking)

MULTIPLE–CHOICE QUESTIONS

Ans: c
Page: 383
Obj: 1
Type: C

1. A ninety-year-old woman kills herself rather than continue suffering with terminal bone cancer. A teenager commits suicide when his girlfriend breaks up with him and his parents are unconcerned. A religious fanatic kills himself to protest religious persecution. These examples of suicide suggest that
   a. suicide cannot be studied in a scientific manner.
   b. all suicide stems from mental disorder.
   c. there are many different causes for suicide.
   d. suicide is basically a sociological phenomenon.

Ans: c
Page: 385
Obj: 1
Type: F

2. Suicide should be discussed separately from depression because
   a. there is little correlation between depression and suicide.
   b. the cause of suicide is biological, while the cause of depression is environmental.
   c. there are many causes of suicide, and it may represent a separate clinical entity.
   d. suicide is more related to schizophrenia than to depression.

Ans: d
Page: 386
Obj: 1
Type: A

3. A psychologist says, "It is not a disorder in the DSM-IV-TR, but it is usually included in abnormal psychology texts in the chapter on depression. It is an irreversible act, but some people advocate a person's right to do it. It makes so many people uncomfortable that they often avoid discussing it." What is it?
   a. Thanatos
   b. Psychosurgery
   c. Drug abuse
   d. Suicide

Ans: b
Page: 386
Obj: 1
Type: C

4. Dr. Elmer is interviewing the friends, family, and therapist of a person who committed suicide so that she can better understand the reasons for suicide. This assessment is
   a. called a medical autopsy.
   b. called a psychological autopsy.
   c. relatively easy to do because it involves direct evidence.
   d. based on the biological approach to mental disorders.

Ans: a
Page: 386
Obj: 1
Type: F

5. It is patterned after a medical procedure and is an attempt to understand the reasons for a person's sudden death through case history analysis and interviews with family and friends. It is called a(n)
   a. psychological autopsy.
   b. psychic post-examination.
   c. anomic assessment.
   d. postmortem analysis.

Ans: c
Page: 387
Obj: 1
Type: F

6. Which of the following is *not* one of the ten common characteristics of suicide?
   a. seeking a solution.
   b. intolerable psychological pain.
   c. a sense that suicide is the right thing to do.
   d. a desire to escape.

Ans: d
Page: 388
Obj: 1
Type: F

7. A study by Furr et al. (2001) found that the suicide rate for college students was:
   a. much higher than for non-college students of the same age.
   b. about the same as for non-college students of the same age.

c.   slightly lower than for non-college students of the same age.
d.   much lower than for non-college students of the same age.

Ans: d
Page: 388
Obj: 1
Type: A

8.   Dr. Nunez says, "Suicide is believed to be among the top ten causes of death in the industrialized world. About 30,000 or more suicides are said to occur in the United States yearly. It is a leading cause of death among young people, but estimates suggest the actual number of suicides is probably 45-50% higher than that recorded. What portion of this statement is *inaccurate*?
     a.   It is inaccurate to say that suicide is a major cause of death.
     b.   It is inaccurate to say that 30,000 or more suicides are said to occur in the United States yearly.
     c.   It is inaccurate to say that suicide is a leading cause of death among young people.
     d.   It is inaccurate to say that estimates are 45-50% higher than that recorded.

Ans: c
Page: 388
Obj: 7
Type: A

9.   The dean of students at a university wonders what percentage of his students have thought about suicide during their four years of college. A good estimate is
     a.   less than 1 percent.
     b.   between 5 and 10 percent.
     c.   as many as 20 percent.
     d.   about half.

Ans: a
Page: 388
Obj: 7
Type: F

10. A ten-year study of suicide by students from the University of California at Berkeley indicates that
     a.   older and foreign-born students are most at risk.
     b.   suicide is most common during final exam week.
     c.   freshmen are most likely to commit suicide.
     d.   females with poor grade point averages are most at risk.

Ans: a
Page: 388
Obj: 7
Type: A

11. A college mental health counselor at a large university is instituting a suicide prevention effort. Based on the study of suicide at the University of California at Berkeley, which group should be targeted for help?
     a.   Foreign-born graduate students who are doing poorly
     b.   Female freshmen during exam week
     c.   Graduate students who are at the top of their class
     d.   Undergraduates who are on academic probation

Ans: c
Page: 388
Obj: 7
Type: F

12. College student suicides are *most likely*
     a.   to occur at small liberal arts and community colleges.
     b.   when people are stressed about taking final exams.
     c.   to involve firearms or drug overdoses.
     d.   to occur when students are on vacation away from campus.

Ans: d
Page: 388
Obj: 7
Type: F

13. The fact that undergraduates with the strongest academic averages are at higher risk for suicide indicates that
     a.   biology is what finally determines who commits suicide.
     b.   socioeconomic factors influence adolescent suicide.
     c.   suicide is basically attention-seeking.
     d.   unrealistically high expectations can make success seem like failure.

Ans: d
Page: 388
Obj: 7
Type: F

14. Gender differences in suicide among college students suggest
a. that sex-role stereotypes are much stronger for college students now than they used to be.
b. increased risk for suicide occurs only in Asian-born women.
c. unrealistic academic standards occur only among men.
d. such differences are much less than in the general population.

Ans: c
Page: 388
Obj: 7
Type: A

15. The dean of students at a large university notes that international students seem more prone to committing suicide. A likely explanation is that international students
a. have a higher prevalence of psychopathology.
b. are more prone to own and use firearms.
c. feel overwhelmed with shame if they do not excel.
d. see their suicide as an irrational choice.

Ans: d
Page: 388
Obj: 7
Type: A

16. Dr. Paris says, "There are two reasons for college student suicide: academic pressure students put on themselves and a sense of shame if their poor performance brings disgrace to their family. Emotional disturbance is not really an issue." Which portion of this statement is *inaccurate*?
a. It is inaccurate to say that student suicide is caused by academic pressure.
b. It is inaccurate to say that student suicide is caused by pressure that students put on themselves.
c. It is inaccurate to say that student suicide is caused by feelings of shame.
d. It is inaccurate to say that student suicide is unrelated to emotional disturbance.

Ans: b
Page: 389
Obj: 1
Type: F

17. _____ are more likely to attempt suicide; _____ are more likely to succeed at committing suicide.
a. White adolescents; Native American adolescents
b. Females; males
c. White males over 40; African American males in their 20s
d. African American females over 40; African American male adolescents

Ans: a
Page: 388
Obj: 1
Type: F

18. Which statement below is *accurate*?
a. Suicide among young people has increased by more than 40 percent in the past decade.
b. For every person who completes a suicide, there are about two who attempt it.
c. Suicide is much less common among college students than among people of the same age who are not in college.
d. It is relatively easy to tell if an "accident" was really a suicide.

Ans: c
Page: 389
Obj: 1
Type: C

19. Statistically, who is at the greatest risk for committing suicide?
a. Bobby, a fourteen-year-old African American male
b. Star, a 35-year-old Native American female
c. Stuart, a fifty-year-old white male
d. Sue, a thirty-year-old Japanese American female

Ans: c
Page: 389
Obj: 1
Type: A

20. Which elderly person is *most likely* to commit suicide if depressed?
a. Harold, a married African American male
b. Lawrence, a married white American male
c. Vern, a single divorced white American male
d. Vivian, a single African American female

Ans: b
Page: 389
Obj: 1
Type: A

21. Which person is at *highest* risk for committing suicide?
    a. Harriet L., a 35-year-old devout Catholic
    b. George T., an elderly white widower
    c. Martha K., a young married professional
    d. Douglas J., a middle class married man of English ancestry

Ans: d
Page: 389
Obj: 1
Type: A

22. Which person would be *most likely* to commit suicide?
    a. A wealthy, female business executive
    b. A twenty-year-old who is not in college
    c. A poor laborer
    d. An elderly psychiatrist

Ans: a
Page: 389
Obj: 1
Type: F

23. When it comes to suicidal behavior, men are *more likely* than women to
    a. complete suicide.
    b. attempt suicide when psychotic.
    c. use drug overdoses as their method.
    d. attempt, but not complete, suicide.

Ans: c
Page: 389
Obj: 1
Type: F

24. The lowest incidence of suicide is found among
    a. divorced women.
    b. widowed men.
    c. married women.
    d. never-married men.

Ans: d
Page: 389
Obj: 1
Type: A

25. An emergency medical squad arrives at the house of a man who has killed himself. The odds are that the method of committing suicide was
    a. jumping off the roof of the house.
    b. ingesting barbiturates or other depressants.
    c. using a knife to cut himself.
    d. using a firearm.

Ans: b
Page: 389
Obj: 1
Type: F

26. A disturbing change in suicidal behavior is that women are now
    a. more likely to use poisoning by barbiturates.
    b. using firearms and explosives as methods of suicide more often.
    c. becoming more influenced by the Catholic Church.
    d. more likely to be in the lower socioeconomic levels of society.

Ans: b
Page: 390
Obj: 1
Type: A

27. Dr. Minton states, "Suicide is a modern phenomenon. It is virtually universal, although the prevalence rates vary across cultures. For example, Japan has a higher suicide rate than the United States." What part of Dr. Minton's statement is *inaccurate*?
    a. It is inaccurate to say that suicide occurs in all cultures; for example, it is rarely present in non-industrialized nations.
    b. It is inaccurate to say that suicide is a modern phenomenon.
    c. It is inaccurate to say that prevalence rates vary across cultures.
    d. It is inaccurate to say that Japan has a higher suicide rate than the United States.

Ans: a
Page: 390
Obj: 1
Type: C

28. What is the primary reason that countries such as Italy and Iran have lower suicide rates?
a. They have strong religious prohibitions against suicide.
b. They do not experience the stressors common to promoting suicide, such as economic difficulties.
c. They have longer summers, so fewer citizens experience seasonal affective disorder, which is often a precursor to suicide.
d. They have better psychological facilities.

Ans: a
Page: 391
Obj: 1
Type: F

29. Which statement is *inaccurate*?
a. It is rare for people to communicate their intention to commit suicide.
b. Suicide rates are generally at their lowest during times of war.
c. In the United States, American Indians have the highest rates of suicide.
d. Most people who attempt suicide are ambivalent about dying.

Ans: a
Page: 391
Obj: 2
Type: F

30. Which form of psychopathology is *most closely* related to suicidal behavior?
a. Depression
b. Schizophrenia
c. Anxiety
d. Obsessive-compulsive disorder

Ans: b
Page: 391
Obj: 2
Type: A

31. Which of the following statements about suicide is *accurate*?
a. In most cases of suicide severe depression is the principal and immediate cause.
b. Hopelessness, or negative expectations about the future, may be a more important factor in causing suicide than depression.
c. Individuals who threaten suicide rarely carry out the act.
d. Approximately two-thirds of individuals diagnosed with depression will attempt suicide at some time during their life.

Ans: c
Page: 391
Obj: 2
Type: C

32. Which statement *accurately* describes the relationship between depression and suicide?
a. Suicide risk is highest in the months before a depressive episode.
b. There is a correlation between depression and suicide in adults but not in children and adolescents.
c. The suicide rate for depressives is much higher than the rate for the general public, but most depressives do not take their lives.
d. Suicide is most likely when people are at the depths of a depression that produces psychomotor retardation.

Ans: b
Page: 391
Obj: 2
Type: A

33. A researcher examines the mental health records of 100 individuals diagnosed with depression and 100 mental patients who completed suicide. The researcher is likely to find that
a. they are the same group of 100 people.
b. more than one-half of the suicidal group were depressed.
c. 90 percent of the depressed individuals attempted suicide.
d. about 10 to 20 percent of the suicidal group were depressed.

Ans: c
Page: 391
Obj: 2
Type: A

34. Consider these suicidal patients: Mary is in the depths of a severe depression. Jack is hospitalized for depression. Larry has just gotten his first weekend pass from the psychiatric hospital. Who is at *highest* risk for suicide?
a. Mary
b. Jack
c. Larry
d. All are at equal risk.

Ans: c
Page: 391
Obj: 2
Type: A

35. A friend of yours says, "I heard that suicide is caused by depression, not by just feeling hopeless. In fact, when people are at the depths of depression, they are most likely to commit suicide." Which portion of your friend's statement is *inaccurate*?
    a. Only the portion saying that suicide is caused by depression is inaccurate.
    b. Only the portion saying that suicide is most likely committed during the depths of depression is inaccurate.
    c. Everything that was said is inaccurate.
    d. Nothing that was said is inaccurate.

Ans: d
Page: 392
Obj: 2
Type: A

36. Based on research by Beck et al. (1985), which of the following people is *most likely* to complete suicide?
    a. Morton, who is very optimistic
    b. Jed, who is depressed
    c. Zach, who thinks about suicide a good deal
    d. Lenny, who is very pessimistic

Ans: b
Page: 392
Obj: 2
Type: F

37. Research seems to show that negative expectations about the future
    a. are unrelated to the likelihood of suicide.
    b. are even more strongly related to suicidal behavior than depression is.
    c. cause suicide but not depression.
    d. cause depression but not suicide.

Ans: a
Page: 392
Obj: 2
Type: A

38. Who is at the greatest risk for committing suicide?
    a. Raul, who is diagnosed with depression and alcoholism
    b. Bob, who is diagnosed with bipolar disorder
    c. Anne, who is diagnosed with schizophrenia
    d. Sandy, who is diagnosed with depression and anxiety

Ans: b
Page: 392
Obj: 3
Type: A

39. Quincy gets very drunk and commits suicide. Most professionals would see
    a. this as extremely uncommon, since alcohol decreases distress and therefore the likelihood of suicide.
    b. alcohol as narrowing Quincy's thinking into an all-or-none state where no alternatives are seen.
    c. alcohol as relaxing Quincy and giving him more alternative answers to his problems.
    d. this as a coincidence, since few suicides occur when individuals are drunk.

Ans: a
Page: 392
Obj: 3
Type: A

40. A mental health professional who wants to reduce the risk of suicide in a client who uses alcohol would probably say,
    a. "Stop drinking. Alcohol constricts your thinking, and that is dangerous."
    b. "If you stop drinking suddenly, you will experience alcohol myopia, a dangerous condition."
    c. "Alcohol myopia is a pleasant state that will probably reduce your likelihood of committing suicide."
    d. "Alcohol relaxes you and lets you see many options to your problems."

Ans: d
Page: 393
Obj: 3
Type: F

41. Mood disorders are one form of psychopathology associated with suicide. What is another?
    a. Sexual dysfunction
    b. Antisocial personality disorder
    c. Social phobia
    d. Schizophrenia

Ans: c
Page: 393
Obj: 4
Type: C

42. If there is one common motive for suicide, it is
    a. the person's desire to gain attention from others.
    b. the person's desire to seek revenge against others.
    c. the person's desire for relief from an unbearable situation.
    d. the person's need to be remembered by others.

Ans: a
Page: 393
Obj: 4
Type: A

43. Dr. Ethan says, "Suicide rates vary with occupation and income group. They also vary depending on the individual's relationship to and interaction with society." Dr. Ethan's remarks reflect which perspective on suicide?
    a. Socio-cultural
    b. Psychodynamic
    c. Behavioral
    d. Cognitive

Ans: b
Page: 393
Obj: 4
Type: A

44. "In my view, suicide is motivated by one of three things: a sudden change in one's relationship with the rest of society, a desire to help the larger group, or a general isolation from others." Who is *most likely* to have made this statement?
    a. Thomas Szasz
    b. Emile Durkheim
    c. Aaron Beck
    d. Sigmund Freud

Ans: c
Page: 393
Obj: 4
Type: A

45. Jewel writes this before she commits suicide: "I am a misfit; I am tortured by my failures. I cannot be who I want, and I cannot change." According to Durkheim , Jewel's suicide probably
    a. occurred while she was psychotic.
    b. was anomic.
    c. was egoistic.
    d. was ageneratic.

Ans: d
Page: 393
Obj: 4
Type: C

46. Connie's family moved to another country, leaving her alone. She is isolated from the rest of the neighborhood and cannot function well on her own. If Connie commits suicide, it would be a(n) _____ suicide, according to Durkheim.
    a. egoistic
    b. altruistic
    c. rational
    d. anomic

Ans: b
Page: 393
Obj: 4
Type: C

47. Sharif is very committed to his religious and political views. He is willing to die for those views. If Sharif commits suicide, we might consider this type of suicide
    a. anomic.
    b. altruistic.
    c. egoistic.
    d. psychopathic.

Chapter 12

Ans: a
Page: 394
Obj: 5
Type: C

48. Anger at others is so violently directed at the self that suicide is the outcome. This is a _____ explanation for suicide.
a. psychodynamic
b. socio-cultural
c. cognitive
d. behavioral

Ans: b
Page: 395
Obj: 5
Type: F

49. Later in Freud's life, when he was suffering from jaw cancer, facing his mortality, and perplexed by war and violence, he posited the existence of
a. libido, a life instinct.
b. thanatos, a death instinct.
c. eros, a love instinct.
d. catharsis, an emotional release.

Ans: a
Page: 395
Obj: 5
Type: C

50. A researcher is investigating the neurotransmitters associated with suicide. She is likely to find that in those who complete suicide,
a. serotonin levels are abnormally low.
b. 5-HIAA levels are abnormally high.
c. adrenalin levels are abnormally low.
d. serotonin levels are abnormally high.

Ans: b
Page: 395
Obj: 5
Type: C

51. Suppose that five years from now there is a blood test that assesses the likelihood of a person's committing suicide. It is likely that this test will measure _____ levels in the blood.
a. dexamethasone
b. serotonin
c. dopamine
d. adrenalin

Ans: c
Page: 395
Obj: 5
Type: F

52. People with abnormally low levels of 5-HIAA
a. are very unlikely to commit suicide.
b. have a history of depression but not suicide attempts.
c. tend to be aggressive and impulsive.
d. commit suicide using the least violent means possible.

Ans: b
Page: 396
Obj: 6
Type: F

53. Which statement about suicide among children and youths is *accurate*?
a. The suicide rate in the United States has not changed over the past twenty-five years.
b. Suicide is second only to auto accidents as the leading cause of death in adolescents.
c. Children who commit suicide tend to have high levels of 5-HIAA in their brains and spinal cords.
d. About 5,000 children between ages five and fourteen commit suicide each year in the United States.

Ans: d
Page: 396
Obj: 6
Type: A

54. A researcher surveys teenagers to find out whether they have ever thought about suicide or done any self-harmful things. The results, if they mirror those of Gallup's recent poll, will show that
a. almost all of them have thought seriously about suicide at least once.
b. many more have done self-harm than have come close to trying suicide.
c. nearly 60 percent have engaged in self-harmful behavior.
d. 6 percent admit to a suicide attempt and another 15 percent to having come close.

Ans: b
Page: 396
Obj: 6
Type: F

55. Among children and teenagers, the group *most likely* to attempt suicide is
 a. boys under age ten.
 b. girls.
 c. those who have never used drugs.
 d. those who do not live with their parents.

Ans: b
Page: 396
Obj: 6
Type: A

56. Based on research, which teenager is at greatest risk for completing a suicide?
 a. Sandy, whose parents are both employed
 b. Sam, who fluctuates between anger and depression
 c. Sarah, who shows little hostility
 d. Steve, who shows no signs of psychological impairment

Ans: d
Page: 396
Obj: 6
Type: A

57. "Samantha had just experienced a major mood swing and became hostile before she took twenty painkillers. Because her parents were not at home, she was lucky to be found and taken to the hospital." Based on Garfinkel and associates' research on more than 500 children and teens who attempted suicide, how typical is this profile of a teen who attempted suicide?
 a. Except for being a female, this case is typical in all respects.
 b. Except for being hostile, this case is typical in all respects.
 c. Except for attempting to take a drug overdose, this case is typical in all respects.
 d. Except for the parents not being at home, this case is typical in all respects.

Ans: a
Page: 397
Obj: 6
Type: A

58. Drew's parents are both unemployed alcoholics. Drew has tried a variety of ways to get his parents to attend to his needs. Now he is severely depressed and angry. When it comes to committing suicide, Drew is
 a. at high risk.
 b. at low risk.
 c. an example of an altruistic suicide.
 d. an example of an anomic suicide.

Ans: d
Page: 397
Obj: 6
Type: F

59. When television newscasters dramatize adolescent suicides, there is the danger of
 a. reducing the early identification of suicide attempters.
 b. increasing the lethality of the methods that adolescent suicide attempters choose.
 c. increasing the sense of depression among adolescents.
 d. generating copycat suicides.

Ans: b
Page: 398
Obj: 8
Type: A

60. Norman is a 71-year-old white widower who is very depressed. He still lives in the small town that he grew up in and attends church every Sunday. He also attends many other regular social activities during the week. What statement regarding Norman's susceptibility to suicide is *most accurate*?
 a. Norman is at minimal risk to commit suicide.
 b. The fact that Norman is an elderly, white, depressed male puts him in a high-risk group, but his social support system is a positive sign.
 c. Norman displays all the risk factors associated with suicide and is likely to commit suicide.
 d. Norman requires immediate hospitalization.

Ans: b
Page: 398
Obj: 8
Type: A

61. If we looked at the death records for a large city, we would probably find that suicide was *most common* among
   a. Hispanic Americans.
   b. elderly white men.
   c. middle-age women.
   d. young white females.

Ans: c
Page: 399
Obj: 8
Type: A

62. A suicide prevention program in San Francisco, where there is a large Asian American population, would target efforts at
   a. elderly women who are second- or third-generation Americans.
   b. college students who have strong family ties.
   c. elderly men who have just arrived in the United States.
   d. young men who are second- or third-generation Americans.

Ans: b
Page: 399
Obj: 8
Type: F

63. Feelings of isolation and a sense of having failed to earn sufficient money are reasons why _____ are so prone to commit suicide.
   a. adolescent females
   b. first-generation Asian immigrants
   c. older black men
   d. third-generation Asian Americans

Ans: a
Page: 399
Obj: 8
Type: C

64. Which group of elderly men is at *highest* risk for suicide?
   a. Chinese who have just arrived in the United States
   b. American Indians
   c. African Americans living in rural areas
   d. Chinese who are acculturated and have strong family ties

Ans: d
Page: 399
Obj: 9
Type: A

65. Sandra has been telling her friends, "I'd be better off dead. I'm not worth anything, and nobody would miss me anyway." How should Sandra's friends interpret her remarks?
   a. They should have Sandra hospitalized immediately.
   b. They should ignore them because the overwhelming majority of people who talk about suicide do not commit suicide.
   c. They should disregard them because Sandra most likely has a personality disorder and her attempts to get attention should not be reinforced.
   d. They should respond to Sandra's suicidal communication because 70 to 80 percent of people who eventually commit suicide give warning signs.

Ans: b
Page: 399
Obj: 9
Type: F

66. Mental health professionals believe that potential suicide victims
   a. always announce their intentions as an attention-seeking device.
   b. are ambivalent about wanting to kill themselves.
   c. cannot be dissuaded because they are psychotic.
   d. are nearly impossible to detect.

Ans: a
Page: 399
Obj: 9
Type: F

67. A psychologist who is asked to assess patients' lethality is being asked to find out
   a. the chances that they will choose to end their lives.
   b. whether they will survive their suicidal actions.
   c. whether other people will copy their actions.
   d. the chances that a psychological autopsy is possible.

Ans: d
Page: 399
Obj: 9
Type: A

68. Which situation represents the person with the *highest* lethality?
   a. A young man who vaguely mentions how he'd be better off dead
   b. A woman who has made suicidal gestures in the past but who has no plan or method of killing herself now
   c. A depressed young woman who has not mentioned killing herself
   d. An elderly man who has planned the time and place for killing himself

Ans: b
Page: 400
Obj: 9
Type: C

69. Some clues of suicide intent are direct, and some are indirect. Which of the following is an *indirect* clue?
   a. A person loading a pistol and saying he knows how to use it on himself
   b. A student giving away his treasured collection of CDs
   c. An employee saying, "If I don't get the promotion, I'll kill myself"
   d. A teenager storing up depressant drugs and scheduling a time to take them

Ans: c
Page: 400
Obj: 9
Type: F

70. Which of the following is *most likely* associated with potential suicide?
   a. Trouble getting to sleep
   b. Birth of a new family member
   c. Loss of a loved one, or chronic or terminal illness
   d. Generalized anxiety

Ans: d
Page: 401
Obj: 9
Type: F

71. "I'd make everyone happier if I just shot myself" is an example of a
   _____; revising one's will and giving away one's record collection are examples of _____.
   a. psychodynamic clue of suicide; behavioral clues of suicide
   b. behavioral clue of suicide; suicidal gestures
   c. suicidal gesture; suicide attempts
   d. verbal clue of suicide; behavioral clues of suicide

Ans: d
Page: 402
Obj: 9
Type: F

72. A counselor who is involved in suicide interventions should
   a. never make decisions for the client; all actions must come from the client's thinking.
   b. avoid behavioral contracts because they lower the barrier against suicide.
   c. avoid involving the family members of the suicidal individual.
   d. be willing to take assertive action with a high-risk client.

Ans: b
Page: 402
Obj: 9
Type: C

73. It is aimed at providing intensive short-term help to assist potential suicide victims in resolving a life crisis. What is it?
   a. Systematic desensitization
   b. Crisis intervention counseling
   c. Suicide prevention center
   d. Insight psychotherapy

Ans: a
Page: 402
Obj: 9
Type: A

74. Gary was hospitalized when he was considered at high risk for suicide. A team of counselors saw him for four hours every day for three days until his suicidal thinking was greatly reduced. The team was extremely active in mobilizing his family and occupational resources outside the hospital. This experience *best* illustrates
   a. crisis intervention.
   b. "right-to-suicide" interventions.
   c. how psychotherapy is used with suicidal people.
   d. suicide prevention programs.

Ans: c
Page: 402
Obj: 9
Type: F

75. High-intensity assessment and treatment during which professionals take charge of the suicidal individual's personal, social, and professional life outside the psychiatric facility characterize
    a. suicide prevention work.
    b. psychological autopsies.
    c. crisis intervention work.
    d. paraprofessional assistance.

Ans: a
Page: 402
Obj: 9
Type: F

76. What is the usual sequence of help in crisis intervention?
    a. First the crisis is dealt with by both the individual and his or her social network, and then traditional therapy is offered.
    b. First the individual is treated as an outpatient, and then the individual comes in for inpatient medical treatment.
    c. First relatives are educated, and then the staff works on the crisis with the individual.
    d. First traditional therapy that examines the motivation for the crisis is offered, and then the individual's social network is educated.

Ans: a
Page: 403
Obj: 9
Type: A

77. A counselor draws up a document for Janie, a suicidal student. The document, which she signs, says that Janie will not attempt to harm herself, that she will get rid of the pills she has stockpiled, and that she will telephone a crisis hot line immediately if she feels like hurting herself. This document is called a
    a. behavioral contract.
    b. lethality assessment.
    c. psychological autopsy.
    d. treatment plan.

Ans: a
Page: 403
Obj: 10
Type: F

78. Which of the following is *not* a goal of treatment following a suicidal attempt?
    a. Assigning the patient to a long-term treatment facility
    b. Determining the underlying problem
    c. Facilitating appropriate problem solving
    d. Preventing further suicidal behavior

Ans: a
Page: 405
Obj: 10
Type: C

79. Imagine that there are two organizations in a community, Help Inc. and Open Door. Help Inc. is available to everyone in the community through a telephone contact. Callers are trained to assess suicidal callers. Open Door has a team of mental health professionals in a clinic where short-term help is given to those who are in immediate danger of suicide. Which description is *accurate*?
    a. Help Inc. is a suicide prevention center.
    b. Open Door is a suicide prevention center.
    c. Help Inc. is a crisis intervention program.
    d. Open Door is a community prevention program.

Ans: c
Page: 405
Obj: 10
Type: F

80. What is the main difference between crisis intervention and suicide prevention centers?
    a. Crisis intervention is done on a large scale for all people in a community.
    b. Suicide prevention involves psychotherapy and medical treatment.
    c. Suicide prevention is done on a large scale and does not involve formal treatment.
    d. Crisis intervention is not involved in treating suicidal behavior.

Ans: c
Page: 403
Obj: 10
Type: C

81. Kyoko is a well-trained suicide prevention hot line worker. She would
    a. never be involved in evaluating a caller's suicidal potential.
    b. always want to allow the suicidal caller to develop his or her own plan of
       action.
    c. always want to establish a good relationship with a suicidal caller.
    d. never want to know the suicidal caller's age, religious preference, or
       name.

Ans: d
Page: 405
Obj: 10
Type: C

82. Ron works as a paraprofessional for a program that receives telephone calls
    twenty-four hours a day. He has been trained to evaluate an individual's risk
    of suicide. What kind of program does Ron probably work for?
    a. A halfway house
    b. An employee-assistance program
    c. A crisis intervention unit in a mental hospital
    d. A suicide prevention center

Ans: a
Page: 403
Obj: 10
Type: A

83. Ignacio calls a telephone hot line because he is thinking of harming himself.
    The telephone counselor asks him if he is married, if he has ever harmed
    himself before, and the stressors he faces. Why are these questions being
    asked?
    a. The counselor is assessing his lethality.
    b. The counselor just wants to establish good rapport.
    c. The counselor is performing a psychological autopsy.
    d. The law requires this information about everyone who calls a telephone
       hot line.

Ans: d
Page: 404
Obj: 10
Type: A

84. John calls a suicide prevention hot line in a desperate state of helplessness. A
    well-trained worker should focus John's attention on
    a. research evidence that helplessness is a product of operant conditioning.
    b. the fact that helplessness is a normal reaction to an absurd world.
    c. specific interpersonal limitations related to his helplessness.
    d. his strengths and resources to cope with his problems.

Ans: c
Page: 404
Obj: 10
Type: F

85. The focus on a clinical approach to suicide intervention makes which of the
    following suggestions?
    a. Even if the person is at high risk for suicide, never make decisions that are
       against the individual's wishes.
    b. Realize that most suicidal people are fully committed to killing
       themselves.
    c. Ask direct questions about the suicidal person's intentions of killing
       himself or herself.
    d. Take plenty of time to assess the background and personality of the
       suicidal individual before listing options.

Ans: a
Page: 404
Obj: 10
Type: F

86. Which statement about research on suicide prevention centers is *accurate*?
    a. Little research has been done on their effectiveness.
    b. Almost every study has shown that they save lives.
    c. Although callers universally find the counselors more helpful than
       friends, they are unlikely to call back a second time.
    d. A great deal of research shows that these centers are actually harmful to
       their clients.

Ans: d
Page: 404
Obj: 10
Type: F

87. A distressing research finding concerning suicide prevention centers is that
    a. most communities are so upset with them that they are forced to close down.
    b. they rarely assess the lethality of clients accurately.
    c. they are open only during weekday business hours.
    d. callers do not perceive the help they get to be any better than what their friends offer.

Ans: b
Page: 404
Obj: 10
Type: A

88. In reference to a suicide prevention center, a psychologist says this to potential financial supporters: "Although 95 percent of callers never use the service again, we know that they see counselors as more helpful than their friends. They may not use the hot line again because they have no further need. Some studies show decreases in suicide after communities institute telephone services." Which portion of the statement is *inaccurate*?
    a. It is inaccurate to say that 95 percent of callers call once.
    b. It is inaccurate to say that callers see counselors as more helpful than friends.
    c. It is inaccurate to say that callers use the service once because they no longer have a need for it.
    d. It is inaccurate to say that some communities have seen decreases in suicide after centers are created.

Ans: d
Page: 404
Obj: 10
Type: F

89. In general, the evaluation of suicide prevention centers' effectiveness indicates that
    a. they are most effective with highly educated callers and least effective with those who are not highly educated.
    b. for the vast majority of callers, they are very helpful.
    c. although they may not stop every suicide, callers feel that the centers provide more help than their friends.
    d. convincing evidence for their success is lacking.

Ans: b
Page: 405
Obj: 11
Type: F

90. A _____ is likely to be used if a school or workplace experiences a suicide; its goals are to facilitate the grieving process and prevent copycat suicides.
    a. suicide prevention center
    b. community prevention program
    c. crisis intervention facility
    d. psychiatric hospital treatment program

Ans: b
Page: 405
Obj: 11
Type: A

91. After two suicides occur in the Plainville School District, the school board institutes a series of talks by mental health professionals to help teachers and students express their emotions about these tragedies. This program illustrates a
    a. mental health halfway house.
    b. community prevention program.
    c. suicide prevention center.
    d. crisis intervention center.

Ans: d
Page: 405
Obj: 11
Type: C

92. Community prevention programs in schools use methods that
    a. emphasize the medical model of psychopathology.
    b. assume that Durkheim was correct about suicide.
    c. unfortunately, have been proven to be ineffective.
    d. assume that suicide be faced directly, allowing survivors to express their feelings.

Ans: b
Page: 405
Obj: 11
Type: F

93. Which component is most likely to be included in school community prevention programs?
   a. Education of funeral home directors
   b. Individual counseling sessions for teachers and students
   c. Free medication to reduce depressive symptoms
   d. A 24-hour telephone hot line

Ans: a
Page: 405
Obj: 11
Type: A

94. After three suicides occur in Springfield's middle school, a community prevention program is set up. A major goal of such a program is likely to be
   a. minimizing the mental health problems of survivors.
   b. explaining everyone's right to commit suicide.
   c. educating individuals about living wills.
   d. protecting students from the ugliness of death and dying.

Ans: b
Page: 407
Obj: 12
Type: A

95. If you hear a presentation by Thomas Szasz, you would *most likely* hear him say,
   a. "Doctors should be encouraged to assist terminally ill patients in their suicides."
   b. "Ending one's life is an individual's moral responsibility, not a professional's."
   c. "Unless we can say words like *death* and *suicide* we can never help our clients cope with their relatives' suicides."
   d. "Prevention is much more efficient and effective than treatment."

Ans: d
Page: 407
Obj: 12
Type: C

96. *Quality of life* and *quality of humanness* are phrases used by
   a. opponents of right-to-die laws.
   b. telephone hot line counselors.
   c. Thomas Szasz to argue for doctor-assisted suicide.
   d. advocates of right-to-die laws.

Ans: d
Page: 406
Obj: 12
Type: F

97. Surgeon General David Satcher laid out all of the following goals to prevent what he saw as an epidemic of suicide except
   a. awareness aimed at broadening the public's awareness of suicide and its risk factors.
   b. Intervention aimed at enhancing services and programs for community and clinical care.
   c. Methodology aimed at advancing the science of suicide prevention.
   d. Legislation aimed at passing laws to deter suicide.

Ans: b
Page: 407
Obj: 12
Type: A

98. In which situation is the right to die seen by *most* individuals as morally acceptable?
   a. A foreign-born student feels that he has disgraced his family name by cheating on an important exam and wants to kill himself.
   b. A 90-year-old man in the last stages of painful bone cancer wants to kill himself.
   c. A 35-year-old business executive who must declare bankruptcy wants to kill himself.
   d. A 13-year-old girl's boyfriend breaks up with her, and she wants to kill herself.

Ans: c   99. Dr. Taylor, a psychologist, says, "Just like our medical counterparts,
Page: 407   psychologists assume that life is worth living only when it is of high quality.
Obj: 12   Clients who are in immediate crisis and are suicidal should not be encouraged
Type: A   to live against their will." What would most other psychologists say to Dr.
                     Taylor?
                     a. Her description is accurate for both psychologists and medical profes-
                         sionals.
                     b. Her description is accurate for psychologists but not medical profes-
                         sionals.
                     c. Her description is inaccurate for members of both professions.
                     d. Her description is accurate for medical professionals but not psycholo-
                         gists.

Ans: b   100. According to Corey, the practicing therapist must confront which of the
Page: 407   following questions when dealing with a suicidal client?
Obj: 12   a. Will the news media treat this client's suicide in a discreet manner?
Type: F   b. Do therapists have the right to prevent a suicide when the client has
                         clearly chosen death over life?
                     c. Does a client's suicide increase the therapist's malpractice insurance
                         premiums?
                     d. Can the client's family be blamed for the client's suicidal manner?

ESSAY QUESTIONS

1. Using facts about the epidemiology of suicide, describe the groups in a large university that are
    most likely to be at risk for suicide. Explain your reasons for including these groups.

2. Discuss how the biological and socio-cultural approaches explain the causes of suicidal behavior.

3. List and describe five different risk factors for suicide.

SAMPLE ANSWERS

1. Although research by Furr et al. Showed that college students are considerably less likely than their
    non-college age peers to attempt suicide, a ten-year study at the University of California, Berkley
    found that suicide on college campuses is more likely among males than among females, but not by
    as large a margin as in the general population. More student suicides occur at large universities
    than at small liberal arts colleges or community colleges. Older postgraduates are more likely to
    commit suicide than undergraduates, as are foreign students and those studying languages or
    literature. Many suicide victims are undergraduates who had better-than-average academic
    records, but lower-than-average grades as graduate students. Suicide may be triggered by
    unrealistically high expectations for academic performance, although the timing of student suicide
    does not support this idea. Earlier points in the semester (February and October) are associated
    with suicide, not months in which finals occur. For international students, pressure from family to
    excel and a sense of shame at letting the family down may be particularly strong motives for
    suicide. Still, those students who are depressed, abuse alcohol, and have experienced
    overwhelming stressors are highly vulnerable to suicide, just as non-students with those
    characteristics are.

2. We have only correlational data on the causes of suicide. Biological theorists propose that
    abnormalities in the nervous system will correlate with suicide, and they have found one that does:

low levels of the chemical 5-HIAA in the cerebrospinal fluid of suicide victims. This chemical is a by-product of the neurotransmitter serotonin, so it seems likely that deficiencies in serotonin might be associated with suicidal tendencies. Research shows that patients with low 5-HIAA levels are more likely to be depressed, aggressive, and impulsive than others, a combination that points toward suicide. Most remarkable is that low levels of 5-HIAA have been discovered in suicidal individuals who had no history of depression. An association exists, but it is not clear whether biology is cause, effect, or directly involved at all in suicide.

Almost one hundred years ago, the great sociologist Emile Durkheim proposed a socio-cultural theory of suicide that is still useful. In his view, there are three motives for suicide, all of them reflecting a relationship between the suicidal individual and his or her community. In egoistic suicide, the individual has failed to develop a nurturing network of social supports and, unable to function adequately, becomes isolated. Disconnected, these individuals end their lives rather than remain alone. Altruistic suicides are culturally supported acts to further a group's goals. Buddhist monks who killed themselves to protest the government of Vietnam in the 1960s and militant Palestinians who blow up buildings and themselves with truck bombs illustrate this kind of suicide. Finally, there are suicides caused by wrenching changes in people's relationship to society. An economic crash, a sudden loss of social status, or being forced to emigrate from one's homeland may trigger what Durkheim called anomic suicides. These categories do more to describe types of suicides than to explain them. Further, as much as the biological approach puts too much emphasis on the inner molecular world, the socio-cultural approach excludes the internal, psychological world. Neither perspective gives a complete answer, but together they give a better picture of what suicide is and how it occurs.

3. Risk factors do not necessarily "explain" suicidal behavior but are those factors which are often found in the backgrounds of suicidal individuals. Five such risk factors include
   a. *Suicidal thoughts and talk*—An estimated 80 percent of suicides are preceded by some kind of warning, either direct or indirect.
   b. *Mental disorders, depressive disorders*—Diagnosable depressive disorders have been implicated in 40 to 60 percent of suicides. About 15 percent of persons with a diagnosis of major depression or bipolar disorder will eventually kill themselves.
   c. *Alcoholism*—This is associated with approximately 25 percent of suicide deaths, and the presence of depression along with alcoholism is a particularly severe risk factor.
   d. *Lethal methods*—Basically, individuals who choose more lethal methods are more likely to complete a suicide than those who use nonlethal methods (e.g., firearms versus pills).
   e. *Isolation, living alone, loss of support*—Being isolated and lacking the support of positive relationships may well limit a person's access to resources that would otherwise counteract hopelessness.

CHAPTER 13

Schizophrenia: Diagnosis and Etiology

LEARNING OBJECTIVES

1. Discuss the general characteristics of schizophrenia (pp. 413-414).

2. Discuss the history of the diagnostic category known as schizophrenia and the current DSM-IV-TR criteria. (pp. 414-415; Table 13.1)

3. Describe the symptoms of schizophrenia, including positive and negative symptoms, delusions, and perceptual distortions. (pp. 415-419; Mental Health & Society)

4. Describe the problems of communication and thought disturbance seen in schizophrenia, including loosening of associations. (p. 419)

5. Describe the motoric disturbances and negative symptoms, and associated features seen in schizophrenia, as well as the role of culture in interpreting symptoms. (pp. 420-423)

6. Differentiate between the various subtypes of schizophrenia, including the paranoid, disorganized, catatonic, undifferentiated, and residual types of schizophrenia. (pp. 423-425)

7. Describe the psychotic disorders once considered schizophrenia including delusional disorder, brief psychotic disorder and schizophreniform disorder, and differentiate them from schizophrenia. Differentiate delusional disorder from paranoid schizophrenia. Describe shared psychotic disorder and schizoaffective disorder. (pp. 426-427; Table 13.2)

8. Describe the three phases of schizophrenia, then discuss research on long-term outcomes of schizophrenia, including studies in developing and developed countries (pp. 427-429; Critical Thinking)

9. Consider the usefulness of combining hereditary and environmental influences for understanding the origins of schizophrenia, then discuss and evaluate the genetic studies, including blood relatives, twin research, adoption and high-risk population studies, and the methodological issues involved with each type of study. (pp. 430-436)

10. Describe the biochemical theories of schizophrenia, including the dopamine hypothesis of schizophrenia and research results that strengthen and weaken this hypothesis. (pp. 436-438; Table 13.4)

11. Describe the neurological impairments, cognitive, and information-processing deficits believed to be associated with schizophrenia. Evaluate the usefulness of a neurological explanation of schizophrenia. (pp. 438-440)

12. Discuss environmental factors in the development of schizophrenic symptoms, including the family environment theories, methodological problems with this research, and the role pf expressed emotion in schizophrenia. (pp. 440-443)

13. Discuss the social class and cross-cultural aspects of schizophrenia (pp. 443-446)

14. Discuss the use of antipsychotic medications in the treatment of schizophrenia and the problems in using these drugs in treatment. Discuss changes in patients' rights to refuse medication. (pp. 446-449; Mental Health & Society; Critical Thinking)

15. Describe the psychosocial therapies including institutional approaches, cognitive-behavioral therapy, Integrated Psychological Therapy, and interventions targeted at relapse prevention by reducing expressed emotion. Discuss the effectiveness of these treatments. (pp. 449-452)

MULTIPLE–CHOICE QUESTIONS

Ans: b
Page: 413
Obj: 1
Type: C

1. Because Jasmine has been hospitalized for this mental disorder so many times, her family's financial resources are very low. When Jasmine is in the acute phase of the disorder, her cognition is severely impaired: She hears voices, firmly holds delusions, and cannot speak coherently. The disorder, which affects about 1 percent of Americans, is called
   a. anxiety.
   b. schizophrenia.
   c. delusional disorder.
   d. major depression.

Ans: a
Page: 414
Obj: 1
Type: A

2. Suppose you looked at the patient records of people diagnosed with schizophrenia at a large psychiatric hospital. You would probably find many more women than men among which of the following groups?
   a. The elderly
   b. African Americans
   c. Teenagers
   d. Hispanic Americans

Ans: d
Page: 414
Obj: 1
Type: A

3. "I have named this organic disorder dementia praecox because insanity comes in youth. The chief symptoms of this terrible illness are hallucinations and delusions, and it is incurable." Who is speaking and about what disorder?
   a. Emil Kraepelin about dissociative identity disorder
   b. Sigmund Freud about schizophrenia
   c. Eugen Bleuler about depression
   d. Emil Kraepelin about schizophrenia

Ans: d
Page: 414
Obj: 1
Type: A

4. "Schizophrenia does not always have an early onset, and it does not always lead to a tragic deterioration in functioning. It is a mental disorder involving self-focus, unconnected ideas, and inappropriate emotions, and its causes involve the interaction of environment and inheritance." Who would be *most likely* to have said this?
   a. Sigmund Freud
   b. Emil Kraepelin
   c. Philippe Pinel
   d. Eugen Bleuler

Ans: b
Page: 3415
Obj: 1
Type: A

5. Charlene has no history of psychological or medical problems, but recently her husband of thirty years died of cancer. Last night she believes she saw her husband sitting in the living room smoking a cigar. Which of the following statements regarding Charlene is probably *accurate*?
   a. Charlene is experiencing auditory hallucinations.
   b. Charlene's perceptual disturbance is probably within the normal limits of behavior, given the loss of her husband.
   c. Charlene's perceptual disturbance is reflective of a slight case of schizophrenia.
   d. Charlene is having a psychotic break caused by the stress over her husband's death.

Ans: a
Page: 415
Obj: 2
Type: C

6. Which statement about the DSM-IV's criteria for diagnosing schizophrenia is *accurate*?
   a. A deterioration in functioning from a previous level must last six months or more.
   b. The chief characteristic of the disorder is uncontrollable emotions.
   c. The criteria are based on subjective judgments, not objective behaviors.
   d. The patient must be delusional.

Ans: d
Page: 415
Obj: 2
Type: C

7. Which of the following symptoms is *critical* for the diagnosis of schizophrenia?
   a. Short-term memory deficits
   b. Fear of being left alone
   c. Feelings of worthlessness
   d. Marked disturbances in thinking

Ans: a
Page: 415
Obj: 3
Type: C

8. There are believed to be three dimensions of schizophrenia. One is psychoticism (hallucinations and delusions). What are the other two?
   a. Disorganization (of thought, affect, and behavior) and negative symptoms
   b. Early onset and long-term deterioration
   c. Disorganization (of thought, affect, and behavior) and obsessions and compulsions
   d. Negative symptoms and unprovoked violence

Ans: b
Page: 416
Obj: 3
Type: A

9. Sylvia says, "I run the FBI, and I know everyone in the Mafia. My husband is Michael Jordan, and Madonna is my sister." Sylvia is suffering from
   a. thought withdrawal.
   b. delusions of grandeur.
   c. auditory hallucinations.
   d. delusions of reference.

Ans: a
Page: 416
Obj: 3
Type: C

10. Delusions of reference are beliefs that
    a. all events revolve around or involve you.
    b. life is absurd and pointless.
    c. other people are stealing your ideas or inserting them in your mind.
    d. everyone is conspiring to kill you.

Ans: c
Page: 416
Obj: 3
Type: A

11. "My father poisons my food, and my mother has hired a hit man to shoot me. My boss is plotting to humiliate me, and my neighbor spies on me." These comments illustrate the schizophrenic symptom called
    a. anhedonia.
    b. catatonia.
    c. delusions of persecution.
    d. delusions of grandeur.

Ans: d
Page: 416
Obj: 3
Type: A

12. Patrick says, "I'm afraid to go to my in-laws' house because I hate them. Whenever I go there, they can hear whenever I think how much I hate them and that I think they should clean their house." What schizophrenic symptom is Patrick displaying?
    a. Thought insertion
    b. Delusions of reference
    c. Nihilistic delusions
    d. Thought broadcasting

Ans: b
Page: 416
Obj: 3
Type: A

13. Angela hears voices that tell her to commit suicide. She also tends to use many neologisms when she speaks and believes that the FBI is spying on her. Which of the following statements regarding Angela is *accurate*?
    a. Angela's negative symptoms are atypical for a psychotic disorder.
    b. Angela exhibits positive symptoms of schizophrenia.
    c. Angela exhibits negative symptoms of schizophrenia.
    d. Angela could be diagnosed with residual schizophrenia.

Ans: a
Page: 416
Obj: 3
Type: C

14. Which term does *not* belong with the rest?
    a. Delusions
    b. Anhedonia
    c. Flat affect
    d. Alogia

Ans: c
Page: 416
Obj: 3
Type: F

15. A false belief that is firmly and consistently held despite contradictory evidence or logic is a
    a. distortion.
    b. loose association.
    c. delusion.
    d. hallucination.

Ans: a
Page: 417
Obj: 3
Type: A

16. Polly thinks that her father and mother have been replaced by two people who are simply acting as her father and mother. She believes that someone found people who look exactly like her parents and exchanged them. Polly's delusion is rare and is called
    a. Capgras's syndrome.
    b. dementia praecox.
    c. delusions of thought broadcasting.
    d. delusions of grandeur.

Ans: a
Page: 417
Obj: 3
Type: C

17. A clinical psychologist is interested in minimizing the delusions in a patient with schizophrenia. The *most* promising method for doing this involves
    a. weakening and then directly challenging the delusions.
    b. relaxation training and response prevention.
    c. exaggeration and humor, followed by aversive conditioning.
    d. agreeing with the delusional ideas until they seem absurd.

Ans: d
Page: 417
Obj: 3
Type: A

18. Eldon, in an interview with his psychologist, is describing the early stages of a schizophrenic episode. Eldon reports that while he was sitting on his front porch one evening, he could hear and see the grass grow. He explained that he could actually see the grass stretching and moving in an upward direction. Eldon's statements are reflective of
a. affective disturbances.
b. nihilistic delusions.
c. delusions of reference.
d. perceptual disturbances.

Ans: a
Page: 417
Obj: 3
Type: A

19. Tuyet-Hoa hears voices in her head. These voices often tell her that she is a bad person and does not deserve to live. Tuyet-Hoa suffers from
a. auditory hallucinations.
b. somatic hallucinations.
c. nihilistic delusions.
d. thought insertion.

Ans: b
Page: 417
Obj: 3
Type: F

20. _____ are sensory perceptions that are not directly attributable to environmental stimuli.
a. Neologisms
b. Hallucinations
c. Delusions
d. Loose associations

Ans: d
Page: 417
Obj: 3
Type: F

21. Which statement about hallucinations is *accurate*?
a. Hallucinations are directly related to environmental stimuli.
b. Hallucinations are pathognomonic to schizophrenia.
c. Hallucinations involve beliefs that are contrary to evidence.
d. Hallucinations seen in schizophrenics tend to be bizarre.

Ans: b
Page: 418
Obj: 3
Type: C

22. Rudolph is experiencing the most common form of hallucination found in schizophrenia. He
a. has no feeling in his fingers or toes.
b. is hearing voices that no one else can hear.
c. is seeing images of God that no one else can see.
d. believes he is being threatened by forces that want to kill him.

Ans: a
Page: 418
Obj: 3
Type: C

23. In what way are hallucinations and delusions related?
a. The voices a person hallucinates often talk about the delusional belief the person holds.
b. Hallucinations involve thoughts, whereas delusions involve perceptual distortions.
c. There is no relationship between the two.
d. The more a person hallucinates, the less he or she has a need for delusions.

Ans: b
Page: 418
Obj: 3
Type: F

24. Individuals who do not have psychotic symptoms and people with schizophrenia have been studied in terms of how they account for their thoughts and feelings. Results show that
   a. only schizophrenic people identify thoughts and feelings as internal stimuli.
   b. only schizophrenic people attribute thoughts and feelings to sources outside themselves.
   c. both schizophrenic and nonschizophrenic people identify thoughts and feelings as internal stimuli.
   d. both schizophrenic and nonschizophrenic people do not have a well-developed way of accounting for thoughts and feelings.

Ans: c
Page: 419
Obj: 4
Type: F

25. Romme et al. (1992) studied 186 schizophrenic individuals who had hallucinations. They found that distraction, ignoring, and selective listening were
   a. ineffective strategies for reducing or preventing these psychotic symptoms.
   b. of use only for negative symptoms such as hallucinations.
   c. effective coping strategies to reduce or prevent psychotic symptoms.
   d. methods therapists used to eliminate the hallucinations.

Ans: d
Page: 419
Obj: 4
Type: C

26. A clinical psychologist does an assessment of a deaf person who is believed to have schizophrenia. Based on a recent investigation,
   a. the person will show only negative symptoms.
   b. only hallucinations will be found; there will be no communication disorder when the person uses sign language.
   c. the person will refuse to use sign language to communicate.
   d. the person's use of sign language will show communication disturbances similar to those of hearing patients.

Ans: c
Page: 419
Obj: 4
Type: A

27. Virginia says, "My thoughts do not come out with me in control. A powerful chaos takes over, and my brain chooses what my mouth says. I just get lost." Virginia is describing which symptom(s) of schizophrenia?
   a. Ideas of reference
   b. Negative affective symptoms
   c. Loosening of associations
   d. Neologisms

Ans: a
Page: 419
Obj: 4
Type: A

28. Daria has been diagnosed with schizophrenia and is being given an intelligence test. The examiner asks Daria what it means when one says, "Strike while the iron is hot." Daria replies, "You cannot iron clothes with a cold iron." Daria's response demonstrates
   a. concrete thinking.
   b. the use of neologisms.
   c. delusional thinking.
   d. poverty of speech.

Ans: a
Page: 420
Obj: 5
Type: A

29. Stefan and Darnell have been diagnosed with schizophrenia. Stefan walks around the room rapidly, talking endlessly and swinging his arms. Darnell stands in one position for hours at a time, responding to nothing.
    a. Both Stefan's and Darnell's behavior occurs in schizophrenia.
    b. Stefan's behavior is typical of schizophrenia; Darnell's is extremely unlikely.
    c. Stefan's behavior never occurs in schizophrenia; Darnell's behavior is typical of schizophrenia.
    d. Neither Stefan's nor Darnell's behavior occurs in schizophrenia.

Ans: b
Page: 420
Obj: 5
Type: C

30. Mary suffers from schizophrenia and usually shows a total lack of emotion. We cannot diagnose her as having primary symptoms of schizophrenia unless
    a. she shows the symptoms of catatonic schizophrenia.
    b. we can rule out the effects of medicine or institutionalization.
    c. we see a complete absence of delusions.
    d. she also shows loosening of associations.

Ans: d
Page: 403
Obj: 5
Type: F

31. The abnormal lack of emotion seen in schizophrenics is termed
    a. emotional rigidity.
    b. affective apathy.
    c. catatonia.
    d. flat affect.

Ans: c
Page: 421
Obj: 5
Type: A

32. Quincy is diagnosed as having schizophrenia because he shows negative symptoms. Which of the following symptoms is likely to be seen in Quincy?
    a. Auditory and visual hallucinations
    b. Neologisms and other symptoms of thought disturbance
    c. Lack of motivation and restricted affect
    d. Wild, inappropriate expression of emotions

Ans: a
Page: 422
Obj: 5
Type: A

33. Which schizophrenic is most likely to be described as rigid, compulsive, withdrawn, and passive?
    a. Anjin, who is Japanese
    b. Paddy, who is Irish-American
    c. Gianni, who is Italian-American
    d. Shlomo, who is Israeli

Ans: a
Page: 424
Obj: 6
Type: A

34. Craig is convinced that the CIA is trying to kill him. He wants to keep a knife under his pillow so that he can stab them before they smother him. Craig illustrates
    a. delusions of persecution.
    b. delusions of grandeur.
    c. delusions of reference.
    d. nihilistic delusions.

Ans: c
Page: 424
Obj: 6
Type: C

35. Shevawn has been diagnosed with paranoid schizophrenia. Her symptoms include false beliefs that she is being followed, flat affect, and auditory hallucinations. What symptom makes a diagnosis of paranoid schizophrenia *inappropriate*?
    a. None of Shevawn's symptoms are inappropriate for the diagnosis.
    b. Paranoid schizophrenics do not have delusions.
    c. Paranoid schizophrenics do not show flat affect.
    d. Paranoid schizophrenics do not have auditory hallucinations.

Ans: a
Page: 424
Obj: 6
Type: C

36. Louis has a number of delusional ideas. How can we tell if he suffers from paranoid schizophrenia rather than delusional disorder?
    a. If functioning is normal in areas unrelated to the delusions, it is delusional disorder.
    b. If there is no symptom other than the delusions, it is paranoid schizophrenia.
    c. If the delusions have lasted less than six weeks, it is paranoid schizophrenia.
    d. If the delusions are very bizarre, it is delusional disorder.

Ans: a
Page: 424
Obj: 6
Type: A

37. Jennie "receives" secret messages from Brad Pitt every time she watches him on television talk shows or in movies. She believes he is in love with her and is telling her that he is planning to leave his wife to be with her. Jennie is most likely suffering from which delusional disorder?
    a. Erotomania
    b. Grandiosity
    c. Jealousy
    d. Persecution

Ans: a
Page: 425
Obj: 6
Type: A

38. Marlene giggles most of the time, fantasizes aloud, and speaks in an incoherent and absurd manner. Her behavior is extremely bizarre and childish. She matches the common conception of "crazy" and has been this way since childhood. The *best* diagnosis is _____ schizophrenia.
    a. disorganized
    b. residual
    c. undifferentiated
    d. catatonic

Ans: c
Page: 425
Obj: 6
Type: C

39. Ardell had a schizophrenic episode ten years ago. He was treated successfully with medication and returned to work. Nonetheless, Ardell still has some problems, including peculiar mannerisms and thoughts and unusual affect. What diagnosis *best* characterizes Ardell?
    a. Schizoid personality disorder
    b. Undifferentiated schizophrenia
    c. Residual schizophrenia
    d. No DSM-IV diagnosis since his schizophrenic episode was ten years ago

Ans: c
Page: 425
Obj: 6
Type: A

40. Milton frightened his family with his wild talking and frantic activity. Confined in a mental hospital for several days, he became completely immobile. He would take awkward postures for hours on end and allow himself to be "arranged" by others. What is the *most likely* diagnosis for Milton?
    a. Disorganized schizophrenia
    b. Bipolar schizophrenia
    c. Catatonic schizophrenia
    d. Paranoid schizophrenia

Ans: d
Page: 425
Obj: 6
Type: C

41. Which of the following descriptions does *not* match up with the diagnosis?
    a. John thinks his thoughts are being broadcast on TV—paranoid schizophrenia.
    b. Sarah hears voices and says neologisms—positive symptoms.
    c. Karen stands in one awkward position for hours—catatonic schizophrenia.
    d. Theodore shows many signs of bizarre thoughts and behavior—residual schizophrenia.

Ans: c
Page: 426
Obj: 7
Type: F

42. Among the psychotic disorders once considered schizophrenia, _____ lasts one month or less.
  a. Capgras's syndrome
  b. schizophreniform disorder
  c. brief psychotic disorder
  d. delusional disorder

Ans: b
Page: 426
Obj: 7
Type: A

43. Herman's thinking processes have been disturbed, and he has complained of hearing voices for the past four months. What can be said of his condition?
  a. He is less likely to recover than if he had schizophrenia.
  b. He should be diagnosed as having schizophreniform disorder.
  c. He is in the residual phase of schizophrenia.
  d. He should be diagnosed as having a non-psychotic delusional disorder.

Ans: d
Page: 426
Obj: 7
Type: C

44. Dr. Henderson is trying to decide whether a new patient should be diagnosed as suffering from schizophrenia, schizophreniform disorder, or brief psychotic disorder. The information she should use is
  a. whether there are positive or negative symptoms.
  b. the pathognomonic symptoms of schizophrenia.
  c. whether the person is old or young.
  d. how long the symptoms have lasted.

Ans: d
Page: 427
Obj: 7
Type: A

45. Lydia Tan has been living with her paranoid schizophrenic husband on an isolated farm for so long that she has come to accept his irrational beliefs. When she visits her sister, her delusions weaken. Mrs. Tan's condition is called
  a. schizophreniform disorder.
  b. Capgras's syndrome.
  c. schizoaffective disorder.
  d. shared psychotic disorder.

Ans: b
Page: 427
Obj: 7
Type: C

46. Jodie was diagnosed with schizoaffective disorder. In addition to cognitive disturbances such as loosening of associations and delusions, we would expect that she
  a. developed the disorder in response to a stressful event.
  b. has experienced periods of extreme depression.
  c. shows motor disturbances such as waxy flexibility.
  d. has negative symptoms such as alogia and neologisms.

Ans: d
Page: 427
Obj: 8
Type: C

47. Iris, usually involved with her friends, has become withdrawn and isolated. She has stopped taking showers and changing her clothes. When asked what she is thinking, she describes, in scattered phrases, a frightening inner world of demons and threats. These symptoms illustrate the _____ phase of schizophrenia.
  a. reactive
  b. residual
  c. active
  d. prodromal

Ans: c
Page: 427
Obj: 8
Type: F

48. Which ordering of the phases of schizophrenia is *accurate*?
  a. Prodromal, residual, active
  b. Active, prodromal, residual
  c. Prodromal, active, residual
  d. Active, residual, prodromal

Ans: b
Page: 428
Obj: 8
Type: A

49. A researcher wants to do long-term outcome research on people with schizophrenia. She looks at those who were diagnosed in 1960 and those who were diagnosed in 1980 (after the DSM-III was published). One problem the researcher faces is the fact that
   a. definitions of recovery have changed since the DSM-III was published.
   b. the DSM-III redefined schizophrenia to be a chronic condition.
   c. treatment was not available in 1960.
   d. schizophrenia used to be considered a chronic disorder.

Ans: c
Page: 429
Obj: 8
Type: A

50. Imagine that Emil Kraepelin came back to earth and saw the results of contemporary follow-up studies of treated schizophrenics. Which of these reactions could we expect from him?
   a. "I used to say that schizophrenia involves rapid deterioration followed by a slow recovery in men but not women; the results support me."
   b. "I always knew that schizophrenics never recover; now I have been proved correct."
   c. "I am shocked; I never thought so many schizophrenics could recover."
   d. "I always knew that schizophrenia was a disorder with many possible outcomes; the research proves me correct."

Ans: c
Page: 430
Obj: 9
Type: C

51. Nadine, age twelve, lives with her mother, who was diagnosed with schizophrenia, and her alcoholic father. The family argues constantly. According to _____, Nadine's chances of developing schizophrenia herself are higher than the average person because _____.
   a. psychosocial theorists; alcoholism in fathers produces schizophrenia in daughters
   b. biological theorists; of poor family communication
   c. biological theorists; she inherited a genetic vulnerability
   d. psychosocial theorists; she inherited a genetic vulnerability

Ans: a
Page: 431
Obj: 9
Type: F

52. According to Meehl's proposed wager, the *best* way to select a schizophrenic out of a large sample would be to
   a. find someone whose identical twin was a schizophrenic.
   b. learn the person's blood type.
   c. find someone whose parents were overprotective but hostile.
   d. measure the size of the person's skull.

Ans: d
Page: 431
Obj: 9
Type: F

53. Which statement about research on the genetics of schizophrenia is *accurate*?
   a. Too little genetic research has been done to come to any conclusions.
   b. Very few people believe that heredity plays a major role in causing schizophrenia.
   c. Such research shows that schizophrenia occurs only among identical and fraternal twins.
   d. Although there is much controversy, evidence indicates that genetic factors play an important causal role.

Ans: b
Page: 431
Obj: 9
Type: C

54. A twins study is performed. The results show that the concordance rate for monozygotic (MZ) twins is 70 percent, but the concordance rate for dyzygotic (DZ) twins is 15 percent. Which interpretation of the results is *most* accurate?
   a. The cause of the disorder must have a strong environmental component.
   b. The cause of the disorder is overwhelmingly genetic in origin.
   c. The disorder is more likely to be found in fraternal twins than in identical twins.
   d. The disorder will occur only when the twins are identical.

Ans: b
Page: 432
Obj: 9
Type: C

55. Why is an adoption study superior to a twins study?
     a.   Because adoption studies allow one to control for the degree of genetic similarity in the probands
     b.   Because twins usually share the same family environment
     c.   Because adopted children have greater stress levels than twins reared at home
     d.   Because very few people are twins, but many people are adopted

Ans: c
Page: 432
Obj: 9
Type: F

56. The results of Heston's (1966) research indicate that
     a.   none of the adoptees with schizophrenic mothers developed schizophrenia.
     b.   all the adoptees with schizophrenic mothers developed schizophrenia.
     c.   none of the adoptees in the control group developed schizophrenia.
     d.   only the adoptees who had high levels of life stress developed schizophrenia.

Ans: d
Page: 433
Obj: 9
Type: A

57. Jason's mother was diagnosed with schizophrenia and gave Jason up for adoption when he was six days old. Based on Heston's (1966) research, what can we predict about Jason's mental health?
     a.   There is an increased likelihood of schizophrenia but no other form of mental disorder.
     b.   There is no increased likelihood of schizophrenia.
     c.   There is an increased likelihood of other mental disorders but not schizophrenia.
     d.   There is nearly a one-in-two chance that he will be creative and well-adjusted as an adult.

Ans: a
Page: 434
Obj: 9
Type: F

58. Kety et al. (1994) report the results of a study that identified the characteristics of adoptive children who developed schizophrenia and those of children who did not. The *most* important distinguishing factor turned out to be
     a.   the degree of psychopathology in the biological family.
     b.   the age at which the child was adopted.
     c.   the degree of stress in the adoptive home.
     d.   whether the biological parent had taken drugs during pregnancy.

Ans: b
Page: 434
Obj: 9
Type: A

59. Dave is thirty years old and was raised by an adoptive mother who was diagnosed with schizophrenia. His biological mother did not suffer from the disorder. Research by Wender et al. (1977) suggests that
     a.   Dave has a 50 percent chance of being diagnosed with a schizophrenia-spectrum disorder.
     b.   Dave has no more chance of developing schizophrenia than anyone else.
     c.   Dave has a 50 percent chance of being diagnosed with schizophrenia.
     d.   Dave has a much greater chance of being diagnosed with schizophrenia than a person who was raised by a non-schizophrenic mother.

Ans: d
Page: 434
Obj: 9
Type: F

60. The advantage of high-risk studies of schizophrenia is that they are
     a.   experimental; they randomly assign subjects to groups.
     b.   controlled; the influence of genes is separated from that of environment.
     c.   correlational; they examine the influence of an independent variable on the dependent variable.
     d.   developmental; they allow observation over time.

Ans: b
Page: 434
Obj: 9
Type: A

61. Based on Mednick and associates' high-risk research on schizophrenia, children whose mothers have schizophrenia are more likely to develop the disorder if
    a. their mothers had relatively mild cases of schizophrenia.
    b. their mothers had serious pregnancy or birth complications.
    c. they were seen by their teachers as passive and dependent.
    d. their autonomic reactions recover quickly when exposed to stimuli.

Ans: a
Page: 434
Obj: 9
Type: C

62. The Israeli study of children who developed schizophrenia is considered prospective. This means that
    a. the studies began before the onset of the disorder.
    b. no one knows whether the child's mother was diagnosed with schizophrenia or not.
    c. the studies began as soon as the children displayed symptoms of the disorder.
    d. the studies do not include a control group.

Ans: c
Page: 435
Obj: 9
Type: A

63. Based on the results of the Israeli high-risk study that compared children with schizophrenic and non-schizophrenic mothers who were raised in a kibbutz or a suburban town, what advice would you give health officials about predicting psychopathology?
    a. Only children raised in suburban towns develop schizophrenia or personality disorders.
    b. High-risk children are vulnerable only to schizophrenia, not to other disorders.
    c. High-risk children are vulnerable to schizophrenia and other disorders.
    d. Only children raised on kibbutzes develop schizophrenia or major affective disorders.

Ans: a
Page: 436
Obj: 9
Type: A

64. Anisa's mother was diagnosed with schizophrenia. Based on the Israeli high-risk study, Anisa's chances of developing schizophrenia herself are
    a. increased only if she does not receive adequate parenting.
    b. between 50 and 75 percent.
    c. no greater than those of children whose mothers did not suffer from schizophrenia.
    d. high if she was seen as outgoing and highly involved with other children while in school.

Ans: d
Page: 436
Obj: 10
Type: C

65. Which description of the history of biochemical explanations for schizophrenia is *accurate*?
    a. Until the 1950s, very little theorizing or research had been done on biochemical explanations.
    b. It has always been assumed that the cause of schizophrenia was related to diet.
    c. Generally, when a researcher discovers an abnormal amount of a chemical in schizophrenics, other researchers confirm this.
    d. Most discoveries concerning biochemical abnormalities have not been replicated.

Ans: b
Page: 436
Obj: 10
Type: A

66. A pharmaceutical company interested in new drugs for treating schizophrenia would want ones that
    a. increase adrenalin levels.
    b. decrease dopamine levels.
    c. act like amphetamine.
    d. increase dopamine levels.

Ans: d
Page: 436
Obj: 10
Type: C

67. The dopamine hypothesis is supported by evidence that
   a. a drug that increases dopamine activity reduces symptoms.
   b. high levels of dopamine are found in people with Parkinson's disease.
   c. high-risk children have lower dopamine levels.
   d. a drug that blocks dopamine activity reduces symptoms.

Ans: d
Page: 436
Obj: 10
Type: A

68. A physician prescribes phenothiazines to a person with schizophrenia. If the person's symptoms are not reduced,
   a. another drug such as L-dopa might be used.
   b. another drug such as amphetamine might be used.
   c. there should be no surprise since phenothiazines increase dopamine activity.
   d. there should be no surprise since one-quarter of schizophrenic patients respond very little to these drugs.

Ans: b
Page: 438
Obj: 10
Type: A

69. Hiroki, who has been diagnosed with schizophrenia, went to the hospital, where imaging techniques showed that he has extensive neuronal loss in his brain and enlarged ventricles. We can guess that Hiroki
   a. will respond quickly to antipsychotic medications and recover.
   b. demonstrates the negative symptoms of the disorder.
   c. never really had schizophrenia.
   d. is actively delusional and hallucinatory.

Ans: a
Page: 438
Obj: 11
Type: F

70. Brain imaging techniques have identified areas of the brain where individuals with schizophrenia have impaired functioning. One of the *most* important areas is the
   a. frontal lobes.
   b. medulla.
   c. occipital lobes.
   d. cerebellum.

Ans: d
Page: 439
Obj: 11
Type: A

71. Ron and Jon are identical twins, but only Jon shows the symptoms of schizophrenia. Brain imaging techniques are *most likely* to show that Jon has
   a. more brain tissue than Ron.
   b. smaller than normal ventricles.
   c. excessive dopamine activity in the frontal lobes.
   d. decreased blood flow in brain areas involved in attention and planning.

Ans: b
Page: 439
Obj: 11
Type: C

72. A researcher investigating the cause of schizophrenia uses the Eye Movement Dysfunction Measure and the Visual Continuous Performance Test to assess individuals with the disorder. The researcher's goal is probably to
   a. discover the relapse rate of individuals given neuroleptics.
   b. identify cognitive markers for schizophrenia.
   c. relate brain abnormalities to the individuals' inheritance of schizophrenia.
   d. distinguish negative symptoms from positive symptoms.

Ans: d
Page: 439
Obj: 11
Type: C

73. Dr. Wallace adheres to family process theories. When she interviews family members of a schizophrenic patient, she is likely to look for
   a. a schizophrenogenic mother.
   b. cognitive markers.
   c. poor modeling by parents and siblings.
   d. unclear or inconsistent communication patterns.

Ans: a
Page: 440
Obj: 12
Type: F

74. Which statement *best* answers the question, "Do environmental factors cause schizophrenia?"
  a. "Since concordance rates are less than 50 percent in identical twins, environmental factors must play a causal role."
  b. "Environmental factors such as poor family communication are usually caused by schizophrenia, not the other way around."
  c. "There is little evidence that environmental factors contribute to the disorder."
  d. "If environmental influences play a causal role, it is probably in adulthood, close to the time when symptoms first appear."

Ans: c
Page: 441
Obj: 12
Type: C

75. Which woman illustrates the "schizophrenogenic mother"?
  a. A physically attractive but flighty woman who must have all the family's attention focused on her
  b. An anxious woman who compulsively cleans her house
  c. An overprotective woman who coldly rejects her children's attempts at gaining affection
  d. A career-oriented woman who is unaware of and uninterested in her children's achievements

Ans: c
Page: 441
Obj: 12
Type: A

76. Which of the following is an example of what Bateson described as a "double-bind communication"?
  a. Becoming stiff and rigid when you are angry at your child
  b. Ignoring a child's request for attention when he or she is physically hurt and crying
  c. Telling your child you are proud of his or her artwork while you throw it in the trash
  d. Telling a child she cannot go outside to play, even though you know she really wants to leave the house

Ans: a
Page: 442
Obj: 12
Type: F

77. Even if a strong correlation is found between poor communication patterns in families and the presence of a schizophrenic child, researchers cannot tell
  a. whether the communication patterns are the cause or the effect of the disorder.
  b. what a suitable control group might be in which schizophrenia does not occur.
  c. whether there has been any stress in the family.
  d. whether the schizophrenia is severe.

Ans: c
Page: 442
Obj: 12
Type: C

78. Steve has just been discharged from the hospital with the diagnosis of residual schizophrenia. Steve's family is marked by high levels of intra-familial criticism, hostility, and emotional over-involvement. Which of the following statements is *accurate*?
  a. Steve's family environment probably influenced the onset of his disorder but will have little impact on his rate of relapse.
  b. Given Steve's diagnosis, his chances of relapse are minimal.
  c. Steve has a greater chance of relapse if he returns to his family than if he does not.
  d. Steve's family would receive a low EE score.

Ans: b
Page: 442
Obj: 12
Type: A

79. Laura is seventeen and has been diagnosed with schizophrenia. Her father often says to her, "You never tell me what's going on in your life. You keep secrets and make terrible mistakes in judgment. I want what's best for you, but you must change your attitude and start behaving like a human being!" The father's comments *best* illustrate which factor in schizophrenia?
    a. Diathesis-stress
    b. Expressed emotion
    c. Cognitive impairment
    d. Double-bind communications

Ans: a
Page: 442
Obj: 12
Type: C

80. Expressed emotion has been shown to have which of the following relationships to schizophrenia?
    a. Families with high expressed emotion are most likely to see relapse in their schizophrenic members.
    b. Families with high expressed emotion are least likely to see relapse in their schizophrenic members.
    c. High expressed emotion causes schizophrenic thought disturbance in children.
    d. High expressed emotion is a genetically determined trait in schizophrenics with positive symptoms.

Ans: d
Page: 444
Obj: 13
Type: A

81. A family therapist interested in cross-cultural studies of psychopathology would find that high expressed emotion
    a. has little or no effect on relapse among Mexican Americans with schizophrenia.
    b. is much more likely to occur in developing countries such as India than in the United States and other Western cultures.
    c. is found only in the families of people who have schizophrenic relatives.
    d. is more likely in the families of schizophrenic patients living in the United States and other Western cultures.

Ans: b
Page: 443
Obj: 13
Type: F

82. Which statement *best* describes the relationship between schizophrenia and social class?
    a. There is no consistent relationship between schizophrenia and social class.
    b. Schizophrenia is most common in the lower classes.
    c. Schizophrenia is found equally in all social classes.
    d. Schizophrenia is most common in the upper classes.

Ans: d
Page: 443
Obj: 13
Type: A

83. In which geographic location is schizophrenia *most* usually found?
    a. Among the elderly members of an exclusive country club
    b. In suburban areas outside cities
    c. In small towns and farm communities
    d. In the poorest areas of large cities

Ans: b
Page: 444
Obj: 13
Type: C

84. There are two theories to explain the correlation between schizophrenia and low socioeconomic status. One, focusing on the stressfulness of poverty, is called the _____ hypothesis. The other, focusing on the loss of income after one becomes sick and cannot function, is called the _____ hypothesis.
    a. diathesis-stress; psychophysiological
    b. breeder; downward drift
    c. diathesis-stress; double-bind
    d. cross-cultural; diathesis-stress

Ans: b
Page: 444
Obj: 13
Type: A

85. Which story supports the downward drift theory of schizophrenia?
    a. Jesse was born in poverty and became psychotic because the stress of crime and hunger was too much for him.
    b. Angela, the daughter of a dentist, lives in poverty because her schizophrenic symptoms prevent her from holding down a job.
    c. Keith, when first diagnosed with schizophrenia, had no delusions but now shows both delusions and hallucinations.
    d. Louis, the son of parents who were over-involved and hypercritical, develops schizophrenia in his mid-twenties.

Ans: c
Page: 444
Obj: 13
Type: A

86. A young man has a brief psychotic reaction that his doctor calls a "possession syndrome." It turns out that the young man was responding to a severe stress in his life and makes a good recovery afterward. This case is *most likely* to have occurred in a
    a. person suffering from disorganized schizophrenia.
    b. developed country such as the United States.
    c. less developed country.
    d. wealthy suburban neighborhood.

Ans: b
Page: 444
Obj: 13
Type: A

87. Since cultural norms affect the symptoms of hospitalized schizophrenic patients, which of the following cases may show negative symptoms associated with schizophrenia?
    a. Lars, a person from a traditional Swedish background
    b. Toshiko, a person from a traditional Japanese background
    c. Seamus, a person from a traditional Irish background
    d. Alberto, a person from a traditional Italian background

Ans: d
Page: 444
Obj: 13
Type: C

88. Which statement *best* describes the diathesis-stress model?
    a. Unconscious conflicts make some individuals very vulnerable to schizophrenia.
    b. The stress of separating identical twins may contribute to the development of schizophrenia-like symptoms.
    c. Dopamine activity leads to exaggerated responses to stress, which in turn result in schizophrenic symptoms.
    d. Individuals with genetic vulnerability develop schizophrenia if exposed to high levels of stress.

Ans: b
Page: 444
Obj: 13
Type: C

89. Which statement about the diathesis-stress model is *accurate*?
    a. It argues that there is a single cause for schizophrenic disorders.
    b. It argues that predispositions interact with environmental factors to cause schizophrenia.
    c. It proposes that, given a certain level of stress, anyone can develop schizophrenia.
    d. It proposes that stress is a cause of schizophrenia only in cultures experiencing great upheaval.

Ans: b
Page: 446
Obj: 13
Type: A

90. Nathan's grandfather and mother had schizophrenia. He has difficulty sustaining attention and has a stressful life. He may *not* experience psychotic episodes if he
    a. lives with a family that shows high expressed emotion.
    b. has good coping skills and contact with social support.
    c. refuses to take antipsychotic medication.
    d. has very high levels of dopamine.

Ans: c
Page: 446
Obj: 14
Type: A

91. Suppose you looked at the medical records of people treated for schizophrenia in the 1940s. You would *most likely* find that their treatment included
    a. tardive dyskinesia.
    b. antipsychotic drugs.
    c. prefrontal lobotomy.
    d. the drug Clozapine.

Ans: a
Page: 447
Obj: 14
Type: A

92. Norma enters a psychiatric hospital. She is diagnosed with paranoid schizophrenia. Which type of treatment is *most likely* to be offered?
    a. Antipsychotic medication and psychosocial therapy
    b. Electroshock therapy
    c. Prefrontal lobotomy
    d. Covert sensitization and antidepressant medication

Ans: c
Page: 447
Obj: 14
Type: A

93. Tina was diagnosed with schizophrenia ten years ago and was given Thorazine and Haldol, but neither was very helpful. Last year she was put on a newer drug that has been effective and has had few side effects. However, if the drug is abruptly stopped, she will experience more symptom rebound than with other drugs. This new drug is called
    a. Haldol.
    b. L-dopa.
    c. Clozapine.
    d. Thorazine.

Ans: b
Page: 447
Obj: 14
Type: A

94. Webster has been treated for schizophrenia for twenty years. He wants to avoid the risk of tardive dyskinesia. The way to do this
    a. requires an increase in the expressed emotion in his family.
    b. is to decrease his dosage of antipsychotic drugs.
    c. avoid taking Clozapine, and restrict medication only to the drug Thorazine.
    d. involves psychosocial therapies that teach social skills.

Ans: d
Page: 447
Obj: 14
Type: C

95. You are a child psychologist doing an evaluation of an eight-year-old girl, Ramona. After you finish interviewing Ramona, you talk with her mother to get a history. During your discussion with Ramona's mother, you notice that she often smacks her lips, blinks her eyes, and thrusts her tongue out of her mouth. With what additional information do these observations of Ramona's mother provide you?
    a. It suggests that Ramona's mother is in the early stages of Parkinson's disease.
    b. It suggests that Ramona's mother is nervous and might have something to hide.
    c. It suggests that Ramona's mother is high on "speed" or "crack."
    d. It suggests that Ramona's mother has been taking an antipsychotic medication for some time and thus might have schizophrenia.

Ans: a
Page: 447
Obj: 14
Type: A

96. At Lakeside Psychiatric Hospital, patients with schizophrenia get the kind of treatment that most clinicians now agree is *most* beneficial:
    a. antipsychotic medication and psychotherapy.
    b. electroshock therapy and individual psychotherapy.
    c. neuroleptic medication.
    d. individual psychotherapy.

Ans: c
Page: 449
Obj: 15
Type: F

97. Because medicated and adequately functioning individuals with schizophrenia have been discharged from hospitals to stressful environments, the *most* logical change in treatment is to
   a. provide aversive conditioning therapy.
   b. reduce the dosage of medication these people take.
   c. involve these people in outpatient therapy.
   d. make the criteria for readmission to the hospital quite strict.

Ans: a
Page: 450
Obj: 15
Type: A

98. A psychologist uses the research of Kingdon and Turkington (1991) to treat individuals with schizophrenia in such a way that they require little medication or hospitalization to function. What components does this therapy have?
   a. Providing patients with understandable explanations and analytic skills to cope with hallucinations and delusions
   b. Role playing and social skills training to increase the amount of expressed emotion the patients can show
   c. Eye movement training to increase attention span and cognitive skills
   d. Increased decision making by patients on a hospital ward so that they can govern themselves

Ans: c
Page: 450
Obj: 15
Type: C

99. Suppose a group of chronic schizophrenics were taught to recognize and respond to social cues and to retrieve appropriate information so that they could communicate clearly. Further, suppose they were taught social skills through role playing. This would illustrate
   a. intervention to reduce expressed emotion.
   b. assertiveness training.
   c. Integrated Psychological Therapy.
   d. milieu therapy.

Ans: c
Page: 450
Obj: 15
Type: C

100. To reduce the relapse rate of the many schizophrenic patients who return to live with their families, a new type of intervention makes use of
   a. psychoanalytic approaches to improving dream interpretation.
   b. family systems methods of getting families to express greater emotion.
   c. behavioral approaches to reduce expressed emotion in family members.
   d. medicines that increase the expression of emotion.

ESSAY QUESTIONS

1. Identify four different clinical characteristics of schizophrenia, and describe the symptoms associated with these characteristics.

2. Compare and contrast the symptoms of catatonic and undifferentiated schizophrenia. To what extent do they involve negative symptoms?

3. Describe a comprehensive treatment approach to schizophrenia that would not only be effective but also reduce the risk of relapse.

SAMPLE ANSWERS

1. The clinical characteristics of schizophrenia can be divided into four, rather global, categories: disturbance of thought and language, perceptual disturbances, affective disturbances, and behavioral disturbances.

   Disturbances of thought and language might involve the following problems:

   a. *Loose associations*—This occurs when an individual has trouble maintaining a consistent train of thought, often changing from one subject to another without any apparent connection between topics.

   b. *Concrete thinking*—This reflects a reduced ability to deal with abstractions and is often observed in an individual's very literal interpretations.

   c. *Peculiar word usage*—Individuals may use words simply because of the way they sound (i.e., clang associations), sometimes they will make up new words (i.e., neologisms), and sometimes they will use speech that is adequate in form but conveys little information because it repeats simple phrases or is overly abstract (i.e., poverty of speech).

   d. *Delusions*—This refers to false beliefs that have no basis in and are not influenced by reality. Delusions may involve believing in one's own special powers or greatness (i.e., delusions of grandeur), believing that others are plotting against you (i.e., delusions of persecution), believing that others can hear your thoughts (i.e., thought broadcasting), or believing that others are putting thoughts into your head (i.e., thought insertion).

   Perceptual disturbances most typically take the form of hallucinations, with auditory and visual hallucinations being the most common.

   Affective disturbances may take the form of flat affect, inappropriate affect, or anhedonia. *Flat affect* refers to lack of emotional expression and speaking in a monotone voice. *Inappropriate affect* refers to exhibiting inappropriate emotions, e.g., laughing at a sad story or crying when something is funny. Finally, *anhedonia* refers to a lack of enjoyment and lack of pleasure in any activity.

   Behavioral disturbances constitute the final category and may involve peculiar mannerisms, postures, or facial expressions; reduced spontaneous movement; social withdrawal or inappropriate social behavior; impairment in social relatedness; and lack of motivation.

2. Catatonic schizophrenia is a relatively rare form in which the central feature is motor disturbance. In one phase of the disorder, individuals are excessively active—hypertalkative, gesturing wildly, and pacing the floor. In another phase, they become immobile. In fact, catatonics can adopt a position and not move for hours. They either reject any changes in their posture by others or allow themselves to be "arranged," a symptom called waxy flexibility. In this catatonic stupor, individuals are mute and extremely withdrawn.

   Undifferentiated schizophrenia is a form of the disorder in which no one feature (delusions, thought disturbance, or motor abnormalities) is sufficiently prominent to warrant a diagnosis of one of the other forms of schizophrenia. This miscellaneous category includes diffuse and less intense positive symptoms.

   Catatonic schizophrenia has elements of negative symptoms: extreme social withdrawal and apathy. Clearly, the lack of movement corresponds with the avolition of negative symptom schizophrenia. However, catatonic schizophrenia is much rarer than negative symptom schizophrenia. Also, the lack of speech is not the same as alogia, which entails a lack of meaningful speech rather than complete mutism. By comparison, undifferentiated schizophrenia is a mixture of positive symptoms rather than negative ones.

3. A comprehensive treatment program would include antipsychotic medications (neuroleptics), psychosocial therapy, and skills training for both the individual and the family. It is quite clear that neuroleptics are effective in reducing symptoms in roughly three-quarters of individuals with schizophrenia. In the remainder, Clozapine is a drug that holds promise. Excessively high doses of these drugs can cause serious side effects and, over long periods of time, the involuntary movements of tardive dyskinesia. For these reasons, a comprehensive treatment approach should monitor drug dosage so that it is at the lowest level while still controlling symptoms.

At the same time, psychosocial therapies should be used to help individuals with schizophrenia gain control of their lives. Milieu therapy in hospital environments provides training in decision making and planning that schizophrenic patients need. Cognitive-behavioral treatments teach necessary coping and social skills. A cognitive therapy devised by Kingdon and Turkington (1991) provided patients with explanations for their delusions and hallucinations and taught them to analyze situations skillfully. These patients' symptoms were alleviated without the need for much medication. Integrated Psychological Therapy, a highly effective therapy, helps patients identify their cognitive deficits and provides skills to overcome them.

However, since more than half of recovering patients return to live with their parents, treatment must extend to training in family communication—ways to reduce expressed emotion. Therapies that provide information to families about the nature of schizophrenia and methods of communicating without expressed emotion have greatly reduced relapse rates. Individuals with schizophrenia also need to learn coping skills so that they can identify and respond appropriately when family members become emotional. In sum, treatment should combine low but effective levels of medication, psychosocial and cognitive-behavior training, and family interventions designed to reduce relapse. Family and social skills training has proved to be more effective in preventing relapse than drug treatment alone.

CHAPTER 14
Cognitive Disorders

LEARNING OBJECTIVES

1. Define cognitive disorders and discuss their possible causes. Compare the prevalence rate for different population groups. List the DSM-IV-TR categories of cognitive disorders and differentiate these disorders from other disorders involving cognitive problems that are not part of the cognitive disorders group. (pp. 455-458)

2. Describe the methods for assessing brain damage and the problem of linking functional loss to a specific brain location. (pp. 458-460)

3. Describe the dimensions by which brain damage is categorized. (pp. 460-461; Table 14.1)

4. Describe how cognitive disorders are categorized by cause and the problems in diagnosing cognitive disorders. (pp. 461-462)

5. Describe and differentiate dementia and delirium and discuss the possible causes of these disorders. (pp. 462-465; Mental Health & Society)

6. Describe the amnestic disorders and differentiate them from dementia and delirium. (p. 465)

7. List and differentiate the types of brain traumas, their symptoms and aftereffects. (pp. 466-467)

8. Describe the health conditions that accompany old age, including the nature and effects of, and risk factors for, cerebrovascular accidents (strokes) and vascular dementia. (pp. 467-468)

9. Discuss the extent and reasons for memory loss in older people. Discuss the characteristics of Alzheimer's disease, brain abnormalities, and what is known about its cause. (pp. 469-472; Mental Health & Society)

10. Describe and differentiate among the following: Parkinson's disease, AIDS-related dementia, neurosyphilis (general paresis), encephalitis, meningitis, Huntington's chorea, cerebral tumors, and epilepsy. (pp. 472-478)

11. Describe methods of treating cognitive disorders, including medication and cognitive and behavioral approaches. (pp. 478-480)

12. Discuss the need for environmental interventions and methods of supporting the caregivers of individuals with cognitive disorders. (p. 480)

13. Discuss the class of disorders known as mental retardation, including different forms of retardation, how mental retardation is diagnosed, the four levels of retardation, and the predisposing factors associated with mental retardation. (pp. 480-483; Table 14.3)

14. Explain the causes of mental retardation, including how environmental factors and nongenetic biogenic factors may be involved. (pp. 483-487)

15. Describe and discuss early intervention and employment programs and living arrangements for people with mental retardation. (pp. 487-488)

MULTIPLE–CHOICE QUESTIONS

Ans: d
Page: 456
Obj: 1
Type: C

1. Jacob is diagnosed with a psychiatric condition that has cognitive symptoms. There is no sign of brain dysfunction. Would Jacob's disorder be considered a cognitive disorder according to the DSM-IV-TR?
    a. Almost 21% of the children in the United States between ages 9 and 17 have a diagnosed mental or addictive disorder associated with at least a minimal level of impairment.
    b. Yes; all problems involving cognitive symptoms are considered cognitive disorders.
    c. Yes, as long as there was no evidence of brain damage.
    d. No; it would be listed elsewhere (perhaps as schizophrenia).

Ans: b
Page: 456
Obj: 1
Type: F

2. In cognitive disorders,
    a. social and psychological factors play no role.
    b. brain pathology causes behavioral disturbance.
    c. there may be symptoms of brain pathology, but no organic cause is assumed.
    d. psychological factors cause the brain to malfunction.

Ans: d
Page: 456
Obj: 1
Type: A

3. Sanjay was diagnosed with a cognitive disorder. Which of the following could *not* be the specific diagnosis?
    a. Dementia caused by infection
    b. Amnestic disorder
    c. Delirium caused by general medical condition
    d. Schizoaffective disorder

Ans: b
Page: 457
Obj: 1
Type: A

4. When a child has a severe disorder that affects psychological functioning in areas of social interaction, communication skills, and display of stereotyped interests and behaviors, the disorder is called a
    a. No; memory and attention problems are not considered symptoms of a cognitive disorder.
    b. Perhaps; if symptoms aren't due to some mental disorder and are traced to a medical condition, it is a cognitive disorder.
    c. Yes; anytime there is delirium, it is assumed to be a cognitive disorder.
    d. No; delirium is not one of the cognitive disorders.

Ans: d
Page: 457
Obj: 1
Type: F

5. Which disorder does not fit with the others?
    a. autistic disorder
    b. Asperger's disorder .
    c. childhood disintegrative disorder
    d. attention deficit/hyperactivity disorder

Ans: c
Page: 457
Obj: 1
Type: F

6. The prevalence of severe cognitive disorders in the United States is
    a. approximately the same for those eighteen to thirty-four years old as for those over seventy-five.
    b. about 10 percent of the general population.
    c. higher among African Americans than European or Hispanic Americans.
    d. twenty-two times greater among men than women.

Ans: c
Page: 459
Obj: 2
Type: F

7. _____ and _____ are neurological tests that use radioactive substances to produce images of the brain.
   a. EEG; cerebral blood flow measurement
   b. MRI; CAT scans
   c. Cerebral blood flow measurement; positron emission tomography
   d. MRI; positron emission tomography

Ans: a
Page: 459
Obj: 2
Type: A

8. Tonya is suspected of having a brain tumor. She goes to the hospital, where a detailed image of her brain is produced using a magnetic field and radio waves. What kind of brain assessment occurred?
   a. MRI
   b. EEG
   c. CAT scan
   d. Neuropsychological testing

Ans: b
Page: 459
Obj: 2
Type: A

9. Dr. Wilson has a patient with a cognitive disorder. She has used a neuroimaging technique but now wants to determine if the particular patterns of the patient's performance will help her locate lesions in the brain. What technique will Dr. Wilson *most likely* use to accomplish this?
   a. Projective personality tests
   b. Neuropsychological tests
   c. Objective personality tests
   d. Mental Status Exam

Ans: d
Page: 459
Obj: 2
Type: A

10. Dr. Pushkin is seeing a new patient whom she suspects has a cognitive disorder. Dr. Pushkin wants to assess quickly the patient's overall cognitive functioning, including the patient's level of awareness, use of language, ability to perform simple mental tasks, and memory. What instrument will Dr. Pushkin *most likely* use to conduct this assessment?
    a. Objective personality testing
    b. Neuropsychological testing
    c. Neuroimaging techniques
    d. Mental Status Exam

Ans: b
Page: 460
Obj: 2
Type: C

11. Which of the following *accurately* describes the relationship between locations in the brain and their observable functions?
    a. Knowing the precise location of brain damage tells you precisely what functions will be impaired.
    b. Knowing the precise location of brain damage gives only an approximation of the functions that will be impaired.
    c. Knowing the function that is impaired tells you precisely the area of the brain that has been damaged.
    d. Knowing what area of the brain is damaged tells you almost nothing about what functions will be impaired.

Ans: a
Page: 461
Obj: 2
Type: A

12. Based on research matching the location of brain damage to functional problems, we can guess that a man who has right frontal and parietal damage is *most likely* to display
    a. impaired motor and tactile function.
    b. intense emotions and vivid hallucinations.
    c. loss of both expressive speech and speech comprehension.
    d. diffuse intellectual decline and loss of reading ability.

Ans: d
Page: 460
Obj: 2
Type: C

13. A doctor explains to his patient, "We cannot match brain areas and their functions perfectly because of diaschisis." By this the doctor means
   a. undeveloped areas of the brain can substitute for damaged areas.
   b. there are certain areas of the brain that seem to have no specific function.
   c. there are ways for the brain to repair damage so lesions do not produce any function loss.
   d. lesions in one area may affect functioning in a distant, intact area.

Ans: c
Page: 460
Obj: 2
Type: A

14. Mr. Tan is forty-seven years old and had a stroke that paralyzed his left side. His doctor tells him that, with treatment, he will probably regain feeling and movement in his left side. The reason the doctor can say this is
   a. that MRI procedures can make the damaged portion of the brain unnecessary.
   b. the phenomenon of diaschisis.
   c. that there is redundancy in the brain.
   d. that brain surgery using plastics can reconnect nerve tissues.

Ans: d
Page: 461
Obj: 2
Type: A

15. Even though three-year-old Janie had a large portion of her brain surgically removed to treat a tumor, doctors are hopeful that she will grow up showing few functional impairments. Why?
   a. The doctors know that dopamine and other drugs can compensate for lost tissue.
   b. The brain can show diaschisis at age three.
   c. The doctors know that neuroregulators, not brain tissue, control functioning.
   d. The brain is not fully specialized at age three.

Ans: c
Page: 461
Obj: 3
Type: C

16. Which of the following is a good example of an exogenous form of brain damage?
   a. Cerebral atrophy due to a genetic disorder
   b. A loss of blood flow due to a stroke
   c. A trauma due to an automobile accident
   d. An infection such as meningitis

Ans: b
Page: 460 - 461
Obj: 3
Type: A

17. A physician says, "The patient is incapable of responding because of an acute, diffuse, and endogenous form of brain damage." Which of the following is a cause for the type of brain damage the physician is talking about?
   a. The patient has a low-growing tumor that has affected the left occipital lobe.
   b. The patient had a sudden infection that affected the brain generally.
   c. The patient was poisoned, but only a small area of the brain was damaged.
   d. The patient was in a car accident that tore a wide area of the brain.

Ans: c
Page: 461
Obj: 3
Type: C

18. Late on Saturday night, Dennie is taken to the hospital after drinking twenty beers. His confusion and hallucinations stop as soon as the alcohol is out of his system. This incident illustrates an _____ cognitive disorder.
   a. endogenous and acute
   b. endogenous and diffuse
   c. exogenous and acute
   d. exogenous and chronic

Ans: a
Page: 461
Obj: 3
Type: A

19. Dr. Kumalo tells the Ryan family, "Your daughter's cognitive disorder involves long-term memory problems. We're sorry to say that it is a condition that is probably not reversible." The doctor is describing a(n) _____ form of brain damage.
    a. chronic
    b. acute
    c. endogenous
    d. specific

Ans: b
Page: 461
Obj: 4
Type: C

20. One major problem in diagnosing brain damage is that
    a. most of the symptoms are too subtle to be detected.
    b. its symptoms and those of affective disorders are very similar.
    c. organic disorders are extremely rare.
    d. little research has been done on methods of assessing such damage.

Ans: d
Page: 461
Obj: 4
Type: A

21. Elsa, seventy-three years old, has been diagnosed with depression because she shows reduced activity and slowed thought. What are the chances that she was misdiagnosed and actually has a cognitive disorder?
    a. Very likely, because slowed thought is a symptom of cognitive disorders, not depression
    b. Very unlikely, because cognitive disorders are rare in women
    c. Very unlikely, because the symptoms of depression and cognitive disorders do not overlap
    d. Fairly likely, because the symptoms of depression and cognitive disorders overlap

Ans: b
Page: 462
Obj: 4
Type: A

22. Phil is diagnosed with schizophrenia. Stephanie is diagnosed with major depression. Using neuropsychological tests, is it likely that either one could be misdiagnosed as having brain damage?
    a. It is unlikely that either Phil or Stephanie would be misdiagnosed.
    b. It is likely that both Phil and Stephanie would be misdiagnosed.
    c. It is likely for Phil to be misdiagnosed but not Stephanie.
    d. It is likely for Stephanie to be misdiagnosed but not Phil.

Ans: d
Page: 462
Obj: 4
Type: F

23. A study of fifty retired teachers showed that
    a. delirium is easily masked when a person has an outgoing personality.
    b. even well-educated people have a rapid drop in intellectual functioning after the age of fifty.
    c. test scores showing brain damage predict poor levels of daily functioning.
    d. even when daily functioning is high, neuropsychological testing can indicate brain damage.

Ans: c
Page: 462
Obj: 4
Type: C

24. Fred's symptoms suggest that he has a cognitive disorder. His doctor recommends that he get neuropsychological and neurological testing at regular intervals. Is this a wise suggestion?
    a. No, because repeated testing will make treatment less effective.
    b. Yes, because for people with cognitive disorders, the testing is a form of therapy.
    c. Yes, because such testing would measure Fred's progress or deterioration.
    d. No, because repeated testing might lead to a change in the diagnosis to a non-cognitive disorder.

Ans: a
Page: 462
Obj: 4
Type: C

25. The case of Larry D. illustrates the fact that organic disorders
   a. are often misdiagnosed.
   b. are typically diagnosed accurately when psychological tests are used.
   c. show symptoms that rarely overlap those of functional mental disorders.
   d. may be biologically caused but are treated successfully only with psychotherapy.

Ans: b
Page: 462
Obj: 4
Type: F

26. How are cognitive disorders classified according to the DSM-IV-TR?
   a. By the effect they have on behavior: emotional, motor, social, or intellectual
   b. By their cause within each of the four major categories: delirium, dementia, amnestic, and not otherwise specified
   c. By four major categories: delirium, dementia, amnestic, and not otherwise specified
   d. By whether they are endogenous versus exogenous and specific versus diffuse

Ans: c
Page: 462
Obj: 4
Type: A

27. Charles has symptoms of delirium caused by a cocaine overdose. Lydia has symptoms of major depression caused by a thyroid deficiency. Using the DSM-IV-TR, how should these people be diagnosed?
   a. Both Charles and Lydia have endogenous, acute cognitive disorders.
   b. Both Charles and Lydia have cognitive disorders caused by a general medical condition.
   c. Charles has a cocaine-induced delirium; Lydia has a depression due to a general medical condition.
   d. Both Charles and Lydia have non-cognitive disorders caused by a general medical condition.

Ans: b
Page: 463
Obj: 5
Type: F

28. Dementia is *best* described as a condition involving
   a. an inability to form new memories and the need to distort previously recalled information.
   b. memory impairments and disturbances such as aphasia, apraxia, and agnosia.
   c. short-term dimming of consciousness that is often related to seizures or convulsions.
   d. hallucinations and delusions that are caused by external traumas to the brain.

Ans: c
Page: 452463
Obj: 5
Type: A

29. Terrance has gradually begun to forget the names of family members and acts in impulsive ways. He cannot remember the names of familiar objects and speaks haltingly, repeating the same phrase over and over. What symptoms of cognitive disorder does Terrance illustrate?
   a. Delirium and Parkinson's disease
   b. Amnestic disorder and epilepsy
   c. Dementia and aphasia
   d. Huntington's chorea and amnestic disorder

Ans: a
Page: 463
Obj: 5
Type: A

30. Jed can see and hear normally. However, when he picks up a fork, he tries to use it as an electric shaver. This failure to recognize the use of an object is called
   a. agnosia.
   b. diaschisis.
   c. aphasia.
   d. delirium.

Ans: d
Page: 463
Obj: 5
Type: A

31. Marcus is eighty-three and has a form of aphasia that makes it difficult for him to find the words he wants to say. He developed this condition very suddenly and has experienced a steady cognitive decline. Marcus was diagnosed with dementia. What aspect of his case is *unusual*?
    a. It is unusual for dementia to show a steady cognitive decline.
    b. It is unusual for dementia to occur in someone over eighty.
    c. It is unusual for dementia to involve speech aphasia.
    d. It is unusual for dementia to have a sudden onset.

Ans: a
Page: 463
Obj: 5
Type: A

32. 89-year-old Rose has had a gradual loss of memory in her daily life activities, such as remembering people's names and phone numbers. However, in her Bible study class she makes insightful comments and understands the topic of discussion. This would suggest that Rose is experiencing:
    a. normal aging.
    b. early signs of Alzheimer's disease.
    c. early signs of dementia.
    d. a cognitive disorder not otherwise specified.

Ans: d
Page: 463
Obj: 5
Type: F

33. Which statement about dementia is *accurate*?
    a. Between 20 and 40 percent of people over age sixty-five have some form of dementia.
    b. Dementia never involves hallucinations or delusions.
    c. The prevalence of dementia decreases after age sixty-five.
    d. Dementia is associated with a wide range of disorders.

Ans: d '
Page: 463
Obj: 6
Type: A

34. Gertrude, a 75-year-old woman, is being evaluated for the presence of a cognitive disorder. Her daughter tells the physician that Gertrude has been experiencing several problems. Although she can speak fluently, she cannot comprehend written words, has difficulty finding the correct words to name objects, cannot remember new information, and has difficulty planning and organizing. What diagnosis or diagnoses would Gertrude *most likely* be given?
    a. Dissociative amnestic disorder
    b. Amnestic disorder
    c. Delirium
    d. Dementia

Ans: a
Page: 465
Obj: 5
Type: F

35. Which of the following characteristic of delirium helps to distinguish it from other forms of cognitive disorder?
    a. Rapid onset
    b. Inability to remember familiar faces
    c. Ritualistic behavior
    d. Memory lapses

Ans: c
Page: 464
Obj: 5
Type: A

36. Ian suddenly became incoherent at 3 a.m. yesterday. He was agitated and unable to focus his attention and did not know where he was when taken to the hospital. After two days, the cocaine was out of his system and his cognitive functioning returned to normal. What form of cognitive disorder did he display?
    a. None; he was experiencing withdrawal.
    b. Amnestic disorder
    c. Delirium
    d. Dementia

Ans: b
Page: 465
Obj: 6
Type: C

37. Because of an inadequate diet and excess consumption of alcohol, Donald has a thiamine deficiency that has caused Wernicke's encephalopathy. Which cognitive disorder is Donald *most* at risk for having?
    a. Huntington's chorea
    b. Amnestic disorder
    c. Chronic delirium
    d. Expressive aphasia

Ans: c
Page: 465
Obj: 6
Type: C

38. Aphasia and apraxia are symptoms that tend to distinguish dementias from delirium and amnestic disorders. What symptom(s) is/are found in all three forms of cognitive disorder?
    a. Hallucinations and delusions
    b. Thiamine deficiency
    c. Memory impairment
    d. Disorientation of place and time

Ans: a
Page: 466
Obj: 7
Type: C

39. The famous case of Phineas Gage, the man who had a $3\frac{1}{2}$ -foot iron rod shot through his brain, illustrates the fact that
    a. brain trauma can alter personality.
    b. brain trauma is the leading cause of aphasia and apraxia.
    c. dementia and delirium cannot be distinguished from one another.
    d. the amount of tissue lost is proportionate to the severity of functional loss.

Ans: b
Page: 466
Obj: 7
Type: A

40. Phineas Gage became moody, impatient, and obstinate after he experienced extensive brain damage when a tamping rod tore through his head after an explosion. What DSM-IV-TR diagnosis would he have received?
    a. Amnestic disorder
    b. Laceration
    c. Concussion
    d. Dementia due to general medical condition

Ans: c
Page: 466
Obj: 7
Type: F

41. "A physical wound or injury to the brain" is a definition of
    a. infarction.
    b. diaschisis.
    c. brain trauma.
    d. cerebrovascular accident or stroke.

Ans: a
Page: 466
Obj: 7
Type: A

42. Harold was involved in a fight and received several kicks to the head. He was dazed and experienced headaches and some memory problems for ten days afterward. Harold's symptoms suggest
    a. that he suffered a concussion.
    b. apraxia and agnosia.
    c. a multi-infarct disorder.
    d. that a brain laceration occurred.

Ans: b
Page: 466
Obj: 7
Type: A

43. When a football player has, as sports announcers say, "his bell rung" (is knocked unconscious by a tackle but then walks off the field), what has occurred according to the DSM-IV-TR?
    a. A diffuse brain laceration
    b. A brain trauma called a concussion
    c. An endogenous head injury called a contusion
    d. An acute form of dementia

Ans: d
Page: 466
Obj: 7
Type: A

44. Paige was in an auto accident that caused her head to crash against the windshield. Her brain was pressed against the skull and bruised by the impact. She lost consciousness for three days, but none of the brain tissue was torn. Paige experienced a
   a. brain laceration.
   b. multi-infarct disorder.
   c. stroke.
   d. contusion.

Ans: a
Page 466 - 467
Obj: 7
Type: A

45. Hilary was involved in a shooting that left her with traumatic brain injury. She spent several weeks in a coma. Afterward, she was depressed and anxious but was unaware that she had these feelings. What aspect of Hilary's case is *unusual*?
   a. Nothing about Hilary's case is unusual.
   b. It is unusual for people with traumatic brain injury to be in a coma for weeks.
   c. It is unusual for people with traumatic brain injury to feel depressed and anxious.
   d. It is unusual for people with traumatic brain injury to be unaware of negative feelings.

Ans: b
Page: 467
Obj: 7
Type: A

46. Andre, age sixteen, had an open-head brain injury that did extensive damage to the right hemisphere. Which of the following is the *most likely* symptom he will experience?
   a. Huntington's chorea
   b. Epilepsy
   c. Long-term loss of cognitive functions
   d. Amnestic disorder

Ans: d
Page: 467
Obj: 7
Type: F

47. Which of the following is a common outcome of severe closed-head injury?
   a. Complete recovery without intellectual or emotional difficulties
   b. Complete intellectual recovery but continuing emotional problems
   c. Complete emotional recovery but continuing intellectual impairment
   d. Continuing intellectual and emotional difficulties

Ans: c
Page: 467
Obj: 7
Type: F

48. Only one-third of patients with _____ can return to gainful employment after traditional rehabilitative therapy.
   a. Alzheimer's disease
   b. epilepsy
   c. severe closed-head injuries
   d. concussions

Ans: a
Page: 468
Obj: 8
Type: F

49. When there is a sudden stoppage of blood flow in the brain that leads to a loss of brain function, a person has experienced
   a. a stroke.
   b. a brain trauma.
   c. aphasia.
   d. dyslexia.

Ans: b
Page: 467
Obj: 8
Type: A

50. The director of medicine at a large nursing home that cares for elderly people is *most likely* to treat which cognitive disorders?
   a. Closed-head injuries and cerebral tumors
   b. Alzheimer's disease and stroke
   c. Stroke and closed-head injuries
   d. Cerebral tumors and meningitis

Ans: d
Page: 468
Obj: 8
Type: F

51. Which statement about cerebrovascular accidents is *inaccurate*?
    a. Survivors of them generally require long-term care.
    b. They are also called strokes.
    c. They involve a sudden loss of brain function.
    d. They kill about 10 to 15 percent of people who have them.

Ans: b
Page: 468
Obj: 8
Type: A

52. Mr. Pappadopolis has a cognitive disorder that has caused an interesting symptom: He no longer acknowledges the left side of his body. For example, he does not shave the left side of his face or button his left shirt cuff. This is a sign that he
    a. has Parkinson's disease.
    b. suffered a stroke.
    c. is recovering from a closed-head injury.
    d. has aphasia and agnosia.

Ans: c
Page: 468
Obj: 8
Type: C

53. *Infarction, atherosclerosis,* and *lack of acknowledgment* are all terms associated with
    a. Alzheimer's disease.
    b. cerebral tumors.
    c. strokes.
    d. meningitis and encephalitis.

Ans: b
Page: 468
Obj: 8
Type: F

54. A series of small strokes or incidents in which portions of the brain die leads to uneven deterioration of intellectual functioning. This is called
    a. Alzheimer's disease.
    b. vascular dementia.
    c. atherosclerosis.
    d. presenile dementia.

Ans: c
Page: 469
Obj: 9
Type: F

55. Age-related decreases in cognitive function
    a. occur in 35 to 45 percent of those over age sixty-five.
    b. usually begin in a person's early forties and fifties.
    c. can be reduced by the person's remaining cognitively active.
    d. rarely can be stopped because they are genetically programmed.

Ans: a
Page: 469
Obj: 9
Type: C

56. Wilma is seventy-six years old and has noticed that her memory is not as sharp as it was earlier in her life. This memory loss might be due to all of the following *except*
    a. epilepsy.
    b. Alzheimer's disease.
    c. vascular dementia.
    d. the normal aging process.

Ans: c
Page: 469
Obj: 9
Type: F

57. The intellectual decline that accompanies aging
    a. is a myth—cognitive skills improve through age eighty.
    b. is sudden and dramatic after age sixty-five.
    c. has been overstated—cognitive skills are quite stable.
    d. is found only in people with Alzheimer's disease.

Ans: d
Page: 469
Obj: 9
Type: A

58. One problem with diagnosing and differentiating Alzheimer's disease and vascular dementia is that a major symptom of both is part of the normal aging process. That symptom is
    a. aphasia.
    b. delusions.
    c. muscular tremors.
    d. memory loss.

Ans: b
Page: 469
Obj: 9
Type: A

59. Olaf is eighty years old. If he is typical of most elderly people, his *greatest* fear of aging is
    a. sudden death due to stroke or heart disease.
    b. loss of mental capabilities.
    c. arthritis and limited movement.
    d. loss of vision and hearing.

Ans: c
Page: 469
Obj: 9
Type: A

60. The senior center in a large town is interested in the cognitive problems that its customers are likely to have. Research suggests that _____ will *most likely* be impaired by the normal aging process.
    a. all general cognitive skills
    b. verbal fluency
    c. problem solving in novel situations
    d. knowledge gained over the course of one's life

Ans: d
Page: 470
Obj: 9
Type: C

61. A seventy-year-old retired accountant is fearful that he is losing his cognitive abilities because he occasionally forgets his keys and cannot think of the names of certain common objects. If he compared his performance with that of other retired accountants, he would be using _____ methods to assess his cognitive aging.
    a. individual normative
    b. population normative
    c. age-group normative
    d. reference-group normative

Ans: a
Page: 470
Obj: 9
Type: A

62. At age sixty-four, Mrs. Willis began a long mental decline. She first showed memory loss and irritability, then delusions, social withdrawal, dementia, and finally death at age sixty-eight. An autopsy showed neurofibrillary tangles and senile plaques in her brain. Mrs. Willis died of
    a. Alzheimer's disease.
    b. aphasia.
    c. epilepsy.
    d. a cerebrovascular accident (stroke).

Ans: c
Page: 470
Obj: 9
Type: A

63. A handout on Alzheimer's disease says, "Alzheimer's is the leading cause of dementia in older persons. It rarely leads to death but causes marked deterioration in emotional and mental functioning and has no cure." Which portion of this statement is *inaccurate*?
    a. No portion of the statement is inaccurate.
    b. It is inaccurate to say that Alzheimer's is the leading cause of dementia in older persons.
    c. It is inaccurate to say that Alzheimer's rarely leads to death.
    d. It is inaccurate to say that Alzheimer's has no cure.

Ans: d
Page: 471
Obj: 9
Type: F

64. Neurofibrillary tangles, memory loss, and senile plaques are all related to
   a. Huntington's chorea.
   b. epilepsy.
   c. severe closed-head injury.
   d. Alzheimer's disease.

Ans: a
Page: 471
Obj: 9
Type: F

65. The cause of Alzheimer's disease is
   a. unknown.
   b. excessive drinking that leads to encephalopathy.
   c. the natural aging process.
   d. excessive blood flow in the brain.

Ans: b
Page: 471
Obj: 9
Type: A

66. Beverly has been diagnosed with Alzheimer's disease. Which of the following is *not* a likely cause?
   a. Genetic anomalies
   b. Deficient levels of dopamine
   c. Decreased blood flow in the brain.
   d. Reduced levels of acetylcholine

Ans: c
Page: 471
Obj: 10
Type: F

67. Tremor, muscle rigidity, and difficulty initiating movement are the primary symptoms of
   a. Huntington's disease.
   b. cerebral vascular disorder.
   c. Parkinson's disease.
   d. Alzheimer's disease.

Ans: c
Page: 472
Obj: 10
Type: A

68. A physician says, "Most people know that AIDS leaves people open to deadly infections, but few are aware that a major symptom of AIDS is a kind of intellectual deterioration called delirium." What about the physician's comments is *incorrect*?
   a. There is nothing incorrect in the physician's comments.
   b. AIDS does not leave people open to deadly infections.
   c. Intellectual deterioration is called dementia.
   d. AIDS does not produce any intellectual deterioration.

Ans: d
Page: 473
Obj: 10
Type: F

69. Why might having AIDS produce dementia?
   a. Most people with AIDS have a history of Alzheimer's disease.
   b. Most people with AIDS are over age sixty-five.
   c. The AIDS virus narrows the capillary walls and produces infarctions.
   d. The AIDS virus infects the brain and affects mental processes.

Ans: a
Page: 473
Obj: 10
Type: F

70. Two cognitive disorders are the result of sexually transmitted disease. They are
   a. AIDS and neurosyphilis.
   b. neurosyphilis and meningitis.
   c. AIDS and encephalitis.
   d. Parkinson's disease and Huntington's disease.

Ans: b
Page: 474
Obj: 10
Type: A

71. Young Billie has shown epileptic seizures followed by fever and constant sleep over three days. When he awakens, he is delirious, hyperactive, and irritable. He is probably suffering from the infection of the brain called
   a. Huntington's disease.
   b. encephalitis.
   c. neurosyphilis.
   d. Parkinson's disease.

Ans: d
Page: 475
Obj: 10
Type: A

72. Dr. Wayne says, "We know that the patient's cognitive disorder was caused by an infectious agent. That automatically rules out _____."
    a. neurosyphilis (general paresis)
    b. encephalitis
    c. AIDS dementia
    d. Huntington's disease

Ans: a
Page: 475
Obj: 10
Type: F

73. It is a rare, genetically transmitted disorder that involves twitching movements, dementia, and death. Its symptoms begin to appear in young adulthood or middle age. What is it?
    a. Huntington's disease
    b. Alzheimer's disease
    c. Parkinson's disease
    d. Benign cerebral tumor

Ans: d
Page: 469; 475
Obj: 10
Type: F

74. Which of the following organic brain disorders are incurable and always fatal?
    a. Alzheimer's disease, Huntington's disease, stroke, and meningitis
    b. Huntington's disease and stroke
    c. Stroke and meningitis
    d. Alzheimer's disease and Huntington's disease

Ans: b
Page: 475
Obj: 10
Type: F

75. Cerebral tumors
    a. produce aphasia and apraxia but rarely are associated with mood changes.
    b. that affect the temporal areas produce the most psychological symptoms.
    c. rarely affect consciousness.
    d. that grow rapidly rarely affect cognitive function.

Ans: d
Page: 476
Obj: 10
Type: F

76. Unlike contusion or Parkinson's disease, epilepsy refers to
    a. a cause of a cognitive disorder, not the disorder itself.
    b. a cognitive disorder that is genetically transmitted.
    c. a cognitive disorder caused by infection.
    d. a set of symptoms, not a disorder or cause.

Ans: a
Page: 476
Obj: 10
Type: F

77. Which statement about epilepsy is *accurate*?
    a. It is the most common form of neurological disorder.
    b. It cannot be diagnosed until young adulthood.
    c. It cannot be acquired through drug use or surgery.
    d. It is among the rarest forms of neurological disorder.

Ans: d
Page: 476
Obj: 10
Type: A

78. Paulo is a young teenager whose eyelids occasionally flutter while he loses consciousness for two to three seconds. He is usually unaware that he has had a kind of seizure. Paulo's cognitive problems *best* illustrate
    a. a cerebral vascular accident.
    b. a cerebral tumor.
    c. early stages of Alzheimer's.
    d. epilepsy.

Ans: c
Page: 477
Obj: 10
Type: F

79. The presence of an aura prior to loss of consciousness and a coma following the tonic and clonic phases is the key to diagnosing
    a. schizophrenia.
    b. general paresis.
    c. tonic-clonic epileptic seizure .
    d. somatization disorder.

Ans: d
Page: 478
Obj: 10
Type: F

80. Which statement about the cause of epilepsy is *accurate*?
    a. Epilepsy is caused by a combination of genetic vulnerability and poor parenting.
    b. It is now clear that epilepsy is caused by a genetic defect in Chromosome 21.
    c. Personality factors are the most important vulnerability factor for the disorder.
    d. A wide range of biological and stress factors seems to cause excessive neuronal discharges.

Ans: b
Page: 478
Obj: 10
Type: F

81. L-dopa is *most* effective in the treatment of
    a. Huntington's chorea.
    b. Parkinson's disease.
    c. encephalitis.
    d. neurosyphilis.

Ans: c
Page: 478
Obj: 11
Type: A

82. Jill is given Dilantin to treat her cognitive symptoms; Patricia is given L-dopa to treat her cognitive disorder. We can guess that
    a. Jill has epilepsy, and Patricia has a psychoactive-induced disorder.
    b. both Jill and Patricia suffer from epilepsy.
    c. Jill has epilepsy, and Patricia has Parkinson's disease.
    d. both Jill and Patricia suffer from Parkinson's disease.

Ans: a
Page: 479
Obj: 11
Type: A

83. Christopher, recovering from a severe head injury, is in psychological counseling to improve his concentration and recall. This cognitive therapy probably focuses on
    a. the way private speech can regulate his distracting thoughts.
    b. increasing his performance on IQ tests.
    c. his unconscious fears.
    d. retraining his neutral tracts so that speech can be relearned.

Ans: c
Page: 480
Obj: 12
Type: F

84. Butler suggests ways that caregivers of people with cognitive disorders can be most helpful. Which of the following is *not* one of the those suggestions?
    a. Schedule diversions such as walks in calm, predictable settings.
    b. Assign the person tasks but do not require perfection.
    c. Free the person from the burden of making personal decisions.
    d. Make sure that interpersonal contact is short and not overwhelming.

Ans: b
Page: 480 - 481
Obj: 13
Type: F

85. Which statement *best* describes the changes in the perception of mental retardation?
    a. Psychologists have come to understand that many forms of retardation lead to psychotic conditions.
    b. Conditions that used to be seen as hopeless are now believed to respond to training.
    c. Conditions that used to be seen as responsive to training are now believed to be hopeless.
    d. Psychologists have come to understand that all forms of retardation produce about the same level of handicap.

Ans: c
Page: 481
Obj: 13
Type: F

86. According to the Association for Retarded Citizens, what percentage of people with mental retardation can be completely self-supporting if they are given appropriate training?
    a. Less than 10 percent
    b. Almost 100 percent
    c. About 75 percent
    d. Around 50 percent

Ans: b
Page: 481
Obj: 13
Type: A

87. Dr. Travis says, "People with mental retardation have an IQ below 90 and must be diagnosed before age eighteen. There are seven million such people in the United States, and many have problems with dependency and low self-esteem." What portion of this statement is *inaccurate*?
    a. It is inaccurate to say that people with mental retardation have problems with dependency and low self-esteem.
    b. It is inaccurate to say that mental retardation involves an IQ below 90.
    c. It is inaccurate to say that mental retardation must be diagnosed before age eighteen.
    d. It is inaccurate to say that seven million Americans have mental retardation.

Ans: d
Page: 481
Obj: 13
Type: A

88. Joan scores 65 on an IQ test but does not show signs of adaptive problems. Can she be considered mentally retarded?
    a. Maybe, but she must first show a low IQ after the age of eighteen.
    b. Yes; her IQ score requires such a diagnosis.
    c. No; her IQ test score is too high.
    d. No; she must show adaptive problems.

Ans: a
Page: 482
Obj: 13
Type: A

89. "African Americans score lower on IQ tests because they go to inadequate schools and, living in poverty, often get poor parental support and models for academic success." This explanation
    a. can be considered a disadvantage/oppression explanation.
    b. agrees with Herrnstein and Murray's genetic theory in their book *The Bell Curve*.
    c. supports the idea that IQ tests are culturally biased.
    d. suggests that African American children show more psychopathology than European American children.

Ans: d
Page: 483
Obj: 14
Type: A

90. Naomi is a child of poverty. She has inadequate nutrition, housing, and educational opportunities. Naomi is mildly retarded. Her mental retardation is considered
    a. organic.
    b. a result of genetic deficiencies.
    c. untreatable.
    d. a result of environmental factors.

Ans: b
Page: 484
Obj: 13
Type: A

91. Bud, age ten, was born with short fingers, slanted eyes, and a protruding tongue; he is moderately retarded. His parents were both in their forties when he was born. He probably has the form of retardation called _____ and has a high likelihood of developing _____.
    a. Alzheimer's disease; fetal alcohol syndrome
    b. Down syndrome; heart problems
    c. fetal alcohol syndrome; Alzheimer's disease
    d. microcephaly; heart problems

Ans: c
Page: 485
Obj: 14
Type: A

92. Dr. Branch tells his pregnant patient, "Because you are thirty-eight years old, we are going to do a chorionic villus sampling procedure to see whether there is the normal number of chromosomes in your baby." What disorder is Dr. Branch concerned about?
a. Phenylketonuria (PKU)
b. Nongenetic biogenic retardation
c. Down syndrome
d. Fetal alcohol syndrome

Ans: d
Page: 486
Obj: 13
Type: F

93. Which statement about the predisposing factors associated with mental retardation is *accurate*?
a. Heredity explains the cause of over one-half of all cases of mental retardation.
b. Down syndrome and fetal alcohol syndrome account for almost 75 percent of all cases of mental retardation.
c. More children develop mental retardation because of infections and brain damage during infancy than because of all other causes put together.
d. In a large minority of cases (30 to 40 percent), the cause of mental retardation is not known.

Ans: b
Page: 486
Obj: 14
Type: A

94. Jack, Jim, and Justin all have mental retardation. Jack's mother was a chronic alcoholic. Jim's mother beat him on the head repeatedly when he was an infant. Justin was born prematurely and suffered from a lack of oxygen at birth. What can be said of these three boys?
a. The cause of Jack's and Jim's retardation can be considered organic.
b. Nongenetic biogenic factors were the cause of retardation for all three.
c. Genetic factors were the cause of retardation for all three.
d. Environmental factors were the cause of retardation for all three.

Ans: d
Page: 486
Obj: 14
Type: F

95. In addition to retardation, children with this problem have unusually small brains. They are often hyperactive. Their mothers' smoking and poor nutrition during pregnancy increase the likelihood of this form of retardation, which is estimated to occur once in every 750 live births. What is being described?
a. Down syndrome
b. Phenylketonuria (PKU)
c. Environmentally caused retardation
d. Fetal alcohol syndrome

Ans: a
Page: 486
Obj: 14
Type: F

96. Although most types of mental retardation have decreasing rates, mental retardation due to _____ is on the increase.
a. postnatal trauma
b. Down syndrome
c. fetal alcohol syndrome
d. prenatal trauma

Ans: c
Page: 486
Obj: 14
Type: F

97. Which cause of mental retardation is 100% preventable?
a. Phnylketonuria (PKU)
b. down syndrome
c. fetal alcohol syndrome (FAS)
d. fragile syndrome

Ans: d
Page: 487
Obj: 15
Type: F

98. Studies of the effects of Head Start programs have shown that
    a. while students enjoy them, their families see the programs as intrusive and their children as more aggressive and defiant.
    b. while they make families happier, the children show no improvement in their school performance.
    c. they lead to dramatic improvements in intellectual abilities and mental health, although these improvements drop off after three years.
    d. they produce modest improvements in school performance that widen until the twelfth grade producing long-term, positive effects.

Ans: c
Page: 487
Obj: 15
Type: A

99. A community is considering funding a Head Start program. Based on long-term follow-up research on other such programs, the community can expect
    a. the program to waste money and have no impact on dropout rates.
    b. that any improvements in children who get the program will fade within six months of the program's completion.
    c. that the parents of children who get the program will see their children as happier and healthier.
    d. the children who get the program will show dramatic increases in intellect.

Ans: c
Page: 488
Obj: 15
Type: A

100. The parents of a moderately retarded 24-year-old want their child to live in the best place for learning living skills. Which piece of advice is *most* reasonable?
    a. "Put your child in an institution; they know how best to deal with a retarded person."
    b. "Independent living is the best situation; it will force your child to adapt."
    c. "The place is not as important as whether the program has a goal of fostering competence."
    d. "Make sure you stay away from group homes; they never help."

ESSAY QUESTIONS

1. Describe the dimensions by which brain damage is categorized. Indicate why it is so difficult to differentiate cognitive disorders from other psychological disorders.

2. Describe the characteristics of dementia in general and Alzheimer's disease in particular. What is known about the cause of Alzheimer's?

3. How is mental retardation diagnosed and subdivided? What are the principal causes of mental retardation?

SAMPLE ANSWERS

1. Brain damage can range from mild to severe, from lesions that affect relatively little tissue to damage that affects a great deal of tissue. However, severity also is influenced by the location of the damage since some structures in the brain have relatively nonspecific functions and can be damaged without noticeable effect and others have highly specialized functions. In addition, three sets of distinctions are used to define damage: endogenous versus exogenous, diffuse versus specific, and acute versus chronic. Exogenous brain damage has a causal agent that is outside the body, such as a brain trauma or drug that induces tissue damage. Endogenous brain damage stems

from internal factors such as infection and degenerative disease processes such as Parkinson's disease. Diffuse damage entails widespread impairment such as loss of judgment, memory, and emotional stability. By contrast, specific damage affects specialized functions such as loss of sensation in a specific limb. Finally, acute damage implies a temporary impairment that is reversible. People who become intoxicated show acute cognitive impairment. Chronic brain damage means that the functional loss is either irreversible or will remain for a long period of time before recovery occurs.

Some of the effects of brain damage are indistinguishable from non-cognitive disorders such as depression and schizophrenia. In those disorders, individuals become lethargic and socially withdrawn, and they have difficulty solving problems. Some people with cognitive disorders experience hallucinations and delusions, classic symptoms of schizophrenia. The experience of having a cognitive impairment can lead one to feel worthless and hopeless, the classic symptoms of depression. Older people are particularly likely to be misdiagnosed. This is true for several reasons. One is that elderly people often take many medications, the cumulative effects of which can be confusion, memory impairment, and even disorientation. A second is that many older people have health, financial, and interpersonal problems that expose them to depression that looks like a cognitive disorder. Older people are prone to hear and see less well than younger people and to perform less well on psychological tests because of anxiety or the timed nature of these tests. All of these factors can give the mistaken impression that an older person who is depressed or simply coping with health or social problems suffers from a cognitive disorder. The reverse also is possible—that a person who is diagnosed with depression or another non-cognitive disorder actually has a form of brain damage. This is most likely with younger populations, since it is often assumed that older individuals have brain damage as the cause of their symptoms while younger people have psychologically caused problems. Combining psychological and neurological tests and carefully checking initial diagnostic impressions are ways to reduce these mistakes in diagnosis.

2. Dementia is defined as a cognitive disorder that produces significant memory impairments and cognitive problems such as aphasia (the inability to understand or express language), apraxia (the inability to carry out motor activities), and agnosia (the inability to recognize or understand the use of objects). Dementia produces such severe memory impairments that social, occupational, and self-care functioning drop significantly from prior levels. Many people with dementia show poor judgment and act impulsively. The onset of dementia is usually gradual; its effects are widespread and chronic, and they involve gradual deterioration.

Alzheimer's disease accounts for 80 percent of dementias in older people. Early signs of the disease are memory loss and irritability. In addition to intellectual impairments, people with Alzheimer's gradually become withdrawn, depressed, delusional, and neglectful of personal hygiene. Memory loss moves from forgetting appointments and how to get home to forgetting who they and relatives are. Death usually occurs within four or five harrowing years of diagnosis. The disease affects 20 percent of those over eighty years old, but an early-onset form exists as well. It occurs more often in women.

Alzheimer's involves significant cortical atrophy and, microscopically, the formation of senile plaques (patches of degenerated nerve endings) as well as neurofibrillary tangles (abnormal, tangled mats of brain tissue filaments). Acetylcholine levels are also reduced in many people with Alzheimer's. The result is impaired transmission of nerve impulses. Why this happens is not clear. Some researchers suspect that a genetic abnormality predisposes individuals to the disorder. This is particularly likely for early-onset Alzheimer's. Others note that excessive levels of aluminum may enter the bloodstreams of people with the disorder, that frequent head injuries produce symptoms, or that decreased blood flow in the brain may be causal. At this point, we simply do not know what is cause, effect, or correlational in this disease.

3. Mental retardation involves substantial intellectual deficits (scoring below 70 on an IQ test), deficiencies in adaptive behaviors expected for the child's age group, and onset before age eighteen. In other words, mental retardation involves impairment in daily living skills, self-care, and other adaptive behaviors in addition to having an IQ below 70. The DSM-IV-TR specifies four subcategories of mental retardation based on a range of IQ scores. Mild mental retardation,

comprising some 85 percent of those with mental retardation, has an IQ range from 50 or 55 to 70. Moderate mental retardation is in the range of 35 to 40 up to 50 or 55. Severe ranges from 20 to 25 up to 35 to 40, and profound mental retardation involves IQ scores below 20 or 25. Social and vocational skills vary widely within these categories. Interestingly, the American Association on Mental Retardation no longer uses IQ scores to subdivide forms of mental retardation. They emphasize the person's need for supportive services. However, they use an IQ cutoff of 75 rather than 70.

A large minority of cases of mental retardation have no clear cause. In some cases, environmental causes such as poverty, lack of attention, poor nutrition, and inadequate stimulation are primary influences. In general, the lower the socioeconomic status, the lower the IQ score. Genetics contributes to mental retardation in several ways. In some cases, mental retardation may be the result of parents who are at the low end of the distribution of IQ scores; there is no physiological anomaly. On the other hand, in Down syndrome, a genetic condition in which there is an extra Chromosome 21, mental retardation results. About 10 percent of children with moderate or severe retardation have Down syndrome. There are other genetic causes of mental retardation including Turner's syndrome, Tay-Sachs disease, and phenylketonuria (PKU).

Non-genetic biological factors account for other cases of mental retardation. For example, when mothers drink heavily during pregnancy, they can give birth to a child with fetal alcohol syndrome, a condition that includes a small brain, attentional problems, and, in many cases, mild mental retardation. Lack of oxygen during birth, head injuries, infections, toxic substances such as lead, and malnutrition are other perinatal or postnatal biological causes of mental retardation. It is alarming that while most types of mental retardation show decreasing incidence, the cases due to postnatal causes such as head injury are increasing. Child abuse may be a more common cause of mental retardation than PKU.

CHAPTER 15
Disorders of Childhood and Adolescence

LEARNING OBJECTIVES

1. Describe the characteristics of pervasive developmental disorders and identify the prevalence of behavior problems in children and adolescents. (pp. 491-493)

2. Indicate the prevalence of autistic disorder and describe the main impairments it entails. Describe diagnostic difficulties and research findings related to autism. Discuss the relation autistic disorder has to retardation and splinter skills. (pp. 493-496)

3. Differentiate between autism and Rett's disorder, childhood disintegrative disorder, Asperger's disorder, and pervasive developmental disorder not otherwise specified. (pp. 496-497; Figure 15.2)

4. Discuss the etiology of autistic disorder, including psychodynamic, family, genetic, central nervous system impairment, and biochemical theories. (pp. 497-500)

5. Describe the prognosis and treatment for children with pervasive developmental disorders. Discuss drug therapy and behavior modification for these children. (pp. 500-501)

6. Discuss the problems with the diagnosis and classification of other developmental disorders. (pp. 501-503; Table 15.1)

7. Describe the symptoms, etiology, and treatment of the attention deficit/hyperactivity disorders. Discuss the difficulty involved in making an ADHD diagnosis accurately. (pp. 503-508; Mental Health & Society)

8. Define and differentiate oppositional defiant disorder and conduct disorder and discuss the prevalence, etiology, and treatment of conduct disorders. (pp. 508-512)

9. Consider the question of whether school violence is a "sign of the times." (p. 510; Critical Thinking)

10. Contrast the anxiety-related disorders of childhood, including separation anxiety disorder and school phobia. Discuss how they can be treated. (pp. 512-513)

11. Describe reactive attachment disorder and how to deal with it. (pp. 513-514)

12. Describe the prevalence, symptoms, and treatment of childhood depression. (pp. 514-515; Mental Health & Society)

13. Describe the symptoms, etiology, and treatment of chronic and transient tic disorders, including Tourette's syndrome. (pp. 515-519)

14. Discuss the various elimination disorders, including enuresis and encopresis. (pp. 519-520)

MULTIPLE–CHOICE QUESTIONS

Ans: a
Page: 492
Obj: 1
Type: F

1. Which statement about psychopathology among children and adolescents in the United States is *accurate*?
    a. Almost 21% of the children in the United States between ages 9 and 17 have a diagnosed mental or addictive disorder associated with at least a minimal level of impairment.
    b. About 2 percent of children have serious emotional or behavioral problems, and three-quarters of them receive treatment.
    c. Nearly one-third of all children and adolescents have a serious emotional or behavioral problem.
    d. Although there are 63 million children with behavioral problems, most of them receive treatment.

Ans: d
Page: 492
Obj: 1
Type: A

2. The mayor of a large town wants to estimate the number of children and adolescents who are likely to have serious emotional or behavioral problems. If the town's population reflects that of the United States in general, the estimate would be
    a. less than 1 percent.
    b. 2 to 3 percent.
    c. 9 to 16 percent.
    d. 20 to 40 percent.

Ans: b
Page: 493
Obj: 1
Type: A

3. A news reporter defines pervasive developmental disorders as "relatively mild childhood disorders that affect verbal and nonverbal communications. These disorders do not involve hallucinations or delusions but involve behavioral abnormalities that are not normally seen in any developmental stage." What portion of this statement is *inaccurate*?
    a. It is inaccurate to say that these disorders involve abnormalities not normally seen in any developmental stage.
    b. It is inaccurate to say that these disorders are relatively mild.
    c. It is inaccurate to say that these disorders affect verbal and nonverbal communications.
    d. It is inaccurate to say that these disorders do not involve hallucinations or delusions.

Ans: c
Page: 493
Obj: 1
Type: F

4. When a child has a severe disorder that affects psychological functioning in areas of social interaction, communication skills, and display of stereotyped interests and behaviors, the disorder is called a
    a. form of childhood schizophrenia.
    b. developmental disability.
    c. pervasive developmental disorder.
    d. personality disorder.

Ans: d
Page: 493
Obj: 1
Type: F

5. Which disorder does not fit with the others?
    a. autistic disorder
    b. Asperger's disorder
    c. childhood disintegrative disorder
    d. attention deficit/hyperactivity disorder

Ans: a
Page: 493
Obj: 1
Type: F

6. Which statement is inaccurate with respect to diagnosing childhood psychiatric disorders?
    a. They parallel characteristics of adult disorders.
    b. They are generally more complex to diagnose than adult disorders.

    c. Some characteristics of mental illness in adults may occur in normally developing children.

    d. Accurate diagnosis and treatment of childhood disorders requires a thorough understanding of normal child development.

Ans: d
Page: 493
Obj: 2
Type: F

7   The term *autistic disorder* comes from the Greek *autos*. This reflects the key characteristic of the disorder, the _____ of these children.

    a. selfishness and guiltlessness

    b. automatic quality of thinking

    c. robot-like movements

    d. profound aloneness

Ans: a
Page: 493
Obj: 2
Type: A

8.   Charles was diagnosed with autistic disorder. He is extremely unresponsive to adults and does not speak. He first showed these abnormalities around the age of six. What aspect of Charles's case is *unusual* for autistic disorder?

    a. It is unusual for a person with autistic disorder to show abnormalities first at age six.

    b. It is unusual for a person with autistic disorder to be male.

    c. It is unusual for a person with autistic disorder to be unresponsive to adults.

    d. It is unusual for a person with autistic disorder not to speak.

Ans: b
Page: 493
Obj: 2
Type: A

9.   A pervasive developmental disorder that affects basic human qualities and has three features, qualitative impairment in social interaction, severe impairments in communication, and restricted, repetitive, and stereotyped patterns of behavior, is called

    a. mental retardation.

    b. autism.

    c. amnestic dissociative disorder.

    d. learning disorder.

Ans: c
Page: 493
Obj: 2
Type: F

10.   Which statement is *correct* about the prevalence of autism?

    a. It is more common among the lower socioeconomic classes.

    b. It is more common among European Americans than among Asian Americans.

    c. It is more common among boys than among girls.

    d. Almost 1% of children in the United States are born with autism.

Ans: c
Page: 493
Obj: 2
Type: F

11.   The prognosis for children with autism

    a. is generally encouraging.

    b. suggests that impairments get progressively more severe until the autistic adult has few remaining capabilities.

    e. generally poor; only about one-third are even partially able to live independently as adults.

    d. is uniformly poor.

Ans: b
Page: 494
Obj: 2
Type: A

12.   Wesley is eight and has been diagnosed with autistic disorder. His symptoms include an extreme unresponsiveness to adults and a lack of meaningful speech. If Wesley has the typical pattern of autistic symptoms, which other symptom can we expect?

    a. Muscle tics of the face, arms, and hands

    b. Repetitive, self-absorbed activities

    c. Highly imaginative play

    d. Anxiety attacks when left alone

Ans: d
Page: 494
Obj: 2
Type: A

13. A child with autistic disorder is observed interacting with his parents in a room full of toys. We are likely to see the child
a. aggressively use the toys, destroying some of them.
b. cling to the parents and refuse to play with the toys.
c. prefer interaction with the father rather than the mother or the toys.
d. make no eye contact with the parents when he is smiling.

Ans: c
Page: 494
Obj: 2
Type: C

14. Oscar is diagnosed as having autistic disorder. When his mother says, "Here's your cereal," Oscar says, "Here's your cereal." What symptom does this illustrate?
a. Splinter skills
b. Differential reinforcement
c. Echolalia
d. Corporalia

Ans: a
Page: 494
Obj: 2
Type: A

15. Three children were diagnosed with autistic disorder. Kim would rather listen to a machine buzzing than hear her mother's voice. Len is perfectly content to be left alone. Matt needs physical contact with his mother all the time. Which child's symptoms are common in autistic disorder?
a. Kim and Len
b. Matt only
c. Kim only
d. Len and Matt

Ans: a
Page: 494
Obj: 2
Type: A

16. Ricky sits in his bed and rocks back and forth for hours while staring off into space. It is likely that Ricky also
a. shows a lack of imagination.
b. is highly creative.
c. has average intelligence.
d. is a savant.

Ans: c
Page: 495
Obj: 2
Type: F

17. What is the relationship between autistic disorder and intelligence level?
a. There is no relationship between the two.
b. Most people with autistic disorder have above-average intelligence.
c. Most people with autistic disorder have below-average intelligence.
d. Most people with below-average intelligence are also autistic.

Ans: a
Page: 495
Obj: 2
Type: A

18. Jason's mother claims that he can multiply large numbers in his head. She says he can figure out, for example, what day of the week it was on February 2, 1846. However, Jason was tested for intelligence and scored in the mentally retarded range. What is a reasonable response to Jason's mother?
a. "Although it is rare, your son sounds as if he is an autistic child with special skills."
b. "What you say he can do is not possible; you must be mistaken."
c. "Your son is demonstrating two common symptoms of autism—echolalia and stimulus over-selectivity."
d. "The testing must have been mistaken; your son is probably an emotionally healthy genius."

Ans: d
Page: 495
Obj: 2
Type: C

19. Autistic children do *not* typically
a. become obsessive about keeping things the same.
b. exhibit self-stimulatory behaviors.
c. become fascinated with inanimate objects.
d. show unique talents in specific areas.

Ans: c
Page: 495
Obj: 2
Type: C

20. Tyrel was diagnosed with autistic disorder and has an IQ in the mentally retarded range. Despite this, he can remember the name of every all-star baseball player for the past thirty years and can tell which day of the week December 3, 1908, fell on. Tyrel's behavior illustrates
   a. superior short-term memory skills.
   b. neurological impairments.
   c. the term *autistic savant*.
   d. echolalia.

Ans: b
Page: 495
Obj: 2
Type: C

21. A splinter skill is said to exist when
   a. a person's language ability is extraordinarily good but his or her motor and visual abilities are extremely poor.
   b. a child does very well on one or more isolated spatial and rote memory tasks but poorly on those requiring language.
   c. a person can develop a relationship with an inanimate object but not with a person.
   d. a child can retain information for only a short period of time.

Ans: c
Page: 495
Obj: 2
Type: A

22. Bennett, now eight years old, was misdiagnosed for five years before being correctly diagnosed as suffering from autistic disorder. Bennett's parents are very angry. How might a psychologist explain the misdiagnosis?
   a. "There is no excuse; autistic disorder is very easy to diagnose."
   b. "Autistic disorder does not usually develop until adolescence."
   c. "Autistic symptoms overlap with medical and neurological conditions."
   d. "The diagnostic category is so new that psychologists are not really sure whether the disorder exists."

Ans: d
Page: 495
Obj: 2
Type: F

23. Diagnosis of autistic disorder is difficult because
   a. most of these children relate well to adults.
   b. many other disorders show splinter skills.
   c. the symptoms do not appear until adolescence.
   d. the children are often assumed to be mentally retarded.

Ans: b
Page: 495
Obj: 2
Type: C

24. Two children are thought to have mental retardation, but one is suspected of being autistic, too. What symptom would help to identify the child with autistic disorder?
   a. If the child spoke fluently and with creativity
   b. If the child showed splinter skills
   c. If the child were a girl
   d. If the child liked to relate to other children

Ans: a
Page: 495
Obj: 2
Type: F

25. Research has compared autistic and nonautistic children. Which difference was found between groups?
   a. Autistic children are worse at identifying human stimuli than are nonautistic children.
   b. Autistic children are better able to identify nonhuman stimuli than are nonautistic children.
   c. Autistic children are better able to identify human stimuli than are nonautistic children.
   d. Autistic children are worse at identifying nonhuman stimuli than are nonautistic children.

Ans: d
Page: 495
Obj: 2
Type: A

26. Audrey, an autistic child, would be expected to respond best to
    a. adults.
    b. babies.
    c. children.
    d. inanimate objects.

Ans: b
Page: 496
Obj: 2
Type: A

27. If Frith (1991) is right and people with autism have no "theory of mind," we can anticipate that an autistic individual will
    a. tend to lie and cheat rather than accept his or her responsibilities.
    b. be unable to understand or tell jokes.
    c. have an easier time developing social skills than intellectual skills.
    d. have an unusually well developed ability to anticipate other people's needs.

Ans: a
Page: 496
Obj: 2
Type: F

28. As autistic children mature into adulthood, they
    a. remain unable to understand other people's mental states.
    b. become better at understanding other people's mental states.
    c. become increasingly independent.
    d. need an increasing amount of care.

Ans: a
Page: 496
Obj: 3
Type: F

29. Which of the following is *not* one of the new pervasive developmental disorders?
    a. Oppositional defiant disorder
    b. Childhood disintegrative disorder
    c. Asperger's disorder
    d. Rett's disorder

Ans: b
Page: 496
Obj: 3
Type: A

30. Natalie has many of the symptoms of autistic disorder but speaks normally and is not mentally retarded. Since she seems to have a "mild" case of autistic disorder, another diagnosis she might get is
    a. encopresis.
    b. Asperger's disorder.
    c. Tourette's syndrome.
    d. Rett's disorder.

Ans: c
Page: 497
Obj: 3
Type: F

31. Which of the following is a reason some psychologists question whether there should be other pervasive developmental disorders besides autistic disorder?
    a. People with Rett's disorder and Asperger's disorder have all been males.
    b. All of them are caused by neurological problems.
    c. People diagnosed with Asperger's disorder may be high-functioning autistic individuals.
    d. Most of them show symptoms seen in schizophrenia.

Ans: d
Page: 497
Obj: 3
Type: A

32. Nicole interacted with her parents in a normal manner until she was two years old. She spoke in several-word sentences. Then, at two, she stopped talking and became increasingly alone and bizarre. There was no medical reason for this change. What is an appropriate diagnosis for Nicole?
    a. Separation anxiety disorder
    b. Autistic disorder
    c. Tourette's syndrome
    d. Childhood degenerative disorder

Ans: c Page: 497 Obj: 3 Type: A	33. Candy is a two-year-old with severe mental retardation. She appeared normal at birth and demonstrated normal motor development until the age of six months. At that time, Candy's head growth decelerated, and she lost control of her hand movements. She also demonstrated a decreased interest in social activities and currently has little communicative skills and poor coordination. What diagnosis would Candy *most likely* be given? a. Childhood disintegrative disorder b. Autistic disorder c. Rett's disorder d. Asperger's disorder
Ans: a Page: 498 Obj: 4 Type: A	34. Dr. Thomas tells the parents of an autistic child, "Your child withdraws because he feels that, since early in life, you have been cold, perfectionistic, and uninterested." Dr. Thomas's statements a. are not supported by the research. b. reject Kanner's original view of autism. c. are widely held by psychologists and psychiatrists today. d. are supported by evidence from genetics.
Ans: c Page: 498 Obj: 4 Type: A	35. Which of the following statements about autism is *unjustified* in light of current research? a. It has been difficult to investigate the genetics of autistic disorder because it is such a rare condition. b. Problems in the way the brain develops cause autistic disorder. c. The cause of autistic disorder is parental neglect. d. The prognosis for most people with autistic disorder is quite good as long as they receive treatment.
Ans: b Page: 499 Obj: 4 Type: A	36. Gregory is diagnosed with autistic disorder. What are the chances that his brother, Keith, will be autistic, too? a. Unknown, because no research has been conducted on the genetics of autistic disorder b. About 100 to 200 times what we would expect in the general population c. About 50 percent d. Almost 100 percent
Ans: a Page: 500 Obj: 4 Type: F	37. Researchers have been searching for central nervous system impairment as a cause of autism because a. so many organic conditions are associated with it. b. there are so many similar central nervous system-like symptoms in autistic children. c. they have so few other clues to pursue. d. the symptoms found in autistic children mimic central nervous system symptoms in their adult relatives.
Ans: c Page: 500 Obj: 4 Type: A	38. Corey is diagnosed with autistic disorder. If biochemical studies conducted on him showed abnormalities, they would probably indicate a. decreased levels of dopamine. b. excessive amounts of acetylcholine. c. elevated blood serotonin. d. cerebral atrophy brought on by alcohol abuse.

Ans: b
Page: 500
Obj: 4
Type: F

39. Nelson et al. (2001) report that children who later develop mental retardation or autism show
   a. decreased levels of neural growth factor.
   b. elevated levels of neural growth factor.
   c. excessive amounts of acetylcholine.
   d. no difference from normal children.

Ans: a
Page: 500
Obj: 5
Type: C

40. In a group of 100 children with autistic disorder, we would expect that, by age eighteen,
   a. those with good verbal skills would have a good chance of either functioning independently or in a supported environment.
   b. almost all would show the hallucinations and delusions of severe schizophrenics.
   c. almost all of them would be functioning like normal young adults.
   d. even those who were considered "high functioning" would be living in institutions.

Ans: c
Page: 501
Obj: 5
Type: F

41. With respect to the use of drug therapy for treating autism,
   a. the antipsychotic medication, Haliperidol offers the most promise overall.
   b. the hormone secretin offers the most promise overall.
   c. the hormone secretin offers promise for a subset of autistic children.
   d. to date, no drugs have been helpful for treating this disorder.

Ans: c
Page: 501
Obj: 5
Type: A

42. The parents of a child with autistic disorder ask you for advice on the *best* treatment to eliminate the child's self-mutilation and improve his language. Your advice should be,
   a. "Drug treatment has been the most effective approach for both symptoms."
   b. "No treatment has been very effective for these symptoms."
   c. "Behavior modification has been used effectively for both symptoms."
   d. "Behavior modification has been used effectively to reduce self-mutilation, but nothing has been effective in teaching language."

Ans: d
Page: 501
Obj: 5
Type: A

43. A researcher reports that in a long-term follow-up of behavioral treatment with high-functioning autistics, IQ scores increased and interpersonal skills improved, although odd behaviors remained. The researcher's report sounds
   a. unimpressive since most autistics improve without treatment.
   b. the same as reports of changes that occur with drug therapy alone.
   c. unrealistically optimistic.
   d. quite realistic.

Ans: b
Page: 501
Obj: 6
Type: F

44. When it comes to deciding whether a child's behavior indicates a disorder,
   a. parents and professionals usually share the same assumptions.
   b. the decision is often based on the tolerance of the referring agent.
   c. the decision is most often based on objective measures such as test results.
   d. cultural differences play little or no role.

Ans: a
Page: 501
Obj: 6
Type: A

45. If the United Nations sent out statisticians to collect data on the problems that bring children to mental health clinics in the United States and Thailand, they would likely find that
   a. clinics in Thailand see over-controlled children, but those in the United States see under-controlled children.
   b. clinics in both nations tend to see under-controlled children.
   c. clinics in both nations tend to see over-controlled children.
   d. clinics in Thailand see under-controlled children, but those in the United States see over-controlled children.

Ans: d
Page: 502
Obj: 6
Type: C

46. Which statement about the diagnosis of childhood disorders using the DSM-IV-TR is *accurate*?
   a. Clinicians no longer have to decide whether behaviors are inappropriate or excessive to diagnose childhood disorders.
   b. In the latest edition, the criteria have become very strict, so there has been a dramatic decrease in the number of children diagnosed.
   c. In the latest edition, there are only seven diagnostic categories so many children's problems are lumped together in overlapping categories.
   d. Guidelines for assessing the degree of deviation from normal development remain vague.

Ans: d
Page: 503
Obj: 7
Type: F

47. There are three types of attention deficit/hyperactive disorders. They are:
   a. associated with aggression, associated with depression, and associated with anxiety.
   b. with learning disabilities, without learning disabilities, and with emotional problems.
   c. primary, secondary, and tertiary.
   d. predominantly hyperactive, predominantly inattentive, and combined.

Ans: a
Page: 503
Obj: 7
Type: A

48. LuAnne is described by her teacher as, "a shy and anxious daydreamer who cannot keep on task and fails to pay attention to details. It takes LuAnne twice as long to complete worksheets as other students." If LuAnne has a childhood disorder, it is probably
   a. attention deficit/hyperactive disorders, predominantly inattentive type.
   b. attention deficit/hyperactive disorders, combined type.
   c. oppositional defiant disorder.
   d. conduct disorder.

Ans: b
Page: 505
Obj: 7
Type: F

49. Which of the following statements about attention deficit/hyperactive disorders (ADHD) is *accurate*?
   a. They are considered a pervasive developmental disorder.
   b. They are relatively common.
   c. They are rarely associated with academic or social problems.
   d. They are more common in females than in males.

Ans: d
Page: 505
Obj: 7
Type: A

50. Kendall, a first grader, is continuously in the principal's office. His teacher complains that he does not listen to instructions, he fails to finish his schoolwork, he fidgets and squirms in his seat, he often leaves his seat without permission, and he cannot seem to wait his turn during class activities. Whenever the principal calls Kendall's mother, she seems baffled by his behavior. She has told the principal that Kendall does not have any problems at home or at daycare. What diagnosis is appropriate?
   a. Attention-deficit hyperactivity disorder, predominantly hyperactive type
   b. Attention-deficit hyperactivity disorder, predominantly inattentive type
   c. Attention-deficit hyperactivity disorder, predominantly combined type
   d. No disorder; his behaviors only appear to occur in one situation—school.

Ans: c
Page: 503
Obj: 7
Type: A

51. Dr. Hamm says, "All children with attention problems are hyperactive, too. They are more frequently boys and have more difficulty in unstructured situations. In most cases, the disorder persists until adolescence." Which portion of this statement is *inaccurate*?
   a. It is inaccurate to say that children with attention problems have more difficulty in unstructured situations.
   b. It is inaccurate to say that attention problems persist until adolescence.
   c. It is inaccurate to say that all children with attention problems are hyperactive.
   d. It is inaccurate to say that attention problems are more frequent in boys.

Ans: d
Page: 503
Obj: 7
Type: A

52. Mr. and Mrs. Martin learn that their son has attention deficit disorder with hyperactivity. They should expect that he will have all of the following problems *except*
   a. having few friends.
   b. doing poorly in school.
   c. being impulsive.
   d. being sluggish and shy.

Ans: c
Page: 505
Obj: 7
Type: A

53. Mrs. McGill learns that her 7-year-old daughter has been diagnosed with attention deficit disorder without hyperactivity. The prognosis for her daughter is
   a. worse than if she had attention deficits with hyperactivity.
   b. poor—almost all children with attention deficits become school dropouts.

   c. excellent—95 percent of children with these problems are symptom-free in adolescence.
   d. mixed—many such children have conduct disorders that get them in trouble with the law.

Ans: c
Page: 505
Obj: 7
Type: F

54. All of the following are difficulties in diagnosing ADHD in preschool children *except*
   a. there is great variability in the attentional skills of preschoolers.
   b. there is great variability in the activity levels of preschoolers.
   c. preschoolers have fewer demands for sustained attention.
   d. parents are more indulgent of their children's behavior before they begin school.

Ans: a
Page: 505
Obj: 7
Type: F

55. Which of the following is *not* one of the central nervous system areas to be associated with ADHD?
   a. the occipital lobe

b.   the reticular activating system
c.   the frontal lobes
d.   the temporal-parietal regions

Ans: b
Page: 505
Obj: 7
Type: F

56.   Imaging procedures have been
a.   useful for diagnosing ADHD.
b.   helpful for providing insight into the psychophysiology of ADHD.
c.   helpful in offering ideas about treatment for ADHD.
d.   of very little use with respect to understanding or treating ADHD.

Ans: d
Page: 505
Obj: 7
Type: C

57.   Researchers have looked for a specific brain impairment to account for attention deficit/hyperactive disorders. Their work has revealed
a.   that the limbic system is under-aroused.
b.   neurological deficits in those with attention deficits who are *not* hyperactive.
c.   that the right frontal lobes are much larger than in normal controls.
d.   no consistent pattern of findings.

Ans: b
Page: 506
Obj: 7
Type: A

58.   Your neighbor, whose daughter has been diagnosed with ADHD, calls to ask your opinion of an article she just read in a popular magazine. According to the article, her daughter's ADHD symptoms are attributable to diet, and if sugar, artificial dyes, and preservatives were cut out of her diet, her symptoms would decrease. What advice do you give your neighbor?
a.   You should tell your neighbor that although research has supported the connection between food additives and preservatives and ADHD, there is no support for the connection between ADHD and sugar.
b.   You should tell your neighbor that scientific evidence has generally failed to support such beliefs.
c.   You should tell your neighbor that although research has supported the connection between sugar and ADHD symptoms, there is no support for a relationship between ADHD and food additives or preservatives.
d.   You should tell your neighbor that the article is supported by ample scientific evidence and that she would be wise to change her daughter's diet.

Ans: d
Page: 507
Obj: 7
Type: A

59.   Dr. Henry did right in recommending that treatment for José's hyperactivity include
a.   medication alone.
b.   cognitive-behavioral treatment alone.
c.   parent-training programs.
d.   a combination of medication and behavior therapy.

Ans: a
Page: 507
Obj: 7
Type: F

60.   Those opposed to the use of medication in treating attention deficit/hyperactive disorders argue that
a.   problems such as antisocial behavior and learning difficulties are not addressed.
b.   the drugs produce tolerance and eventual physical dependence.
c.   most drugs being prescribed are illegal.
d.   there is no evidence that stimulants have even a short-term benefit.

278   *Chapter 15*

Ans: d
Page: 506
Obj: 7
Type: C

61. Which statement about treating attention deficit/hyperactive disorders (ADHD) is *accurate*?
    a. Stimulant medication usually reduces attention span but leads to improved social behavior.
    b. Stimulant medication works in about 30 percent of cases.
    c. Modeling, parent training, and classroom contingency management programs have been far superior to drug therapy in effectiveness.
    d. Although stimulant medications do not treat the causes, they do produce positive results in 75-90 percent of children with ADHD.

Ans: d
Page: 507
Obj: 7
Type: F

62. Which of the following is not a type of drug that is commonly used to treat childhood disorders?
    a. tranquilizers
    b. stimulants
    c. antipsychotics
    d. narcotics

Ans: b
Page: 507
Obj: 7
Type: F

63. The most commonly used class of drugs for treating ADHD are:
    a. tranquilizers
    b. stimulants
    c. antipsychotics
    d. narcotics

64. A study by the National Institute of Mental Health has concluded that is helpful for reducing the symptoms of ADHD.

Ans: a
Page: 508
Obj: 7
Type: F

    a. carefully managed and monitored use of medication
    b. intensive behavioral therapy
    c. combination of behavioral and family therapy
    d. cognitive behavioral therapy

Ans: b
Page: 508
Obj: 8
Type: F

65. Which statement concerning oppositional defiant disorder (ODD) is *true*?
    a. It is characterized by violence and other antisocial behaviors.
    b. It involves negativistic and hostile behavior but *not* serious violations of the rights of others.
    c. Its symptoms have little or no overlap with those of attention deficit/hyperactive disorders.
    d. It is an old category that is widely recognized around the world.

Ans: d
Page: 508
Obj: 8
Type: C

66. Donald, age thirteen, refuses to obey his parents and blames others for his mistakes, but he does not engage in vandalism or other criminal acts. If Donald were to be diagnosed with a mental disorder, it would likely be
    a. conduct disorder, adolescent onset type.
    b. attention deficit/hyperactive disorders.
    c. separation anxiety disorder.
    d. oppositional defiant disorder.

Ans: b
Page: 508
Obj: 8
Type: A

67. Sam is chronically getting in trouble at school. He fights with other boys, has destroyed school property, and cheats on his assignments. Sam also has been arrested by the local police for setting fires and stealing. Sam *most likely* would be diagnosed with
    a. antisocial personality disorder.
    b. conduct disorder.
    c. attention-deficit hyperactivity disorder.
    d. oppositional-defiant disorder.

Ans: a
Page: 508
Obj: 8
Type: F

68. They represent a serious problem in the United States, where approximately 83,000 juveniles are housed in correctional institutions for antisocial behavior. They are more common in boys than in girls, and the prognosis is poor. What is being described?
   a. Conduct disorders
   b. Attention deficit disorders
   c. Anxiety disorders
   d. Pervasive developmental disorders

Ans: c
Page: 508
Obj: 8
Type: A

69. Ronny, a twelve-year-old, has numerous behavioral problems. He loses his temper quickly and easily, often initiating physical fights. In fact, just last week he pulled a knife on a peer at school. Ronny hates to follow rules and frequently refuses his teacher's requests. He intentionally annoys others and is often physically cruel to animals and people. Overall, he appears resentful, spiteful, and vindictive. What diagnosis is *most appropriate* for Ronny?
   a. Attention-deficit hyperactivity disorder
   b. Both conduct disorder and oppositional-defiant disorder
   c. Conduct disorder
   d. Oppositional-defiant disorder

Ans: d
Page: 509
Obj: 8
Type: A

70. Dr. Quinlan offers this explanation of conduct disorders: "When parents have an inadequate relationship, they produce emotional deprivation that leads to deep conflicts. Without a superego, the anxiety conflict leads to antisocial behavior." Dr. Quinlan supports the _____ perspective on abnormal behavior.
   a. humanistic-existential
   b. behavioral
   c. genetic
   d. psychodynamic

Ans: a
Page: 511
Obj: 8
Type: C

71. Based on Patterson's learning viewpoint on conduct disorders, the *most* effective treatment would be
   a. training parents to control the child's behavior better.
   b. covert sensitization to reduce attention problems.
   c. giving children more control over their environment.
   d. systematic desensitization to reduce anxiety.

Ans: c
Page: 511
Obj: 9
Type: A

72. Clinton Junior High School wants to engage in a prevention program to reduce the risk of violence. Consistent with current beliefs, the administration would support all of the following activities *except*
   a. encourage students to report harassment and threats of violence.
   b. a school-wide awareness program of characteristics of students at risk for violent behavior.
   c. use of harsh consequences for aggressive or violent behavior.
   d. comprehensive individualized intervention with students who display behaviors of significant concern.

Ans: b
Page: 511
Obj: 8
Type: F

73. When treating delinquent youth, Dishion et al. (1999) suggest that
   a. behavioral therapy works well.
   b. group interventions may increase substance abuse as well as antisocial and violent behavior.
   c. group interventions may help youngsters learn appropriate forms of social interaction.
   d. drug therapy should be avoided because it may lead to substance abuse.

Ans: c
Page: 511
Obj: 8
Type: F

74. Which treatment for conduct disorders appears to be *most* effective?
    a. Systematic desensitization and insight therapy for parents
    b. Stimulant medication and social skills role playing
    c. Parent management training and cognitive-social skills
    d. Hypnosis and psychoanalysis

Ans: d
Page: 512
Obj: 8
Type: C

75. Douglas is diagnosed with an internalizing disorder. He is over-controlled and frequently anxious. It is likely that
    a. he will be impulsive and insensitive to others.
    b. even with treatment, he will continue to be anxious.
    c. the disorder will evolve into conduct disorder.
    d. he will improve even without treatment.

Ans: a
Page: 512
Obj: 10
Type: A

76. Katrina has been diagnosed with separation anxiety disorder. She comes from a close-knit family. When she must go to school, she complains of headaches. What aspect of this case is *unusual*?
    a. Nothing about this case is unusual.
    b. It is unusual for separation anxiety to occur in a girl.
    c. It is unusual for separation anxiety to occur in a close-knit family.
    d. It is unusual for separation anxiety to involve headaches.

Ans: d
Page: 512
Obj: 10
Type: F

77. All the following are examples of internalizing disorders *except*
    a. shyness.
    b. depression.
    c. anxiety.
    d. aggressive behavior.

Ans: b
Page: 510
Obj: 8
Type: F

78. Which of the following disorders is an example of an externalizing disorder?
    a. separation anxiety disorder
    b. Conduct disorder
    c. reactive attachment disorder
    d. Generalized anxiety disorder

Ans: c
Page: 510
Obj: 8
Type: A

79. Donny frequently gets into fights with other children and has been expelled several times from school for his misconduct. Which statement about Donny's behavior is *most likely* true?
    a. Donny has a school phobia disorder.
    b. Donny is internalizing his depression.
    c. Donny has an externalizing disorder.
    d. Donny's aggressive behavior will greatly reduce over time.

Ans: a
Page: 512
Obj: 10
Type: F

80. All the following are considered childhood anxiety disorders in DSM-IV-TR *except*
    a. overanxious disorder.
    b. school phobia.
    c. reactive attachment disorder
    d. separation anxiety disorder.

Ans: c
Page: 513
Obj: 10
Type: F

81. Children who are treated with cognitive-behavioral therapy for separation anxiety disorder that develops early in life
    a. have, at best, mixed results.
    b. have much worse outcomes than adolescents who receive the same treatment.
    c. have excellent outcomes.
    d. usually do not benefit unless they also receive medication.

Ans: a
Page: 514
Obj: 11
Type: A

82. Angela was removed from her parents' home when she was two years old because of severe abuse. Over the past five years, she has been in six different foster homes. She has difficulty initiating social interactions, even with her foster parents. Angela would be diagnosed with
   a. reactive attachment disorder, inhibited type.
   b. reactive attachment disorder, disinhibited type.
   c. mood disorder.
   d. separation anxiety disorder.

Ans: b
Page: 514
Obj: 11
Type: F

83. A five-year longitudinal study of depression among third-grade students found that
   a. almost none of the children who were depressed at the beginning of the study were depressed at the end of it.
   b. those who were depressed at the beginning of the study tended to be depressed at the end of it.
   c. over 50 percent of the children showed "serious" levels of depression.
   d. less than 1 percent of the children showed "serious" levels of depression.

Ans: d
Page: 515
Obj: 12
Type: F

84. Depressed mood tends to be
   a. more common in boys than in girls.
   b. more common in young children than in adolescents.
   c. extremely common in non-clinical populations.
   d. more common in adolescents than in young children.

Ans: c
Page: 515
Obj: 12
Type: C

85. A clinical psychologist is comparing her case notes for adults and adolescents she has treated for depression. In general, she is likely to find that
   a. in both groups environmental factors have little effect on depressed mood.
   b. adolescents have positive self-concepts, while adults have negative self-concepts.
   c. there are more females than males in both groups.
   d. adolescents do not benefit from social skills training and cognitive-behavioral therapy, but adults do.

Ans: d
Page: 515
Obj: 12
Type: A

86. A large mental health facility provides treatment services for people with depression from ages two to twenty-one. The majority of their clients are likely to be
   a. females between six and nine.
   b. males between ten and thirteen.
   c. males between eighteen and twenty-one.
   d. females between thirteen and sixteen.

Ans: c
Page: 515
Obj: 12
Type: C

87. If children are vulnerable to depression, it is probably because they are
   a. more likely to be overindulged by their parents.
   b. expected to be depressed, according to socio-cultural values.
   c. less able to cope with environmental stressors.
   d. more likely to have a genetic vulnerability to the disorder.

Ans: a
Page: 515
Obj: 13
Type: F

88. Unusual, repetitive, and involuntary movements are key symptoms of _____ disorders.
   a. tic
   b. attention deficit
   c. conduct
   d. eating

Ans: b
Page: 516
Obj: 13
Type: A

89. When Nick was seven years old, he would involuntarily blink his eyes and sometimes flex his fingers and elbows. This went on for about six months and gradually disappeared. What would be an *appropriate* diagnosis for Nick's condition?
   a. Childhood anxiety disorder
   b. Transient tic disorder
   c. Chronic tic disorder
   d. Tourette's syndrome

Ans: d
Page: 517
Obj: 13
Type: F

90. Which statement about tic disorders is *accurate*?
   a. Most children with tic disorders also show attention deficit/hyperactive disorders and conduct disorder.
   b. Tic disorders occur in less than 5 percent of children.
   c. A chronic tic disorder is one that lasts for more than four weeks.
   d. It is impossible to determine whether a tic will disappear or turn into a chronic condition.

Ans: c
Page: 518
Obj: 13
Type: A

91. Arthur makes involuntary grunting sounds that may evolve into shouted obscenities unless he concentrates very hard to stop them. It is always worse when he is under stress. The *most likely* diagnosis for Arthur is
   a. chronic verbal tic disorder.
   b. autistic disorder.
   c. Tourette's syndrome.
   d. pervasive language disorder.

Ans: d
Page: 518
Obj: 13
Type: F

92. The term that refers to a condition in which an individual utters, calls, or screams obscenities is
   a. antisocial personality disorder.
   b. enuresis.
   c. encopresis.
   d. coprolalia.

Ans: b
Page: 518
Obj: 13
Type: F

93. Tourette's syndrome is the only disorder to involve the symptom of
   a. vocal tics such as coughing and grunting.
   b. coprolalia—the compulsion to shout obscenities.
   c. multiple facial tics.
   d. echolalia—the repetition of others' words.

Ans: c
Page: 516
Obj: 13
Type: F

94 Which of the following is *inaccurate* with respect to child abuse?
   a. approximately one child in ten is the victim of severe physical abuse each year.
   b. approximately 20% of abused children live below the poverty line.
   c. child abuse has increased dramatically since the 1960s.
   d. children who are abused are more prone to exhibit significant physical and psychological problems.

95. If your local community wants to reduce the incidence of child abuse, the best intervention would probably be

Ans: c
Page: 517
Obj: 13
Type: A

   a. a billboard and local television advertising campaign.
   b. harsh penalties for abusers.
   c. parent education programs.
   d. teaching children how to avoid abuse.

Ans: a
Page: 518
Obj: 13
Type: A

96. Dr. Aniston says that Joanne's tics are unconscious attempts to block out thoughts of her parents engaging in sexual intercourse. Dr. Aniston is reflecting which view?
   a. psychodynamic
   b. learning theory
   c. biological
   d. cognitive

Ans: b
Page: 518
Obj: 13
Type: A

97. Dr. Rasmussen believes that Juan's tics are conditioned avoidance responses initially invoked by stress. Dr. Rasmussen is reflecting which view?
   a. psychodynamic
   b. learning theory
   c. biological
   d. cognitive

Ans: d
Page: 519
Obj: 14
Type: F

98. Research suggests that the most effective treatment for enuresis is
   a. medications such as imipramine.
   b. dry-bed training.
   c. cognitive restructuring.
   d. constant reinforcement from parents, awakening the child to use the toilet, and having the child become responsible for making her or his own bed.

Ans: c
Page: 519
Obj: 14
Type: A

99. Lakisha is eleven but still urinates into her clothes or in her bed. Her father also wet the bed when he was a youth. The prognosis is good that Lakisha's problems will end without treatment. The disorder she best illustrates is
   a. tic disorder.
   b. attention deficit disorder.
   c. enuresis.
   d. encopresis.

Ans: c
Page: 520
Obj: 14
Type: A

100. Matthew is eight years old and defecates inappropriately almost daily. He has a history of constipation that has not been helped with laxatives, high-fiber diets, or other suggested remedies. Matthew would be diagnosed with

   a. enuresis.
   b. oppositional defiant disorder.
   c. encopresis.
   d. lazy bowel syndrome.

ESSAY QUESTIONS

1. Describe the DSM-IV-TR criteria for autistic disorder.

2. Compare and contrast the symptoms involved in attention deficit/hyperactive disorders, oppositional defiant disorder, and conduct disorder. What is the prognosis if a child has a combination of these disorders?

3. Compare anxiety disorders with reactive attachment disorder, considering symptoms, etiology, prognosis.

SAMPLE ANSWERS

1. Symptoms of autistic disorder fall into one of three categories according to the DSM-IV criteria. The first category is *qualitative impairment in social interaction* and includes the following: marked impairment in the use of multiple nonverbal behaviors such as eye-to-eye contact, facial expression, body posture, and gestures to regulate social interactions; failure to develop peer relationships appropriate to developmental level; lack of spontaneous seeking to share enjoyment, interests, or achievements with other people; and lack of social or emotional reciprocity. The second category is *qualitative impairments in communication* and includes the following: delay in or total lack of the development of spoken language in individuals with adequate speech; in individuals with adequate speech, marked impairment in the ability to initiate or sustain a conversation with others; stereotyped and repetitive use of language or idiosyncratic language; and lack of varied spontaneous make-believe play or social imitative play appropriate to developmental level. The third category is *restricted repetitive and stereotyped patterns of behavior, interests, and activities* and includes the following: encompassing preoccupation with one or more stereotyped and restricted patterns of interest that are abnormal either in intensity or focus; apparently compulsive adherence to specific, nonfunctional routines or rituals; stereotypes and repetitive motor mannerisms; and persistent preoccupation with parts of objects. Furthermore, the child must have developed such problems before the age of three.

2. Attention deficit hyperactivity disorder (ADHD), oppositional defiant disorder (ODD), and conduct disorder all involve disruptive behaviors that may make school achievement less likely and increase conflicts between the children who have these disorders and peers, parents, teachers, and others. ADHD is believed to take three forms: one in which attention problems are predominant, one in which hyperactivity is predominant, and, most common, one that combines both problems. Children with predominant attention problems are least likely to get in trouble with peers, parents, and teachers. Their prognosis is rather good. However, the many children with ADHD involving hyperactivity are impulsive, engage in a great deal of motor activity, and lack self-control. They are more likely to have coexisting disruptive behavior problems. One of these is ODD, a pattern of hostile, negativistic behavior in which the child loses his or her temper and defies adult requests. Anger and resentment are common emotions for these children, and they may engage in spiteful actions, but they usually do not break the law or act cruelly or viciously toward others. Conduct disorders are characterized by just this kind of behavior. Children with conduct disorders violate the rights of others by stealing, fighting, bullying, lying, destroying property, or acting cruelly toward animals or small children.

   Particularly because ODD is a new diagnosis (and not included in the International Classification of Diseases), the borders between ADHD, ODD, and conduct disorders are not clearly defined. However, it seems that there is an increasing level of antisocial behavior from ADHD, which can involve no disruptive behavior, to conduct disorder, which is defined by such behavior. ODD often precedes the development of conduct disorders and exists concurrently with ADHD. Children who develop conduct disorders before the age of ten have a particularly poor prognosis since they do not seem to outgrow these behavior patterns. Criminal behavior, antisocial personality disorder, and marital and occupational problems are common for people who have ADHD and conduct disorders. Many become involved with alcohol and illegal drugs at an early age. Highly aggressive (and especially sexually aggressive) children are inclined to engage in continued violent behavior. Prognosis is best for males with high IQ scores and for females.

3. Anxiety disorders (e.g., fears, school phobia, shyness, separation anxiety) are considered internalizing and over-controlled. They may be due to the child's innate temperament, physiological factors that cause the child to be highly sensitive, or to learning. Prognosis is good, even without treatment, for most childhood anxiety disorders.

   Reactive attachment disorder is much more serious and is expressed primarily in the child's extreme disturbance in relating to others socially. The inhibited type involves children who have difficulty responding to or initiating social interactions; the disinhibited type socializes indiscriminately. There is a history of circumstances, such as extreme abuse or neglect, or repeated changes in primary caregivers, that results in an inability to meet the child's physical or emotional needs and that affects the formation of basic attachments. The abuse or trauma may result in neurobiological changes in brain areas affecting emotion. There is potential for lifelong attachment disturbance.

CHAPTER 16
Eating Disorders

LEARNING OBJECTIVES

1. Describe the prevalence and characteristics of eating disorders. (pp. 523-526)

2. Discuss the symptoms and subtypes of anorexia nervosa. (pp. 526-528)

3. Consider the physical complications that can arise from anorexia nervosa and why it is difficult to overcome. (pp. 528-529; Mental Health & Society)

4. Delineate other characteristics and mental disorders that are associated with anorexia nervosa. (pp. 529-530)

5. Describe the course and outcome of anorexia nervosa. (p. 530)

6. Discuss the characteristics of bulimia nervosa, as well as its physical complications, associated features, and course and outcome. (pp. 530-532)

7. Discuss the characteristics of binge-eating disorder, as well as its associated features, and course and outcome; briefly describe the eating disorders not otherwise specified that are categorized in DSM-IV-TR. (pp. 532-534)

8. Describe the risk factors for and etiology of eating disorders and evaluate the degree to which society creates eating disorders. (pp. 534-543)

9. Compare the attitudes toward weight of European American and African American females. (pp. 540-542)

10. Compare the treatments for anorexia nervosa, bulimia nervosa, and binge-eating disorder. (pp. 543-546)

MULTIPLE–CHOICE QUESTIONS

Ans: c
Page: 523
Obj: 1
Type: F

1. Nearly _____ percent of adolescent females and _____ percent of adolescent males report dieting to control their weight.
   a. 20;10
   b. 20;20
   c. 50;20
   d. 50;50

Ans: c
Page: 523
Obj: 1
Type: A

2. Professor Aron describes factors associated with eating pattern disorders to include being overweight, low self-esteem, mania, and substance use. Which of these factors is *inaccurate*?
   a. being overweight
   b. low self-esteem
   c. mania
   d. substance use

Ans: b
Page: 523
Obj: 1
Type: A

3. All other things being equal, which college student is *most likely* to give a satisfactory self-rating of attractiveness?
   a. Alvin, an American male who is underweight.
   b. Gerhard, a German male who is overweight
   c. Fanny, an American female who is overweight
   d. Etienne, a French male who is underweight

Ans: d
Page: 524
Obj: 1
Type: F

4. In a study of body weight in Germany, France, and the United States
   a. men and women both agreed that women prefer men to have a muscular body.
   b. men believed that women prefer a lean body, but women indicated they prefer muscular men.
   c. men and women both agreed that women prefer men to have a lean body.
   d. men believes women prefer men who have muscular bodies, while women stated a preference for an ordinary male body.

Ans: d
Page: 524
Obj: 1
Type: A

5. Who would be expected to be *least likely* to have an eating disorder?
   a. Pilar, a Hispanic-American.
   b. Therese, a Native-American.
   c. Yeh, an Asian-American.
   d. Shawnuita, an African-American.

Ans: a
Page: 525
Obj: 1
Type: F

6. Which eating disorder is characterized by a refusal to maintain a body weight above the minimum normal weight for one's age and height, and intense fear of becoming obese, body image distortion, and amenorrhea in females?
   a. anorexia nervosa
   b. bulimia nervosa
   c. body dysmorphic disorder
   d. binge eating disorder

Ans: d
Page: 525
Obj: 1
Type: A

7. Yoriko is a seventeen-year-old girl who is so fearful of gaining weight that she starves herself. She has missed five consecutive menstrual cycles. Although she correctly sees herself as having a skeletal figure, she does not think she has an eating disorder. Yoriko was diagnosed with anorexia. What is unusual about this case?
   a. It is unusual for an anorexic to deny having an eating disorder.
   b. It is unusual for a seventeen-year-old girl to have anorexia.
   c. It is unusual for an anorexic to miss five menstrual cycles.
   d. It is unusual for an anorexic to have an accurate body image.

Ans: a
Page: 525
Obj: 1
Type: F

8. Anorexia nervosa is defined by all of the following *except*
   a. a binge-purge cycle.
   b. an intense fear of becoming obese.
   c. a distorted self-perception of body image.
   d. the cessation of menstruation in females.

Ans: b
Page: 525
Obj: 1
Type: F

9. What is the *most likely* course for someone with anorexia nervosa?
    a. complete recovery
    b. continue to be of low weight
    c. continue to meet diagnostic criteria ten years after treatment
    d. death

Ans: a
Page: 526
Obj: 1
Type: F

10. Which statement about anorexia nervosa is *accurate*?
    a. Despite having a skeleton-like appearance, most anorexics will think they are still overweight.
    b. Anorexics who continually fast tend to be outgoing individuals.
    c. Although anorexics are phobic about gaining weight, they often maintain weight at normal or above-normal levels.
    d. Although self-starvation changes the anorexic's appearance, there are no serious physical complications to the disorder.

Ans: b
Page: 527
Obj: 2
Type: F

11. There seem to be two subgroups of anorexia:
    a. conduct and attention-deficit.
    b. binge-eating/purging and restricting.
    c. binge-eating/purging and binge-eating alone.
    d. anxious and depressive.

Ans: a
Page: 528
Obj: 2
Type: A

12. Kimberly is in a treatment program for eating disorders. She is more introverted than many of the other girls in the program and denies that she is hungry or has any psychological distress. Kimberly has:
    a. restricting anorexia.
    b. binge-eating/purging anorexia.
    c. bulimia nervosa.
    d. binge eating disorder.

Ans: a
Page: 528
Obj: 3
Type: A

13. Jean has been diagnosed with anorexia. Jean also has osteoporosis, substance use disorder, and antisocial personality disorder. Jean is
    a. most likely a male.
    b. most likely a female.
    c. most likely homosexual.
    d. equally as likely to be male or female.

Ans: c
Page: 528
Obj: 3
Type: F

14. One result of complications from anorexia is a mortality rate of up to
    a. 5 percent.
    b. 10 percent.
    c. 20 percent.
    d. 25 percent.

Ans: c
Page: 529
Obj: 3
Type: F

15. A common Axis I disorder that often accompanies anorexia nervosa is:
    a. bipolar disorder.
    b. schizophrenia.
    c. obsessive-compulsive disorder.
    d. paranoid personality disorder.

Ans: d
Page: 530
Obj: 3
Type: C

16. Which of the following is *not* one of the reasons stated for the difficulty in interpreting the relationship between anorexia and personality disorders?
    a. They could represent the misfortune of having two or more disorders by chance.
    b. It could indicate that anorexia is an expression of a personality disorder.
    c. They could be the result of common environmental or genetic factors that underlie both anorexia and the personality disorder.
    d. The personality disorder may be a consequence of the anorexia.

Ans: b
Page: 530
Obj: 5
Type: F

17. A follow-up study by Ben-Tovim and colleagues (2001) found that:
    a. ten percent of the patients had died from complications of the anorexia.
    b. most still showed disturbed eating patterns and psychosocial difficulties.
    c. most had greatly improved their body image.
    d. family therapy had been the most successful treatment for this group.

Ans: c
Page: 530
Obj: 6
Type: F

18. Irene eats large quantities of high-calorie foods at least three times a week, when she is alone or nervous. After binging, she induces vomiting. She is constantly concerned about her appearance, although she is of normal weight. an appropriate diagnosis for Irene is
    a. anorexia nervosa.
    b. overanxious disorder.
    c. bulimia nervosa.
    d. binge-eating disorder

Ans: d
Page: 530
Obj: 6
Type: A

19. Emily has the purging type of bulimia nervosa. She is likely to engage regularly in all of the following *except*
    a. vomiting.
    b. use of laxatives or diuretics.
    c. use of exercise.
    d. fasting.

Ans: b
Page: 531
Obj: 6
Type: F

20. Compared to anorexia nervosa, bulimia
    a. is much easier to diagnose on the basis of appearance.
    b. is much more prevalent.
    c. has little to do with self-control.
    d. is unrelated to body size concern or weight.

Ans: a
Page: 531
Obj: 6
Type: A

21. Sarah has the nonpurging type of bulimia. She is most likely to follow a binge episode with all of the following *except*
    a. use of enemas.
    b. commitment to a severely restrictive diet.
    c. fasting.
    d. engaging in excessive exercise of physical activity.

Ans: c
Page: 531
Obj: 6
Type: F

22. The person with bulimia nervosa is *most likely* to be
    a. underweight.
    b. overweight.
    c. of normal weight.
    d. obese.

Ans: a
Page: 531
Obj: 6
Type: A

23. Bess eats large quantities of high-calorie foods about once a month. What other symptoms must she show to be diagnosed with bulimia?
    a. Negative body image and compensatory actions after eating.
    b. None, because binge eating is the critical symptom of bulimia.
    c. The absence of at least three consecutive menstrual cycles.
    d. Self-starvation.

Ans: b
Page: 531
Obj: 6
Type: F

24. Common complications of bulimia nervosa include all of the following *except*
    a. erosion of tooth enamel.
    b. stomach cancer.
    c. dehydration.
    d. heart problems that may lead to cardiac arrest.

Ans: a
Page: 531
Obj: 6
Type: F

25. A bulimic woman is *more likely* than those in a nonclinical sample to give which type of response to life stressors?
    a. "Food was the first thing I loved that loved me back."
    b. "I need to outline my priorities."
    c. "I guess I need to think about how I can solve this problem."
    d. "This approach didn't work, so I'll have to come up with another one."

Ans: a
Page: 532
Obj: 6
Type: F

26. Which of the following is *not* generally a comorbid condition with bulimia nervosa?
    a. schizoaffective disorder
    b. seasonal affective disorder
    c. borderline personality disorder
    d. depression

Ans: a
Page: 532
Obj: 6
Type: A

27. Belle had a later onset of her bulimia than Amanda did with her anorexia. What outcomes would be *expected*?
    a. Belle would probably have a more positive prognosis than Amanda
    b. Amanda would probably have a more positive prognosis than Belle.
    c. Both would have a relatively poor prognosis.
    d. There's no way to guess at a prognosis for either of them.

Ans: a
Page: 532
Obj: 7
Type: F

28. In a lecture on eating disorders, Professor Lublin noted that binge-eating has been classified as an Axis I disorder characterized by consumption of large amounts of food over a short period of time, an accompanying feeling of loss of control, but unlike bulimia the episodes are not generally followed by use of compensatory behaviors like vomiting or fasting. Which of Professor Lublin's statements in *inaccurate*?
    a. Binge-eating has been classified as an Axis I disorder.
    b. Binge-eating is characterized by consumption of large amounts of food over a short period of time.
    c. Binge-eating is characterized by a feeling of loss of control.
    d. Binge-eating is not characterized by not generally followed by use of compensatory behaviors like vomiting or fasting.

Ans: c
Page: 532
Obj: 7
Type: F

29. The primary difference between bulimia nervosa and binge-eating disorder is that
    a. bulimics tend to be grossly underweight from their eating disorder.
    b. individuals with binge eating disorder are grossly underweight.
    c. binge-eating does not involve compensatory behaviors as seen with bulimics.
    d. fewer binge-eating disordered individuals are able to be treated.

Ans: c
Page: 532
Obj: 7
Type: F

30. Which of the following is *not* one of the documented differences between African American and European American women with binge-eating disorder?
    a. African-American women are less likely to have been treated for eating problems.
    b. African-American women are more likely to be obese.
    c. African-American women are more likely to be show symptoms of psychiatric distress.
    d. African-American women appear to have fewer attitudinal concerns.

Ans: d
Page: 533
Obj: 7
Type: F

31. Approximately what percent of women in weight-control programs have binge-eating disorder?
    a. 5-10
    b. 10-20
    c. 20-30
    d. 20-40

Ans: a
Page: 533
Obj: 7
Type: F

32. Which of the following is *not* a comorbid feature associated with binge-eating disorder?
    a. bipolar disorder
    b. depression
    c. obsessive-compulsive personality disorder
    d. avoidant personality disorder

Ans: d
Page: 533
Obj: 7
Type: A

33. Which of the following women has the *best* prognosis for recovery from her eating disorder?
    a. Andrea, who has restricting anorexia.
    b. Bridgette, who has binge-eating/purging anorexia.
    c. Carla, who has bulimia nervosa.
    d. Darlene, who has binge eating disorder.

Ans: b
Page: 534
Obj: 7
Type: A

34. All of the following would fit the DSM-IV-TR category of eating disorder not otherwise specified *except*
    a. Allegra, who meets all the criteria for anorexia nervosa but has regular menses.
    b. Bernadette, who meets all the criteria for anorexia nervosa and has lost a significant amount of weight, but is only 25 lbs below normal weight.
    c. Claudia, who engages in binge eating and compensatory activities less than twice a week.
    d. Darlene, who engages in binge-eating.

Ans: d
Page: 534
Obj: 8
Type: F

35. Which of the following is *not* a psychological risk factor for eating disorders?
    a. dissatisfaction or distorted body image
    b. low self-esteem
    c. childhood sexual abuse
    d. eating-disordered mothers

Ans: a
Page: 534
Obj: 8
Type: F

36. What percent of American women are able to achieve the size required for fashion models?
    a. five
    b. seven
    c. nine
    d. ten

Ans: b
Page: 534
Obj: 8
Type: F

37. Society's emphasis on thinness over the past twenty years has resulted in the belief that
    a. women like Marilyn Monroe and Betty Grable are no longer considered beautiful.
    b. approval and self-worth are dependent on body size and shape.
    c. no woman can ever achieve the standard that has been set.
    d. by becoming thin a woman can have whatever she wants.

Ans: d
Page: 534
Obj: 8
Type: F

38. By fifth grade, what percentage of girls are dieting?
    a. over five
    b. over ten
    c. over twenty
    d. over thirty

Ans: c
Page: 535
Obj: 8
Type: F

39. Lucy is a small-framed woman. She is 5'4". According to the Height and Weight Table for Women, she should weigh between
    a. 108-121.
    b. 111-124.
    c. 114-127.
    d. 121-135.

Ans: a
Page: 535
Obj: 8
Type: F

40. Which of the following is not one of the reasons that most adolescent girls give for dieting and concern over their bodies?
    a. their health
    b. mass media.
    c. peer influences
    d. criticisms by family members

Ans: d
Page: 535-57
Obj: 8
Type: F

41. In a study by Cauffman and Steinberg (1996), high school and college females picked out all of the following as potentially harmful female stereotypes *except*
    a. those that portray women as helpless or dumb.
    b. those that portray women as sex objects.
    c. those that portray women using alcohol or cigarettes.
    d. those that portray women as ultra-thin models.

Ans: c
Page: 537
Obj: 8
Type: F

42. Research by Forbes et al. (2001) found that
    a. males perceived their bodies as larger than what most men or women would prefer.
    b. males perceived their bodies as the same size that most men would prefer, but larger than what women would prefer.
    c. females perceived their bodies as larger than what most men or women would prefer.
    d. females perceived their bodies as larger than they would prefer, but smaller than what men would prefer.

Ans: a
Page: 537
Obj: 8
Type: F

43. There is a tendency for pre-teen and early teen-age girls to want
    a. thinner bodies than they think boys found attractive.
    b. thinner bodies because that's what they think boys find attractive.
    c. normal weight bodies because that's what they think boys find attractive.
    d. rounder bodies because they think boys want them to have more "curves."

Ans: a
Page: 538
Obj: 8
Type: A

44. Who would be *most likely* to express the most concern over body size and appearance and *most likely* to exhibit disturbed eating patterns?
    a. Jim, a gay male.
    b. Dan, a straight male.
    c. Danielle, a lesbian female.
    d. Eldon, a heterosexual male.

Ans: b
Page: 538
Obj: 8
Type: A

45. Societal emphasis on thinness is
    a. a major cause of eating disorders.
    b. related to an increase in eating disorders.
    c. a sufficient explanation of eating disorders.
    d. only mildly related to eating disorders.

Ans: a
Page: 539
Obj: 8
Type: A

46. Trudy is afraid of having to grow up because it would lead to having to separate from her family and develop her own sense of who she is. By staying thin and not menstruating, she is able to remain a child. This scenario is consistent with what explanation of anorexia?
    a. psychodynamic
    b. behavioral
    c. cognitive
    d. family systems

Ans: d
Page: 539
Obj: 8
Type: A

47. Annie comes from a family that does not openly express conflict. It is an enmeshed family, with no personal boundaries and strong parental control. This would help explain Annie's anorexia according to which approach?
    a. psychodynamic
    b. behavioral.
    c. cognitive.
    d. family systems.

Ans: b
Page: 539
Obj: 8
Type: C

48. The major problem with the family systems theory of anorexia is that
    a. it conflicts with other interpretations.
    b. it has not been empirically tested.
    c. it does not fit all cases of anorexia.
    d. it lacks a logical rationale.

Ans: b
Page: 539
Obj: 8
Type: F

49. Socialization agents, such as peers, family members, and the media, help create
    a. externalized notions of "thin is in" or "you can never be too rich or too thin."
    b. internalization of the thin ideal body image.
    c. externalization of one's inner insecurities.
    d. internalization of family values.

Ans: c
Page: 539
Obj: 8
Type: F

50. The depressive feelings related to an internalization of family and societal pressures to be thin derive from a belief that
    a. the person is letting others down by not being "thin and beautiful."
    b. being of "average weight" infers being an "average person."
    c. being thin is under a person's voluntary control.
    d. by being thin a person will be able to achieve anything and everything.

Ans: d
Page: 539
Obj:
Type: F

51. Vincent and McCabe (2000) found that teasing and criticism about body weight or shape by family members predicts all of the following *except*
 a. ideal-body internalization.
 b. body dissatisfaction.
 c. dieting and eating problems.
 d. body dysmorphic disorder.

Ans: b
Page: 540
Obj: 8
Type: C

52. Which of the following is *not* an accepted psychological explanation for anorexia nervosa?
 a. It develops as women become obsessed with obtaining the cultural ideal.
 b. It develops out of traumatic experiences involving overweight people.
 c. It is symbolic of sexual conflicts.
 d. It reflects a controlling, demanding conviction that the person must lose weight.

Ans: b
Page: 540
Obj: 8
Type: F

53. As early as grade _____, girls are beginning to diet
 a. second.
 b. fourth.
 c. sixth.
 d. eighth.

Ans: c
Page: 540
Obj: 8
Type: F

54. Approximately what percent of nine-year-old girls are worried about being fat?
 a. ten
 b. twenty-five
 c. thirty
 d. forty-five

Ans: d
Page: 540
Obj: 8
Type: F

55. By age thirteen, what percent of girls in America report having dieted
 a. twenty.
 b. forty.
 c. sixty.
 d. eighty.

Ans: b
Page: 540
Obj: 8
Type: F

56. Nancy is planning to undergo the leading cosmetic surgery performed in the United States. She is planning to have
 a. rhinoplasty (a "nose job").
 b. liposuction.
 c. a face lift..
 d. breast implants.

Ans: d
Page: 540
Obj: 8
Type: F

57. Over percent of women in the United States exhibit symptoms of eating disorders.
 a. twenty-five.
 b. forty.
 c. fifty.
 d. sixty.

Ans: a
Page: 540
Obj: 8
Type: C

58. Which woman is the *least likely* to exhibit an eating disorder?
 a. Mei Li, who lives in China.
 b. Shoshana, who lives in Israel.
 c. Candice, who lives in Canada.
 d. Delores, who lives in the United States.

Ans: c
Page: 540
Obj: 8
Type: A

59. Professor Van Exel was discussing the how family and peer relationships affect eating disorders. She stated that girls are influenced about weight loss by their mothers, friends, or sisters, and that it is the direct influence of these people rather than the quality of the relationships that predicts eating disorders for girls. For boys, though, there is no strong relationship between family and peer factors and eating disorders. Which part of Professor Van Exel's statement is *inaccurate*?
   a. Girls are influenced about weight loss by their mothers, friends, or sisters.
   b. It is the direct influence of mothers, friends, and sisters, rather than the quality of the relationships, that predicts eating disorders for girls.
   c. There is no strong relationship between family and peer factors for eating disorders with boys.
   d. All of the statements are accurate.

Ans: a
Page: 541
Obj: 9
Type: F

60. Fijian girls who had developed eating disorders reported that _____ had influenced their beliefs about ideal body image.
   a. television.
   b. magazines.
   c. interacting with western tourists.
   d. school.

Ans: d
Page: 541
Obj: 9
Type: C

61. Jacquee is an African American woman. Unlike the typical European American woman, she is *likely* to
   a. feel that being underweight is better than being overweight.
   b. describe herself as being too fat and old.
   c. believe that thinness is the same thing as beauty and success.
   d. be satisfied with her weight and body size.

Ans: a
Page: 541
Obj: 9
Type: A

62. Which girl is *least likely* to be dieting?
   a. Lashawna, an African American.
   b. Shawna, a European American.
   c. Selena, a Hispanic American.
   d. Audrey, an Asian American.

Ans: c
Page: 541
Obj: 9
Type: A

63. Which girl is *most likely* to engage in bingeing and purging?
   a. Lashawna, an African American.
   b. Shawna, a European American.
   c. Selena, a Hispanic American.
   d. Audrey, an Asian American.

Ans: a
Page: 541
Obj: 9
Type: A

64. Which boy is *least likely* to report a pattern of bingeing and purging?
   a. Adam, a European American.
   b. Nelson, an Asian American.
   c. Carlos, an Hispanic American.
   d. Desmond, an African American.

Ans: c
Page: 541
Obj: 9
Type: F

65. With respect to cross-cultural comparisons of African American women with European American women, which statement is *inaccurate*?
   a. Fewer African American women than European American women appear to have anorexia.
   b. Fewer African American women than European American women appear to have bulimia.
   c. Fewer African American women than European American women appear to engage in bingeing and purging.
   d. African American women are less distressed by weight gain during pregnancy than their European American counterparts.

Ans: b
Page: 541
Obj: 9
Type: C

66. All of the following appear to be factors the insulate African American women from internalizing the message that "thin is in" *except*
   a. Media messages have less impact on African American women because African American women don't identify with European American women.
   b. Due to higher incidences of diseases such as diabetes and coronary heart disease, African American women are more conscious of maintaining a healthy weight than are European American women.
   c. The African American woman's definition of attractiveness is broader than that for European American women, and does not focus only on external traits such as body shape and weight.
   d. Because African American women have roles that include being assertive and egalitarian in relationships and in the community, they are less influenced by gender-restrictive messages.

Ans: d
Page: 542
Obj: 9
Type: F

67. Which of the following is an *inaccurate* statement when comparing African American females with European American females?
   a. 70 percent of African American females, compared with 11 percent of European American females, are satisfied with their current weight or body shape.
   b. African American women perceived themselves to be thinner than they actually are, whereas European American women perceived themselves as being heavier than they actually are.
   c. African American women believe it is better to be a little overweight than underweight, while European American women fear being overweight
   d. Both African American women and European American women believe that beauty is fleeting and decreases with age.

Ans: d
Page: 542
Obj: 9
Type: A

68. Mary, an anorexic, is perfectionistic, obedient, an excellent student and athlete, and a model child. Dieting and weight loss are the only areas of her life where she feels she has control. Which part of this statement is *inconsistent* with the portrait of an anorexic?
   a. Mary is perfectionistic, obedient, and an excellent student and athlete.
   b. Mary is a model child.
   c. Dieting and weight loss are the only areas of her life where she feels she has control.
   d. The entire statement is an accurate portrait of anorexics.

Ans: a
Page: 542
Obj: 9
Type: F

69. Which characteristic is a predictor of both anorexia and bulimia?
   a. perfectionism
   b. obedience
   c. lack of control
   d. academic excellence

Ans: a
Page: 542
Obj: 9
Type: F

70. All of the following characteristics are typical of both males and females with eating disorders *except*
   a. aggressiveness
   b. low self-esteem
   c. passivity
   d. dependence

Ans: b
Page: 542
Obj: 9
Type: A

71. The psychologists who are administering the support group that Calista attends are doing research to look at psychological traits for families of the men and women in the disordered eating group. These psychologists are *most likely* to find
   a. no consistent psychological traits.
   b. high rates of affective disorders.
   c. high rates of personality disorders.
   d. high rates of anxiety disorders.

Ans: c
Page: 543
Obj: 10
Type: F

72. Blouin et al. (1992) found an interesting pattern for patients with bulimia that led these researchers to hypothesize which disorder is related to the bulimia?
   a. dysthymia
   b. major depression
   c. seasonal affective disorder
   d. bipolar disorder

Ans: d
Page: 543
Obj: 10
Type: F

73. Which statement concerning the relationship between eating disorders and sexual abuse is *accurate*?
   a. There is no relationship between sexual abuse and eating disorders.
   b. There is a direct link between sexual abuse and eating disorders.
   c. Sexual abuse leads to eating disorders.
   d. Sexual abuse may be indirectly related to eating disorders.

Ans: c
Page: 543
Obj: 10
Type: A

74. A clinical psychologist treating a woman with eating disorders says, "Eating problems are associated with depressed mood, although we are not clear whether depression is the cause or the effect. What is clear is that sexual abuse is a causal factor in eating disorders." Research indicates that these remarks are
   a. entirely false. Research fails to support either assertion.
   b. partially true. Research rejects the association with depression but supports the idea that sexual abuse causes eating disorders.
   c. partially true. Research supports the association with depression but rejects the idea that sexual abuse causes eating disorders.
   d. entire true. Research supports both assertions.

Ans: b
Page: 543
Obj: 10
Type: F

75. Which of the following is *not* associated with eating disorders?
   a. Wanting to be attractive to men
   b. Attention deficit/hyperactivity disorder.
   c. Depression.
   d. Genetics.

Ans: c
Page: 543
Obj: 10
Type: F

76. Which of the following did Strober et al. (200) find with respect to first-degree relatives of patients with anorexia and bulimia?
     a.   Relatives of those with anorexia were likely to have anorexia, but not bulimia.
     b.   Relatives of those with bulimia were likely to have bulimia, but not anorexia.
     c.   Relatives of those with anorexia or bulimia were as likely to have either eating disorder.
     d.   There seemed to be no clear relationship.

Ans: d
Page: 543
Obj: 10
Type: C

77. Research exploring the relationship between genetics and eating disorders suggests that
     a.   there is a strong genetic link for eating disorders.
     b.   there is a strong genetic link for anorexia and bulimia, but not for other eating disorders.
     c.   there is only a weak link between genetics and eating disorders.
     d.   although there is strong support for a connection between familial factors and eating disorders, it is unclear whether this connection is primarily genetic or environmental.

Ans: a
Page: 544
Obj: 10
Type: C

78. A school-based group intervention program described by Daigneault (2000) for adolescent girls at risk for eating problems involved all of the following goals *except*
     a.   learning the appropriate ways to diet.
     b.   learning to develop a more positive attitude toward their bodies.
     c.   increasing their comfort in expressing their feelings to others.
     d.   increasing assertiveness skills.

Ans: d
Page: 544
Obj: 10
Type: C

79. Sands (1998) suggests all of the following interventions for girls to deal with eating disorders *except*
     a.   a gender analysis by identifying sex role messages (e.g., "girls must be thin, pretty, and sexy")
     b.   identifying the consequences of gender-related messages (e.g., "I'm going to starve myself to be thin").
     c.   choosing statements of change and implementing them (e.g., "Being healthy is important to me so I will eat and exercise sensibly").
     d.   developing aggressiveness skills to resist media messages (e.g., "Don't you dare tell me how I'm supposed to look!")

Ans: b
Page: 544
Obj: 10
Type: C

80. Karen is dangerously thin and has been admitted to the hospital because of her anorexic condition. The initial goal of treatment will be to
     a.   get her to understand that she is in danger of killing herself.
     b.   restore weight.
     c.   force feed her.
     d.   involve her in a group program with other anorexic girls. .

Ans: a
Page: 544
Obj: 10
Type: C

81. In order not to sabotage weight gain, it is important that the patient receive _____ at the same time that restoration of weight is undertaken.
     a.   psychological support
     b.   group therapy
     c.   family therapy
     d.   nutritional education

Ans: c
Page: 544
Obj: 10
Type: A

82. Millie has been hospitalized because of her anorexia. She will receive psychological intervention to help her with all of the following *except*
    a. understanding and cooperating with nutritional and physical rehabilitation.
    b. identifying and understanding the dysfunctional attitudes related to the eating disorder.
    c. learning the Internet websites that focus on issues of anorexia and other eating disorders.
    d. improving her interpersonal and social functioning.

Ans: c
Page: 544
Obj: 10
Type: C

83. Henry has been hospitalized because of his extreme anorexic condition. His treatment team should include a core of all of the following *except* (noting, though, that the exception might be included in the team)
    a. physician.
    b. psychiatrist.
    c. psychiatric social worker.
    d. psychologist.

Ans: b
Page: 544
Obj: 10
Type: F

84. Which approach to treating anorexia is designed to correct irrational preoccupation with weight and to encourage weight gain by allowing the patient to watch television, use the telephone, have visits from family and friends, and wear street clothes as weight is gained?
    a. psychodynamic
    b. behavioral
    c. cognitive-behavioral
    d. family systems

Ans: a
Page: 544
Obj: 10
Type: A

85. Amy has just begun therapy for anorexia nervosa. She is in the hospital, where medical staff are giving her feedings to increase her weight. After she has gained sufficient weight, _____ should be implemented because it helps maintain treatment gains achieved in the hospital.
    a. family therapy
    b. stimulant medication
    c. systematic desensitization
    d. aversive conditioning

Ans: b
Page: 544
Obj: 10
Type: F

86. When do conditions that might contribute to purging need to be identified for hospitalized bulimic patients?
    a. prior to admission
    b. during the initial assessment
    c. after treatment has begun
    d. as soon as the patient is willing to discuss them

Ans: c
Page: 544
Obj: 10
Type: A

87. Priscilla has been hospitalized because of her bulimia. All of the following physical conditions might be expected to have resulted from her disorder *except*
    a. esophageal reflux disease and dental erosion.
    b. cardiac arrhythmias and electrolyte imbalance.
    c. bowel obstructions.
    d. dehydration.

Ans: a
Page: 545
Obj: 10
Type: F

88. Important goals in treating bulimia are to normalize the eating pattern and to eliminate the binge-purge cycle. The disordered eating pattern typically broken up
     a. with a routine of eating three meals a day with one to three snacks a day.
     b. with a routine of eating five meals a day.
     c. by having the patient work with a nutritionist to learn the appropriate ways of combining healthy foods.
     d. with shock therapy whenever the patient considers vomiting.

Ans: c
Page: 545
Obj: 10
Type: C

89. Paula is searching for the most effective treatment for bulimia. Research suggests it is a combination of
     a. response prevention and family therapy.
     b. relaxation training and cognitive-behavioral therapy.
     c. cognitive-behavioral therapy and antidepressant medication.
     d. psychoeducational groups and stimulant medication.

Ans: d
Page: 545
Obj: 10
Type: A

90. Xanath is in a psychoeducational group for treating her bulimia. Which of the following is *not* one of the techniques she can expect to learn?
     a. To eliminate binges, she must eat regularly.
     b. She will be taught how to anticipate the urge to binge and how to prevent or delay binges.
     c. She will learn to delay purging for as long as possible after an eating binge.
     d. She will learn that each binge is part of her entire bingeing pattern.

Ans: a
Page: 545
Obj: 10
Type: F

91. Which of the following is *not* one of the common components of cognitive-behavioral treatment plans for bulimia and binge-eating disorder?
     a. snapping a rubber band around the wrist to snap whenever a thought of bingeing occurs,
     b. encouraging the consumption of three or more balanced meals a day.
     c. reducing rigid food rules and body image concerns.
     d. developing cognitive and behavioral strategies.

Ans: c
Page: 545
Obj: 10
Type: F

92. The most successful treatment for bulimia has been a combination of cognitive-behavioral therapy and antidepressant medication. How successful has this treatment been?
     a. Completely successful, with rates of recovery up to 90%.
     b. Modestly successful, with rates of recovery up to 75%.
     c. Somewhat successful, with rates of recovery of about 50%.
     d. Not very successful, with rates of recovery less than 20%.

Ans: b
Page: 545
Obj: 10
Type: F

93. Which of the following is predictive of treatment failure for bulimics?
     a. family dysfunction
     b. poor social adjustment
     c. low level of intelligence
     d. socioeconomic status

Ans: d
Page: 545
Obj: 10
Type: F

94. What strategies is being used to help bulimics who have not been successful in other treatment programs?
     a. developing social skills
     b. improving family communication
     c. enhancing self-esteem
     d. regulating emotions

Ans: c
Page: 545
Obj: 10
Type: C

95. How does treatment for binge-eating disorder compare with treatment for bulimia nervosa?
   a. They are the same.
   b. Treatment for bulimia nervosa is more successful because it has been used for a longer period of time.
   c. Treatment for binge-eating disorder presents fewer physical complications because there is no purging.
   d. Because binge-eating disorder has not really been classified by the DSM, there have not been enough comparison studies to allow for any conclusions.

Ans: a
Page: 545
Obj: 10
Type: A

96. Marcia has been diagnosed with binge-eating disorder. We would expect her to have all of the following characteristics *except*
   a. she is not concerned with her eating habits.
   b. she is overweight.
   c. she overeats without regular compensatory behaviors.
   d. she has to deal with stereotypes of overweight individuals.

Ans: b
Page: 545
Obj: 10
Type: A

97. Gary is in treatment for binge-eating disorder. Which of the following would not be one of the typical phases involved in his treatment?
   a. Determining the cognitive factors underlying the eating disorder.
   b. Developing behavioral techniques to maintain good eating habits.
   c. Employing cognitive strategies regarding his distorted believes about eating.
   d. Using relapse prevention strategies to identify potential obstacles and setbacks.

Ans: a
Page: 545
Obj: 10
Type: A

98. Clarissa is in a treatment program for her binge-eating disorder. She records her body weight weekly, implements healthy eating patterns, keeps a food diary, and learns about obesity, proper nutrition, and physical exercise. Clarissa is *most likely* in the _____ phase of her program.
   a. first
   b. second
   c. third
   d. maintenance.

Ans: b
Page: 545
Obj: 10
Type: A

99. Dorit has been asked to prepare a list of "forbidden" foods and to rank them in order of "dangerousness." Dorit is *most likely* in the _____ phase of her treatment program for binge-eating disorder.
   a. first
   b. second
   c. third
   d. maintenance

Ans: b
Page: 546
Obj: 10
Type: F

100. How effective is cognitive-behavioral therapy in treating binge-eating disorder?
   a. It is very successful in getting most patients to stop bingeing and to lose weight.
   b. It is successful in getting patients to stop bingeing, but not particularly successful in helping them lose weight.
   c. It is successful in getting patients to lose weight, but not particularly successful in helping them to stop bingeing.
   d. It has not been particularly successful in either helping patients stop bingeing or losing weight.

ESSAY QUESTIONS

1. Identify two eating disorders and describe the symptoms that characterize these disorders.

2. What etiological explanations are there for the eating disorders?

3. What treatment strategies are effective in the treatment of eating disorders?

SAMPLE ANSWERS

1. (Answers may vary)
   a. In anorexia nervosa, a disorder found almost exclusively in women, fear of weight gain leads to self-starvation or eating and purging, which such consequences as low blood pressure and heart disease. Sufferers possess a distorted body image.
   b. The criteria for bulimia nervosa include eating large quantities of high-caloric foods at least twice weekly for three months, feeling a loss of control over eating, and following eating with compensatory behaviors: self-induced vomiting, purging, or fasting. Much more prevalent than anorexia, bulimia is unrelated to an individual's weight. Binges tend to be related to negative emotions.
   c. Binge-eating disorder is similar to bulimia nervosa, however, the binge eating is not following by vomiting, excessive exercise, or fasting (i.e., compensatory behaviors).

2. A primary factor in eating disorders is societal emphasis on thinness, most particularly noted in western industrialized nations, although countries that are influenced by western standard s are now beginning to report increased problems with eating disorders in women. Women tend to suffer from some body image distortion, believing they weigh more than they actually do; men are also influenced by mass media presentation of muscular male bodies, and the disorders are beginning to become a problem for them as well. Genetics are seen to have some effect, but it is difficult to tease out how much is genetics and how much environment. Family interactions, as well as influence from peers, are also important in the development of these disorders.

3. Individuals with eating disorders tend to suffer from low self-esteem, depression, and perceived lack of control. Initial treatment for anorexia focuses on weight gain (by feeding tube, contingent reinforcement for weight gain, or both). Cognitive behavioral and family therapy sessions are common after weight gain, but relapse and continued obsession with weight are common. Bulimia has been somewhat successfully treated with psychotherapy, cognitive-behavioral therapy, and antidepressant medications; the most successful has been a combination of cognitive-behavioral therapy and use of antidepressant medications. Binge-eating disorder is most commonly treated with cognitive behavior therapy, although it has been more successful in eliminating the bingeing than in reducing weight.

CHAPTER 17
Psychotherapeutic Interventions

LEARNING OBJECTIVES

1. Discuss the various biological therapies, including electroconvulsive therapy (ECT) and psychosurgery, and their use and effectiveness in treating mental disorders. (pp. 549-551)

2. Define psychopharmacology. Describe and evaluate the use of antianxiety, antipsychotic, antidepressant, and antimanic medications. (pp. 551-555)

3. Define psychotherapy and describe its basic characteristics. Discuss why traditional psychotherapy may not be effective with individuals from non-Western cultures and ethnic minority groups. (pp. 555-556)

4. Describe the goals and techniques of psychoanalysis and post-Freudian psychoanalytic therapy. Evaluate the effectiveness of psychoanalytic therapy. (pp. 556-559)

5. Describe the therapies based on the humanistic/existential perspective, including person-centered therapy, existential analysis, and gestalt therapy. (pp. 559-560)

6. Describe the therapeutic techniques based on classical conditioning, including systematic desensitization, flooding and implosion, and aversive conditioning. (pp. 560-562)

7. Describe the therapeutic techniques based on operant conditioning, including token economies and punishment. (pp. 562-563)

8. Describe observational learning techniques and cognitive-behavioral therapies. (pp. 563-564)

9. Discuss the goal of health psychology and describe the techniques used to promote lifestyle changes, including biofeedback. (pp. 564-566)

10. Discuss research on the effectiveness of individual psychotherapy. (pp. 566-569)

11. Describe the common components and types of group therapy; evaluate the effectiveness of group therapy. Describe the functions of couples and family therapy, and the different emphases of the communications and systems approaches. (pp. 569-573)

12. Evaluate the factors involved in choosing a therapist. (p. 570; Critical Thinking)

13. Discuss the movement toward systematic integration and eclecticism. (pp. 573-574)

14. Consider the issues raised with respect to culturally diverse populations and psychotherapy. (pp. 574-579)

15. Discuss the changes in mental health service delivery caused by managed health care. (pp.579-581)

16. Describe primary, secondary, and tertiary prevention and give examples of each. (pp. 581-583)

MULTIPLE–CHOICE QUESTIONS

Ans: c
Page: 549
Obj: 1
Type: F

1. Treatment that uses physical means to alter the physiological and psychological state of people with mental disorders is considered a(n) _____ treatment technique.
   a. biofeedback
   b. action-oriented
   c. biology-based
   d. insight-oriented

Ans: d
Page: 549
Obj: 1
Type: F

2. Which statement about electroconvulsive therapy (ECT) is *accurate*?
   a. ECT is an effective treatment for both schizophrenia and endogenous depression.
   b. ECT improves the mood of depressed individuals by changing their hormones.
   c. Although it is clear that ECT cures schizophrenia, the reasons for its success are not clear.
   d. Although it is clear that ECT effectively treats depression, the reasons for its success are not clear.

Ans: d
Page: 549
Obj: 1
Type: C

3. Laura suffers from major depression. She is treated with electroshock applied to one hemisphere of her brain. The shock lasts about six minutes but produces only slight memory loss for events just before and after treatment. What aspect of Laura's treatment is *unusual*?
   a. It is unusual for shock to produce memory loss.
   b. It is unusual to treat major depression with electroshock.
   c. It is unusual for electroshock to be applied to one hemisphere.
   d. It is unusual to sustain shock for more than one-half second.

Ans: a
Page: 549
Obj: 1
Type: A

4. Yussef is scheduled to have an electroconvulsive therapy treatment tomorrow. He can expect
   a. some confusion and short-term memory loss after the treatment.
   b. to remain awake throughout the procedure.
   c. to feel alert and less depressed immediately after the treatment.
   d. that the shock will be applied to his hands and feet.

Ans: d
Page: 549
Obj: 1
Type: F

5. In the 1960s, how frequently were electroconvulsive therapy (ECT) and the psychosurgery procedures of prefrontal lobotomy and transorbital lobotomy used to treat functional mental disorders?
   a. There was an increase in the use of both forms of treatment.
   b. Neither treatment was used at all.
   c. There was an increase in the use of ECT, but lobotomies were extremely rare.
   d. There was a decrease in both.

Ans: a
Page: 551
Obj: 1
Type: C

6. Prefrontal lobotomy, electrical cauterization, and videolaserscopy are all forms of
   a. psychosurgery.
   b. drug therapy.
   c. biofeedback.
   d. electroshock therapy.

Ans: b
Page: 551
Obj: 1
Type: A

7. Imagine that you are reading the medical chart for a psychiatric patient treated for schizophrenia during the 1930s and 1940s. Which of the following notes would *not* be included in the chart?
   a. "Patient has not responded well to electroconvulsive therapy."
   b. "Patient given another dose of phenothiazines."
   c. "Considering giving patient another insulin shock treatment."
   d. "Patient may be a good candidate for psychosurgery."

Ans: d
Page: 551
Obj: 1
Type: A

8. In 1946, Mrs. Mendez was treated for schizophrenia in a way that left her calm but impaired cognitively. The treatment produced permanent brain damage. Mrs. Mendez was probably treated with
   a. high doses of lithium carbonate.
   b. high doses of phenothiazines.
   c. electroconvulsive therapy.
   d. psychosurgery.

Ans: c
Page: 551
Obj: 1
Type: A

9. Suppose you were looking through old medical charts at a psychiatric institution. You notice that prefrontal lobotomies and transorbital lobotomies were extremely common at the institution during the 1940s and early 1950s but almost completely disappeared from the charts by 1958. What explains this?
   a. Electroconvulsive therapy was found to be more effective than psychosurgery.
   b. Psychosurgery was made an illegal medical procedure in the mid-1950s.
   c. Effective medications made psychosurgery unacceptably dangerous.
   d. Deinstitutionalization made psychosurgery unnecessary.

Ans: a
Page: 551
Obj: 1
Type: F

10. What form of treatment revolutionized mental health care in the 1950s?
    a. Antipsychotic medications
    b. Cognitive behavioral therapy
    c. Psychoanalytic therapy
    d. Milieu therapy

Ans: d
Page: 551
Obj: 2
Type: F

11. Psychopharmacology is best defined as the
    a. "study of the psychological factors involved in the development of substance abuse."
    b. "biological treatment of mental disorders."
    c. "use of psychological principles to improve biological conditions."
    d. "study of the effects of drugs on the mind and behavior."

Ans: a
Page: 551
Obj: 2
Type: F

12. Since the 1950s, this form of biologically based treatment has allowed the early discharge of hospitalized mental patients and has permitted them to function in the community. What is this treatment?
    a. Drug therapy
    b. Electroconvulsive therapy
    c. Behavioral medicine
    d. Psychosurgery

Ans: c
Page: 551
Obj: 2
Type: C

13. Dr. Kramer is a critic of psychopharmacology approaches to treating mental patients. Which of the following is Dr. Kramer *not* accurate in claiming?
    a. "Medication may be a way of oppressing women; twice as many women are prescribed antianxiety drugs."
    b. "We are too dependent on drugs as a cure; more patients get medication than all other therapies put together."
    c. "Drug therapy is far less effective than psychosurgery for treating most forms of mental disorder."
    d. "Antianxiety medication can be abused because it has high potential for addiction."

Ans: a
Page: 551
Obj: 2
Type: C

14. Meprobamate, Librium, and Valium are all _____ drugs.
    a. antianxiety
    b. antimanic
    c. antipsychotic
    d. antidepressant

Ans: c
Page: 553
Obj: 2
Type: C

15. Krishna was originally diagnosed as having an anxiety disorder. Then the diagnosis was changed to schizophrenia. If his medication changed to reflect the different diagnoses, he probably went from taking a _____ to taking a(n) _____.
    a. meprobamate; benzodiazepine
    b. tricyclic; MAO inhibitor
    c. benzodiazepine; phenothiazine
    d. phenothiazine; tricyclic

Ans: a
Page: 553
Obj: 2
Type: F

16. A side effect of taking phenothiazines is, which is characterized by psychomotor symptoms of involuntary movement of the head, tongue, and extremities.
    a. tardive dyskenisia
    b. tardive dyskenisia
    c. multiple sclerosis
    d. Tourette's syndrome

Ans: b
Page: 553
Obj: 2
Type: A

17. Hannah is fifty-three years old and has been taking a drug for twenty-five years to control her schizophrenic symptoms. Although the drug has been helpful, she has developed symptoms that resemble Parkinson's disease and, more recently, has developed involuntary movements of the head and tongue that are side effects of the medicine. What type of drug has Hannah probably been taking?
    a. A benzodiazepine
    b. A phenothiazine
    c. An antimanic
    d. A meprobamate

Ans: a
Page: 553
Obj: 2
Type: F

18. Antidepressant drugs are classified in three ways. One type is called tricyclics. The other two are
    a. MAO inhibitors and SSRIs.
    b. MAO inhibitors and meprobamates.
    c. lithium derivatives and tricyclics.
    d. phenothiazines and lithium derivatives.

Ans: c
Page: 553
Obj: 2
Type: A

19. Lance's psychiatrist says, "I am taking you off your current medication because it isn't helping with your depression much and has the danger of interacting with certain foods to cause severe illness. The new drug stops the re-uptake of serotonin and, despite any bad press you have heard, is safe and has only mild side effects." Lance's first drug was probably _____; the new drug is probably _____.
   a. an MAO inhibitor; lithium
   b. Clozapine; a tricyclic
   c. an MAO inhibitor; an SSRI
   d. Clozapine; an SSRI

Ans: d
Page: 554
Obj: 2
Type: A

20. Which pairing of drug and disorder is *most* appropriate?
   a. Schizophrenia—barbiturates
   b. Schizophrenia—imipramine
   c. Depression—phenothiazines
   d. Bipolar disorder—lithium carbonate

Ans: a
Page: 554
Obj: 2
Type: A

21. Iris is on a drug to control her mood swings. Because its effective dosage is close to its toxic level, Iris is supposed to have her blood levels of the drug monitored often. The drug is probably
   a. lithium.
   b. Clozapine.
   c. imipramine.
   d. Prozac.

Ans: c
Page: 555
Obj: 3
Type: C

22. Psychological therapies vary in many ways, but they all share some important features. Which of the following statements is *not* true for all therapies?
   a. All therapies seek to increase the client's adaptive functioning.
   b. All therapies are designed to be corrective.
   c. All therapies focus on changing observable behavior.
   d. All therapies involve an interpersonal relationship between therapist and client.

Ans: b
Page: 555
Obj: 3
Type: F

23. "The purchase of friendship"; "A conversation with a therapeutic purpose"; "The systematic application of techniques derived from psychological principles to help troubled people." What do all these definitions refer to?
   a. Community psychology
   b. Psychotherapy
   c. Insight
   d. Psychopharmacology

Ans: a
Page: 555
Obj: 3
Type: C

24. Which of the following is a common characteristic of psychotherapy?
   a. The opportunity to relearn or develop behaviors
   b. The use of hypnosis
   c. The use of psychoactive medications
   d. The avoidance of emotional experiences

Ans: d
Page: 556
Obj: 3
Type: C

25. Which of the following is not characteristic of all types of psychotherapy?
   a. There is a chance for the client to relearn.
   b. Clients have the opportunity to generate new emotionally important experiences.
   c. Clients have certain motivations and expectations.
   d. Clients become aware of unconscious forces that drive their behavior and feelings.

Ans: a
Page: 556
Obj: 3
Type: C

26. Dr. Stockton emphasizes the need for clients to understand their feelings, become conscious of their daily motivations, and appreciate conflicts hidden within themselves. Dr. Stockton's approach to therapy reflects the
   a. insight-oriented approach.
   b. biology-based approach.
   c. eclectic approach.
   d. action-oriented approach.

Ans: d
Page: 556
Obj: 3
Type: C

27. Dr. Calderon says, "I do not have my clients look deeply into their childhood memories or unconscious motives. I teach them how to act and think differently, and after they practice these techniques, they improve quickly and dramatically." Dr. Calderon's thinking reflects that of _____ therapists.
   a. community-oriented
   b. insight-oriented
   c. biologically oriented
   d. action-oriented

Ans: c
Page: 556
Obj: 4
Type: C

28. The goal of psychoanalysis is to
   a. force clients to see the totality of their experience in the here and now.
   b. increase the client's control over formerly automatic body functions.
   c. induce ego weakness so that repressed conflicts can be uncovered and resolved.
   d. teach new skills in stressful situations.

Ans: a
Page: 556
Obj: 4
Type: C

29. Which of the following statements regarding traditional psychoanalysis is *inaccurate*?
   a. Because of its stress on underlying unconscious processes, psychoanalysis is well suited for individuals with severe psychopathology.
   b. Psychoanalysis seems best suited for individuals who are verbal and intelligent.
   c. Many of the basic tenets of psychoanalysis have not yet been tested adequately.
   d. Psychoanalysts typically do not adhere to the scientific method when evaluating their therapeutic outcomes.

Ans: c
Page: 557
Obj: 4
Type: A

30. Frank comes home from his first therapy session saying, "All she asked me to do was say anything that came to my mind. Then I described a dream I had last night. She said it probably symbolized something important that I wasn't aware of." Frank's therapist is
   a. probably a humanistic-existential therapist.
   b. using transference to develop a therapeutic alliance.
   c. using the techniques of psychoanalysis.
   d. probably an action-oriented therapist.

Ans: d
Page: 556
Obj: 4
Type: A

31. Ken has been seeing Dr. Hammond for several years in an attempt to relieve his stress and anxiety. If Dr. Hammond is a psychoanalyst, her goal with regard to Ken's treatment would be to help him
   a. dispute his irrational thoughts.
   b. learn different coping mechanisms.
   c. produce change in himself through personal growth and self-actualization.
   d. gain insight into his defenses and unconscious conflicts.

Ans: c
Page: 557
Obj: 4
Type: A

32. Alyssa has a recurrent, distressing dream that she arrived at work only half-dressed. The rest of her dream is spent trying to get back home so that she can get dressed before anyone notices that she forgot some of her clothing. When Alyssa describes this dream to her therapist, he suggests that Alyssa might be feeling anxious about forgetting to do something important at work or worried about not doing a complete job. The therapist has
   a. fixated the dream's manifest content.
   b. encouraged Alyssa in her transference.
   c. interpreted the latent content of the dream.
   d. engaged in counter-transference.

Ans: b
Page: 557
Obj: 4
Type: A

33. Zelda became very angry at her therapist for not being willing to lower her therapy fees. Zelda's therapist replied, "You are angry at me now just like you have been angry at your mother for not giving you the love you needed as a child." Zelda's therapist is
   a. working through.
   b. interpreting transference.
   c. interpreting free association.
   d. interpreting counter-transference.

Ans: a
Page: 557
Obj: 4
Type: A

34. After several months in therapy, Gina is angry with her therapist and demands to know why he will not give her several hours of counseling each day. The psychodynamic concept that *best* explains this is
   a. transference.
   b. dream symbolism.
   c. interpretation.
   d. free association.

Ans: b
Page: 557
Obj: 4
Type: A

35. Here is a very brief transcript from a therapy session:
   Therapist: So how does Jim treat you?
   Client: First he seems interested, then he gets bored with me.
   Therapist: Like your father.
   Client: Exactly! Yes. I see. Jim treats me the way Dad did!
   This interaction *best* illustrates the psychoanalytic technique of
   a. free association.
   b. interpretation.
   c. counter-transference.
   d. analysis of resistance.

Ans: c
Page: 557
Obj: 4
Type: F

36. Freud believed that all psychoanalysts need to undergo psychoanalysis themselves because he feared that unless they had gone through the process themselves, _____ might occur and spoil the benefits of the transference relationship.
   a. resistance
   b. interpretation
   c. counter-transference
   d. latent content

Ans: d
Page: 558
Obj: 4
Type: C

37. A primary difference between traditional and contemporary psychodynamic therapy is that
   a. traditional psychodynamic therapy emphasizes dysfunctional ego processes.
   b. traditional psychodynamic therapy de-emphasizes unconscious conflicts among the id, ego, and superego.
   c. contemporary psychodynamic therapy de-emphasizes unconscious conflicts among the id, ego, and superego.
   d. contemporary psychodynamic therapy emphasizes ego processes and de-emphasizes id processes.

Ans: a
Page: 558
Obj: 4
Type: F

38. Many psychotherapists now predict that psychoanalysis
   a. will decline in use.
   b. will be viewed in the future as an action-oriented form of psychotherapy.
   c. will become the dominant method of treatment for ethnic minorities.
   d. will become the dominant method of treatment for most individuals with mental disorders.

Ans: c
Page: 559
Obj: 5
Type: F

39. A belief in free will and an emphasis on self-concept and phenomenology underscore the _____ approach to therapy.
   a. action-oriented
   b. psychoanalytic
   c. humanistic-existential
   d. cognitive-behavioral

Ans: d
Page: 559
Obj: 5
Type: A

40. Kyle says, "I want a therapist who focuses on the wholeness of a person and how that person sees the world. My self-concept is what's important, not my unconscious." Kyle will feel most comfortable seeing a _____ therapist.
   a. biofeedback
   b. psychoanalytic
   c. behavior
   d. humanistic-existential

Ans: c
Page: 559
Obj: 5
Type: C

41. A therapist who does exclusively client-centered therapy probably would subscribe to the idea that
   a. when conflicts remain unresolved, no amount of behavior change can produce long-lasting success.
   b. all people have within them unconscious drives dictating their behavior.
   c. the therapist's way of relating to the client is more important than the techniques he or she uses.
   d. positive reinforcement shapes all people regardless of whether a person has a mental disorder or is "normal."

Ans: b
Page: 559
Obj: 5
Type: F

42. Rogers is to _____ therapy as Perls is to _____.
   a. humanistic-existential; behavioral medicine
   b. person-centered; Gestalt
   c. person-centered; psychoanalytic therapy
   d. insight-oriented; action-oriented therapy

Ans: c
Page: 559
Obj: 5
Type: A

43. Dr. A says, "The exact techniques I use in therapy are not nearly as important as the quality of the therapeutic relationship I develop with a client." Dr. B. says, "Therapy should involve clients in the totality of their current experiences and feelings so that their typical fragmentation is brought into a whole." Dr. A probably does _____ therapy; Dr. B. probably does _____ therapy.
   a. existential; psychoanalytic
   b. humanistic-existential; psychoanalytic
   c. person-centered; gestalt
   d. gestalt; cognitive-behavioral

Ans: b
Page: 559
Obj: 5
Type: A

44. Julia comes home after her first therapy session and says, "We talked about my feelings of being lonely, about death, and about my philosophy of life. The therapist said I was responsible for my own existence. It was very thought-provoking." Julia's therapist is
   a. using the techniques of psychoanalysis.
   b. probably an existential therapist.
   c. using the techniques of action-oriented therapists.
   d. probably a gestalt therapist.

Ans: d
Page: 559
Obj: 5
Type: C

45. Dreams and their interpretation are important in both
   a. person-centered and existential therapies.
   b. psychoanalysis and action-oriented therapy.
   c. existential and cognitive-behavioral therapies.
   d. psychoanalysis and gestalt therapy.

Ans: a
Page: 559
Obj: 5
Type: C

46. Which term is *correctly* paired with its form of therapy?
   a. Here and now—gestalt
   b. Counter-transference—gestalt
   c. Transference—client-centered
   d. Existential crisis—psychoanalysis

Ans: c
Page: 559
Obj: 5
Type: F

47. _____ and _____ therapies have generated little research, so it is difficult to evaluate their effectiveness.
   a. Insight-oriented; action-oriented
   b. Classical conditioning; operant conditioning
   c. Existential; gestalt
   d. Cognitive-behavioral; family

Ans: b
Page: 560
Obj: 6
Type: C

48. Which list includes *only* therapies based on classical conditioning principles?
   a. Behavioral medicine, person-centered therapy, and aversive conditioning
   b. Systematic desensitization, implosion, and flooding
   c. Gestalt, systematic desensitization, and modeling
   d. Systematic desensitization, token economy, and aversive conditioning

Ans: d
Page: 560
Obj: 6
Type: F

49. Systematic desensitization is based on _____ learning principles.
   a. observational
   b. operant conditioning
   c. psychodynamic
   d. classical conditioning

Ans: c
Page: 560
Obj: 6
Type: A

50. Marcel is a pianist but is terribly frightened to give recitals. His therapist first teaches him how to relax. Then Marcel develops a hierarchy of scenes having to do with playing the piano, which increase in the amount of anxiety they cause him. Finally, he relaxes while imagining each scene. This *best* illustrates
   a.   covert sensitization.
   b.   gestalt therapy.
   c.   systematic desensitization.
   d.   implosion.

Ans: d
Page: 560
Obj: 6
Type: A

51. Dr. Erdstrom is thinking about her upcoming session with Mary Lou. Mary Lou sought Dr. Erdstrom's services as a result of her extreme fear of public speaking. Dr. Erdstrom treated Mary Lou by having her imagine herself in various situations giving speeches while at the same time trying to remain relaxed. The process has been gradual, with Dr. Erdstrom having Mary Lou imagine situations that are more and more anxiety provoking. The treatment technique that Dr. Erdstrom is using is
   a.   exposure with response prevention.
   b.   exposure.
   c.   flooding.
   d.   systematic desensitization.

Ans: a
Page: 560
Obj: 6
Type: A

52. Dr. Wu says, "Systematic desensitization (SD) is based on classical conditioning principles and is more effective than psychotherapy for treating phobias. SD has the advantage of requiring fewer sessions than insight therapies but forces clients to experience very high levels of anxiety." Which portion of this statement is *inaccurate*?
   a.   It is inaccurate to say that SD requires clients to experience high levels of anxiety.
   b.   It is inaccurate to say that SD is based on classical conditioning principles.
   c.   It is inaccurate to say that SD is more effective than psychotherapy for treating phobias.
   d.   It is inaccurate to say that SD requires fewer sessions than insight therapies.

Ans: b
Page: 560
Obj: 6
Type: C

53. What is the main difference between systematic desensitization and flooding?
   a.   Flooding is done in the imagination.
   b.   In desensitization, the feared situation is paired with relaxation.
   c.   Desensitization relies on classical conditioning, whereas flooding relies on operant conditioning.
   d.   Desensitization makes use of psychoactive medications.

Ans: d
Page: 561
Obj: 6
Type: A

54. Caleb has a phobia about insects and spiders and sees a therapist who uses flooding to treat fears. At some future session, Caleb can expect
   a.   to be guided through an imaginary journey through a field full of insects and spiders.
   b.   to learn how to relax his muscles completely.
   c.   the therapist to challenge his irrational beliefs about insects and spiders.
   d.   to experience insects and spiders actually walking over his hands and arms.

Ans: b
Page: 561
Obj: 6
Type: F

55. When an unacceptable behavior is paired with an unpleasant stimulus, the therapy being used is called
    a. systematic desensitization.
    b. aversive conditioning.
    c. a shaping procedure.
    d. a non-contingent reinforcement procedure.

Ans: a
Page: 560
Obj: 6
Type: C

56. Stacey is frightened of flying in airplanes. Lana is addicted to cigarettes. Which of the following is the *best* match of client and behavior therapy?
    a. Stacey—systematic desensitization; Lana—aversive conditioning
    b. Stacey—token economy; Lana—flooding
    c. Stacey—aversive conditioning; Lana—token economy
    d. Stacey—punishment; Lana—systematic desensitization

Ans: c
Page: 562
Obj: 6
Type: A

57. Imelda wants to quit smoking. She has signed up for a rapid-smoking (aversive conditioning) treatment program. The problem she is likely to discover with this form of treatment is that
    a. it is rarely effective at suppressing smoking even temporarily.
    b. it is based on operant conditioning principles, which are inappropriate for treating smoking.
    c. its use of noxious stimuli may make her quit treatment too soon.
    d. it relies heavily on one's ability to imagine unpleasant situations.

Ans: d
Page: 560
Obj: 6
Type: C

58. What do covert sensitization, implosion, and systematic desensitization have in common?
    a. They are all based on operant conditioning principles.
    b. They are all insight-oriented approaches.
    c. They all use aversive conditioning.
    d. They all use the client's imagination.

Ans: b
Page: 562
Obj: 7
Type: A

59. In a school for behaviorally disturbed children, the teacher has a list of desirable behaviors every child should do every day. She gives each child a sticker for each behavior the child does. At the end of the day, the stickers are exchanged for toys, play time, and privileges. The teacher is using
    a. covert sensitization.
    b. a token economy.
    c. aversive conditioning techniques.
    d. a combination of modeling and punishment.

Ans: d
Page: 563
Obj: 7
Type: F

60. Research indicates that, in the treatment of hospitalized schizophrenic patients, token economies
    a. harm staff morale even if they improve patient behavior.
    b. are virtually worthless.
    c. change behavior permanently.
    d. may not be continued outside the hospital.

Ans: c
Page: 563
Obj: 7
Type: A

61. A child with severe mental retardation repeatedly bangs his head against a wall. He has already done some permanent damage to his brain yet continues to bang his head. Which behavior therapy will be *most* effective with this child?
    a. Systematic desensitization
    b. Token economy
    c. Punishment
    d. Observational learning

Ans: d
Page: 563
Obj: 7
Type: F

62. When Lovaas used electric shocks as punishment for twin children who were diagnosed with schizophrenia
    a. the children's thought processes were improved, although their undesirable behaviors were unchanged.
    b. the frequency of temper tantrums went up.
    c. behaviors learned in the hospital setting were not maintained outside.
    d. tantrums were eliminated, while affectionate responses developed.

Ans: c
Page: 563
Obj: 8
Type: F

63. In an experiment comparing the effectiveness of different treatments for an intense fear of snakes, the greatest improvement was seen in the group that
    a. underwent relaxation training and watched a movie of people handling snakes.
    b. received systematic desensitization.
    c. watched a live model handle snakes and then did it themselves.
    d. was punished for fear responses.

Ans: a
Page: 563
Obj: 8
Type: A

64. A teacher wants to develop an instructional film to show how students can take tests without becoming unduly anxious. Based on research about effective modeling, the actors demonstrating test-taking in the film should
    a. explain what they are doing and display some anxiety while taking a test.
    b. consistently display confidence while taking tests.
    c. not explain what they are doing, just show it.
    d. verbalize irrational beliefs that induce feelings of anxiety.

Ans: d
Page: 563
Obj: 8
Type: A

65. If newly treated alcoholics learn how to stay sober by watching the behavior of "veteran" recovering alcoholics, we might assume that the learning is based on
    a. classical conditioning principles.
    b. insight learning.
    c. delayed reinforcement.
    d. modeling.

Ans: c
Page: 563
Obj: 8
Type: C

66. Which element is *not* shared by cognitive-behavioral therapies?
    a. Teaching problem-solving strategies for dealing with specific life difficulties
    b. Skills training to manage and overcome stress
    c. A reward system that provides points for desirable behavior
    d. Restructuring distorted thinking to become more rational

Ans: b
Page: 564
Obj: 8
Type: A

67. Craig is seeing a therapist because he is very shy and worries constantly that if he says no, he will hurt other people's feelings. His therapist says, "Listen to how irrational your beliefs are—saying no is your right. You worry because you think you have to be perfect; no one is." The therapist probably
    a. is using a combination of observational learning and aversive conditioning techniques.
    b. is supportive of Albert Ellis's rational-emotive concepts.
    c. rejects the cognitive-behavioral approach.
    d. is supportive of the humanistic-existential approach.

Ans: d
Page: 564
Obj: 8
Type: C

68. Which therapy is *correctly* paired with its description or concept?
    a. Beck's cognitive behavioral therapy—classical conditioning
    b. Beck's cognitive behavioral therapy—confrontation of irrational beliefs
    c. Ellis's rational emotive therapy—observing competent models
    d. Ellis's rational emotive therapy—attack on irrational beliefs

Ans: a
Page: 564
Obj: 8
Type: C

69. Which two psychologists' forms of therapy have the *most* in common?
    a. Beck and Ellis
    b. Ellis and Freud
    c. Rogers and Ellis
    d. Perls and Beck

Ans: b
Page: 564
Obj: 8
Type: F

70. Which statement about cognitive-behavioral therapies is *accurate*?
    a. Because none of the therapies seeks to alter thinking patterns, skills learned in treatment are quickly lost afterward.
    b. They may be at least as effective as medication in treating certain types of depression.
    c. They have never been evaluated through research, so it is unclear whether they are effective.
    d. A survey of psychotherapists showed that they believe this form of treatment will decline in use in the future.

Ans: c
Page: 564
Obj: 9
Type: F

71. _____ is the merger of the behavioral and biomedical sciences for the purpose of helping people change their lifestyles to improve their health.
    a. Eclecticism
    b. Cognitive-behavioral psychotherapy
    c. Health psychology
    d. Psychosomatic medicine

Ans: d
Page: 565
Obj: 9
Type: A

72. Which of the following problems is the *most likely* target of behavioral medicine treatment?
    a. Paraphilias
    b. Paranoid schizophrenia
    c. Bipolar disorder
    d. Cigarette smoking

Ans: b
Page: 565
Obj: 9
Type: A

73. Susan has headaches caused by muscle tension in her shoulders. As treatment, she is hooked up to a machine that indicates shoulder tension by making a sound. Susan is told to lower the pitch of the sound, indicating reduced muscle tension. After several sessions, she can control her muscle tension, and her headaches are gone. This illustrates
    a. observational learning.
    b. biofeedback.
    c. the principles of resisting stress.
    d. systematic desensitization.

Ans: a
Page: 534
Obj: 9
Type: A

74. Dr. Myers works at a clinic where he teaches people who have had heart attacks how to improve their diet, manage stress more successfully, and exercise more. Dr. Myers's work *best* illustrates
    a. the field of health psychology.
    b. primary prevention.
    c. the value of insight-oriented treatment.
    d. community psychology.

Ans: d
Page: 565
Obj: 9
Type: F

75. Which statement about biofeedback is *accurate*?
    a. It has not been effective in reducing high blood pressure.
    b. It is similar to aversive conditioning.
    c. It is a form of insight-oriented treatment.
    d. It can help reduce high blood pressure.

Ans: c
Page: 565
Obj: 9
Type: F

76. Exercising regularly, eating right, and learning to relax are all components of
    a. psychopharmacology.
    b. insight-oriented psychotherapy.
    c. health psychology techniques.
    d. tertiary prevention efforts.

Ans: a
Page: 565
Obj: 9
Type: A

77. Health psychology techniques would be valuable for all of the following people *except*
    a. Rochelle, who has chronic memory lapses.
    b. Jim, who has recurring headaches.
    c. Marilyn, who has chronic backaches.
    d. Preston, who has repeated problems with insomnia.

Ans: d
Page: 565
Obj: 10
Type: C

78. Which of the following is *not* a criticism of the behavioral therapies?
    a. Behavior therapy is applicable only to a narrow range of problems.
    b. Behavior therapy is dehumanizing.
    c. Behavior therapy is mechanical and manipulative.
    d. Behavior therapy is suited only for individuals with mild psychopathology and those who are at least average in intelligence.

Ans: a
Page: 567
Obj: 10
Type: F

79. What did Eysenck conclude about psychotherapy back in 1952?
    a. Psychotherapy in general is no more effective than no treatment at all.
    b. Behavioral treatments are more effective than insight-oriented approaches.
    c. Insight-oriented approaches are more effective than behavioral treatments.
    d. Psychoactive medication is more effective than either insight- or action-oriented therapies.

Ans: d
Page: 567
Obj: 10
Type: F

80. Persons's (1991) criticism of past outcome studies of psychotherapy points out that
    a. few studies ever standardize the type of treatment that is being evaluated.
    b. few studies make use of specific diagnoses when comparing different treatment approaches.
    c. regardless of their theoretical viewpoints, real therapists collect virtually the same information about their clients.
    d. real treatment is based not so much on a diagnosis as on information related to the therapist's theoretical viewpoint.

Ans: a
Page: 568
Obj: 10
Type: C

81. A researcher examines a large number of research studies on the outcome of family therapy. She calculates the effect size of treated versus untreated individuals. What kind of research procedure is this?
    a. Meta-analysis
    b. Outcome measurement
    c. Idiographic analysis
    d. Group treatment

Ans: d
Page: 568
Obj: 10
Type: F

82. Results of two recent meta-analyses of therapy outcome studies show that people who receive psychotherapy are
    a. better off than 93 percent of those who get no treatment.
    b. not much better off than those who are not treated at all.
    c. better off than 50 percent of those who get no treatment.
    d. better off than 79 percent of those who get no treatment.

Ans: b
Page: 568
Obj: 10
Type: A

83. Dr. Akbar says, "Reviews of therapy outcome studies indicate that people who get treatment show more desirable changes than people who are untreated. The largest gains occur within the first few months. Clearly, insight-oriented therapy is superior to the other types." What portion of this statement is *inaccurate*?
    a. It is inaccurate to say that the largest gains occur within the first few months.
    b. It is inaccurate to say that insight-oriented therapy is superior to other types.
    c. No portion of the statement is inaccurate.
    d. It is inaccurate to say that outcome studies indicate that people who are treated show more desirable changes than untreated people.

Ans: d
Page: 570
Obj: 12
Type: C

84. Denise is searching for a therapist to treat her anxiety and depression. Which of the following would be *most* important for her to consider in selecting a therapist?
    a. The therapist's orientation, since research indicates that psychoanalysis is most effective with anxiety and depression
    b. The therapist's orientation, since research indicates that behavioral approaches are more effective than medications in treating anxiety and depression
    c. Selecting a psychiatrist, since research shows that medications are more effective than psychotherapy in treating anxiety and depression and psychologists cannot prescribe medications
    d. The match between Denise's values and beliefs and her therapist's

Ans: c
Page: 570
Obj: 10
Type: A

85. Gina leaves her group therapy session feeling as though she can trust the other members, reveal her true feelings, and be protected from harm. Gina's feelings
    a. illustrate the goal of preventing disorder that is found in most groups.
    b. are unusual, since groups stress individual responsibility.
    c. illustrate the support function of group therapy.
    d. reveal that she was in an action-oriented group.

Ans: a
Page: 570
Obj: 11
Type: F

86. "The simultaneous treatment of two or more clients involving one or more therapists" is a definition of
    a. group therapy.
    b. psychotherapy.
    c. community therapy.
    d. family therapy.

Ans: c
Page: 571
Obj: 11
Type A

87. What advantage of group therapy does the following dialogue illustrate?
    Don: Mary, when do you think you'll be ready to work on your problems?
    Mary: Shut up! Stop picking on me.
    Don: I asked a simple question, and you flared up again.
    a. Feeling less isolated about problems
    b. Social support
    c. Feedback on social behavior
    d. Uncovering of hidden conflicts

Ans: b
Page: 571
Obj: 11
Type: A

88. Myrna is experiencing a lot of problems with her fifteen-year-old daughter, Sally. Until a year ago, Sally was a straight "A" student who rarely got into trouble. Now Sally is failing her classes, breaking her curfew, and openly defiant toward her mother and stepfather. If the therapist uses family therapy, his primary goal is *most likely* to
    a. help Myrna and her husband as a couple learn how to lessen Sally's problems.
    b. focus on the interpersonal relationships among all members of the family.
    c. help Sally to interact with other peers who have similar problems.
    d. target Sally as the primary focus of treatment and help her alleviate her distress.

Ans: b
Page: 571
Obj: 11
Type: F

89. Communications and systems are two approaches to _____ therapy.
    a. psychoanalytic
    b. family
    c. marital
    d. action-oriented

Ans: c
Page: 572
Obj: 11
Type: A

90. A therapist says, "When I work with a family, I focus on how members express their feelings and perceptions to others in the system. I need to be active but not dominant in getting the family to become aware of how they send messages and practice new ways of responding to them." This therapist probably supports the
    a. systems approach to family therapy.
    b. humanistic-existential approach to group therapy.
    c. communications approach to family therapy.
    d. rational emotive approach to group therapy.

Ans: a
Page: 573
Obj: 11
Type: F

91. Which statement about couples therapy is *accurate*?
    a. It attempts to clarify communication, not save marriages.
    b. It places primary emphasis on the maintenance of the marriage.
    c. It is not considered a form of group therapy.
    d. It is almost always insight-oriented.

Ans: c
Page: 573
Obj: 13
Type: F

92. Because no one theory or therapy is always effective, most clinicians are moving toward
    a. cognitive-behavioral approaches to treatment.
    b. biologically based forms of treatment.
    c. integrative approaches to treatment.
    d. community psychology approaches to treatment.

Ans: d
Page: 574
Obj: 14
Type: C

93. The Surgeon General's Report on Mental Health (DHHS, 1999) indicated that using Euro-American standards to judge normality or abnormality is dangerous for all of the following reasons *except*

    a. it may result in denying appropriate treatment for minority groups.
    b. it may oppress rather than help culturally different clients.
    c. it is important for mental health practitioners to recognize and respond to cultural concerns of ethnic minorities.
    d. the research demonstrates that techniques that are effective for Euro-American clients are not effective for members of other groups.

Ans: b
Pages: 578
Obj: 14
Type: C

94. When dealing with members of minority groups, a therapist should be particularly sensitive to communication style differences (such as lack of eye contact) with
   a. African American and Asian American clients.
   b. Hispanic American and Native American clients.
   c. African American and Hispanic American clients.
   d. Asian American and Hispanic American clients.

Ans: b
Page: 579
Obj: 15
Type: C

95. The movement toward managed health care has changed treatment in several ways. One of them is
   a. greater reliance on the services of people with Ph.D.'s and M.D.'s.
   b. the emphasis on short-term treatment.
   c. the decline in treatment provided by health maintenance organizations.
   d. a tendency to use newer treatment methods that cannot demonstrate their effectiveness.

Ans: d
Page: 579
Obj: 15
Type: C

96. A recent reform, endorsed by the American Psychological Association, is for clinical psychologists to
   a. engage in community psychology rather than direct treatment.
   b. stop providing short-term treatment to clients who do not have insurance.
   c. abandon their efforts at behavioral medicine.
   d. prescribe medications if they have been adequately trained.

Ans: c
Page: 581
Obj: 14
Type: C

97. Jason is getting graduate training in community psychology. Which of the following topics is *most likely* to be a part of his education?
   a. Marital counseling
   b. Psychopharmacology
   c. Methods of preventing mental disturbance
   d. Psychoanalytic group therapy

Ans: b
Page: 581
Obj: 16
Type: C

98. A junior high school teaches its students about nutrition, how to assert their rights to act independently, and the ability of regular exercise to reduce the incidence of eating disorders. This program *best* illustrates
   a. managed health care.
   b. primary prevention.
   c. "manualized" treatment.
   d. secondary prevention.

Ans: a
Page: 582
Obj: 16
Type: F

99. The goal of _____ is to shorten the duration of mental disorders by detecting problems early and getting individuals into effective treatment.
   a. secondary prevention
   b. community psychology
   c. primary prevention
   d. managed health care

Ans: d
Page: 582
Obj: 16
Type: A

100. A psychologist works with fast-food managers in a small city to increase their willingness to hire individuals who have been hospitalized for mental disorders or mental retardation. This work, which alters attitudes and makes the former patients' re-entry into the community easier, is an example of
   a. primary prevention.
   b. managed health care.
   c. group therapy.
   d. tertiary prevention.

ESSAY QUESTIONS

1. Using the following hypothetical case, describe how treatment would proceed if the person received drug therapy, psychoanalysis, or cognitive-behavioral treatment.

   Margaret, age thirty-six, is a wife, part-time secretary, and mother of two school-age children. She has been depressed for the past ten months. She sleeps poorly because of nightmares, is constantly fatigued, and has no energy to perform her expected tasks at work or at home. She feels like a terrible failure and worries that her husband will divorce her because she imagines he sees her as worthless.

2. How do therapies based on classical conditioning treat individuals with phobias?

3. How are the goals and methods of community psychology different from those of clinicians who provide individual or group therapy?

SAMPLE ANSWERS

1. If treated with medication, Margaret would be given antidepressants. There are three major types of antidepressants: monoamine oxidase (MAO) inhibitors, tricyclics, and drugs like Prozac that block the re-uptake of serotonin. The MAO inhibitors alter the norepinephrine and serotonin levels in the brain and are effective but produce serious side effects if taken with certain foods or other drugs. Tricyclics are also effective and have fewer side effects. Imipramine, one tricyclic drug, has been found to be at least as effective in relieving depressive symptoms as psychotherapy. Prozac and other drugs like it produce only mild side effects such as nervousness and nausea. Because Prozac can also produce insomnia, it might not be helpful for Margaret. Claims that Prozac contributes to suicidal or other violent behavior have been largely ruled out by recent investigations.

   A psychoanalyst would want Margaret to say anything that came to her mind (free association) so that repressed material could be made conscious. The analyst would probably ask her to describe her frightening dreams so that they could be understood for their latent (underlying) content. The psychoanalyst would expect and interpret signs of resistance from Margaret. For instance, if she repeatedly came late to sessions, this might be discussed as a way of avoiding the difficult conflicts that therapy reveals. Her relationship with her husband would probably be linked with one she had with her father: Perhaps her father led her to believe she was worthless. A transference relationship with the therapist, one in which strong feelings are expressed, would be encouraged. The therapist would want to remain unknown so that Margaret could re-enact her childhood issues in the present. Throughout treatment, the analyst would offer interpretations of Margaret's comments, dreams, resistance, and transference so that she could gain insight into the underlying causes of her depression.

   A cognitive-behavioral therapist would emphasize Margaret's current thinking patterns, especially her beliefs that she is worthless and that her husband will divorce her. Albert Ellis's rational emotive therapy would actively challenge irrational beliefs, such as the need to be perfect in everything she does or else people will abandon her. Such a therapist would help her develop more rational beliefs and give her homework assignments so that she could practice new ways of thinking and acting between sessions. Beck's cognitive therapy would be less confrontational. This kind of therapy would focus on Margaret's cognitive triad (negative beliefs about the world, the future, and the self). Together, Margaret and the therapist would uncover her underlying assumptions and test their validity and logic. She would be given small challenges at work or at home so that she could experience some success before moving on to more difficult tasks.

2. There are three forms of treatment based on classical conditioning that can be used to treat phobias: systematic desensitization, implosion, and flooding. Each attempts to reduce anxious responses by using classical conditioning principles. In systematic desensitization, a response incompatible with anxiety—relaxation—is paired with stimuli that typically arouse anxiety. The elimination of the anxiety response occurs in a gradual fashion. In implosion and flooding, extinction occurs rapidly. High levels of anxiety are induced so that, after repeated exposures, they have less capacity to produce anxious responses.

   More specifically, in systematic desensitization, phobic clients are taught to relax, usually by employing the progressive muscle relaxation method, in which muscles are alternately tensed and relaxed. Then the client and therapist construct an anxiety hierarchy, a list of scenes that produce increasing amounts of anxiety related to the phobic stimulus. Finally, the client is instructed to imagine the least anxiety-provoking scene while remaining relaxed. After that scene can be imagined without the client's becoming anxious, the next scene in the hierarchy is mastered. Finally, the client can imagine and face situations that he or she had previously feared and avoided. A variation on systematic desensitization called in vivo sensitization involves gradual direct exposure to the feared stimuli rather than using the imagination.

   In implosion, the client begins by confronting the most feared situation in imagination and is required to face it rather than avoid it. This generates intense anxiety, but after the client "survives" the anxiety, his or her fear subsides. In flooding, the client faces the feared stimulus directly: A person afraid of dogs would be in the same room with a dog and be required to pet it. Although quite effective in treating specific phobias, flooding is so traumatic for some clients that they discontinue treatment.

   Empirical studies show that systematic desensitization is effective in treating phobias. Even when the procedure is modified—using music to produce relaxation or simply talking about the fear—anxiety responses can be eliminated. Although there has been less research on flooding and implosion, they appear to be as effective as systematic desensitization and take less time.

3. Clinicians who provide treatment focus on the individual's problems and resources after problems have developed to the point where help is requested. The individual is expected to change so that he or she can better understand and cope with internal conflicts (insight-oriented therapies) or develop skills for thinking and behaving more effectively (action-oriented therapies). Community psychologists focus on the environmental factors that cause psychological problems and seek to prevent full-blown disorders. They are concerned about community institutions and the effectiveness of services provided. Rather than treating sickness (psychological or physical), community psychologists seek to prevent it and maintain health. For example, in primary prevention, the goal is to reduce the number of new cases of disorders. This is accomplished by strengthening or adding to resources in the community that promote health or by eliminating environmental conditions that threaten health. Primary prevention efforts can occur at the community level, affecting many more people than any form of individual or group therapy. Secondary prevention seeks to reduce the duration of disorders by detecting problems early and making referral to effective treatment. For example, teachers might be trained to identify children who are not adapting to the school environment and refer them to counselors, parents, or others who can help. Tertiary prevention is designed to improve the re-entry into the community of people who were hospitalized for mental disorders. These efforts may require designing transitional living experiences or altering the attitudes of community members so that stereotyped thinking and discrimination in employment and housing are eliminated. In all of these ways, we can see the differences between traditional therapies, which emphasize the individual and the internal and provide help after disorders have "flowered," and community psychology, which emphasizes the environment and large populations and provides preventive interventions.

CHAPTER 18
Legal and Ethical Issues in Abnormal Psychology

LEARNING OBJECTIVES

1. Describe the range of legal and ethical issues relevant to abnormal psychology. (pp. 587-590; Table 18.1)

2. Define criminal commitment processes and discuss criminal law's position on free will. (pp. 590-591)

3. Discuss the rationale for the insanity defense and the legal precedents that have shaped the current standing of the insanity defense, including the M'Naghten Rule, the irresistible impulse test, the *Durham* standard, the American Law Institute (ALI) Model Penal Code, and diminished capacity. (pp. 591-594)

4. Discuss the arguments for and against the plea "guilty, but mentally ill," including Thomas Szasz's arguments against the insanity defense and involuntary commitment. (pp. 594-597; Mental Health & Society)

5. Describe the criteria for finding a defendant competent to stand trial and the procedures involved in determining it, including due process. (pp. 595-596)

6. Describe the concept of civil commitment and the criteria by which individuals are committed. Explain why the assessment of dangerousness is difficult. (pp. 596-599)

7. Explain the rationale for civil commitment, the procedures involved, and the protections that exist against its abuse. Outline the criticisms of civil commitment. (pp. 599-601; Mental Health & Society)

8. Discuss the key legal rulings concerning the rights of mental patients, including the level of proof necessary for commitment (*Addington v. Texas*), the least restrictive environment principle, and the right to treatment (*Wyatt v. Stickney* , *O'Connor v. Donaldson*, and *Youngberg v. Romeo*). (pp. 601-603)

9. Discuss the legal rulings concerning the right to refuse treatment (*Rennie v. Klein* and *Rogers v. Okin*) and the arguments for and against this right. Define the term *least intrusive treatment*. (p. 603)

10. Discuss the reasons for and the impact of the deinstitutionalization of mental patients. Evaluate the present living conditions of many ex–mental hospital patients and the prospects for mainstreaming and alternative community programs. (pp. 603-605)

11. Distinguish between the concepts of confidential and privileged communications. Discuss when therapists may disclose confidential information and where there are exemptions to privileged communications. (p. 605-606)

12. Describe the duty-to-warn principle, the legal rulings related to it (*Tarasoff v. Board of Regents of the University of California*), and the criticisms of the duty-to-warn principle. (pp. 606-609; Critical Thinking

13. Identify the position of professional organizations on the issue of sexual intimacies between therapist and client. Discuss the research on the impact of therapists' sexual involvement with clients. (pp. 609-610)

14. Discuss how mental health professionals need to accommodate the changes in the ethnic profile of Americans. Describe the ethical guidelines for working with culturally different clients and the information in DSM-IV that deals with multicultural influences. (pp. 610-611)

MULTIPLE–CHOICE QUESTIONS

Ans: c
Page: 587
Obj: 1
Type: F

1. At one time, psychologists were primarily involved in evaluating criminal defendants for competency to stand trial. Now psychologists
   a. primarily do evaluations for competency cases that involve the new "guilty, but mentally ill" defense.
   b. are forbidden from doing such evaluations.
   c. have expanded roles including giving expert opinions on child custody and suicide, among other issues.
   d. evaluate civil defendants for competency to stand trial.

Ans: a
Page: 588
Obj: 1
Type: A

2. Due to a mental condition, Jonathan seems unable to feed or care for himself. His family wants to put him in a treatment facility against his will. Joanna has told her therapist that she plans to kill her husband. The therapist is contemplating breaching this confidence so that the husband can be warned. Which case involves behavior that has legal and ethical implications?
   a. Both Jonathan's and Joanna's cases
   b. Neither Jonathan's nor Joanna's case
   c. Joanna's case only
   d. Jonathan's case only

Ans: d
Page: 588
Obj: 2
Type: C

3. A homeless man suffers from schizophrenia and cannot take care of himself. His friends want him to be admitted to a psychiatric hospital, but he refuses to go. This case raises issues of
   a. confidentiality.
   b. insanity.
   c. competency to stand trial.
   d. civil commitment.

Ans: b
Page: 590
Obj: 2
Type: F

4. The basic premise of criminal law in the United States suggests that behavior is
   a. fundamentally uncontrollable.
   b. freely chosen.
   c. a result of genes and our environment.
   d. a product of both culture and family upbringing.

Ans: a
Page: 590
Obj: 2
Type: F

5. Which statement about criminal commitment is *accurate*?
   a. It means the incarceration of someone for having committed a crime.
   b. It occurs when people suffering from mental disorders are admitted to a psychiatric hospital against their will.
   c. It always requires a hearing to assess competency to stand trial.
   d. It leads to incarceration of only those people who are not responsible for their actions.

Ans: c
Page: 591
Obj: 3
Type: A

6. James says that he killed his mother but that, at the time of the crime, he was suffering from delusions brought on by schizophrenia and was therefore unable to control his actions. James's statement illustrates the concept of
    a. privileged communication.
    b. the M'Naghten Rule concerning civil commitment.
    c. not guilty by reason of insanity.
    d. incompetency to stand trial.

Ans: a
Page: 592
Obj: 3
Type: F

7. Which of the following statements is *accurate* regarding the term *insanity*?
    a. *Insanity* is a legal term that has been defined in several ways.
    b. *Insanity* is a psychological term used to describe severe pathology.
    c. *Insanity* has no psychological or legal meaning, it is a colloquialism used in this culture.
    d. *Insanity* is a legal term that is comparable with a psychological disorder.

Ans: a
Page: 592
Obj: 3
Type: F

8. In the case of Kenneth Bianchi, psychologists sought to determine whether his criminal behavior was actually due to the disorder called
    a. multiple personality.
    b. paranoid schizophrenia.
    c. amotivational syndrome.
    d. presenile dementia.

Ans: b
Page: 592
Obj: 3
Type: F

9. Martin Orne, through clever questioning, was able to discover that Kenneth Bianchi was
    a. suffering from schizophrenia at the time of the trial but not at the time of his crimes.
    b. faking the symptoms of multiple personality disorder.
    c. guilty but mentally ill.
    d. suffering from multiple personality disorder and was therefore insane at the time of his crimes.

Ans: c
Page: 593
Obj: 3
Type: F

10. What legal ruling established that defendants can be acquitted of a crime if it is proven that during the act of the crime the individual did not know the nature of his or her actions or did not know that what he or she was doing was wrong?
    a. The American Law Institute's Model Penal Code
    b. The Durham Rule
    c. The M'Naghten Rule
    d. Irresistible impulse

Ans: b
Page: 593
Obj: 3
Type: F

11. According to the _____, defendants can be acquitted of a crime if, at the time of their actions, they did not know what they were doing or could not comprehend that the act was wrong.
    a. irresistible impulse concept
    b. M'Naghten Rule
    c. principle of competency to stand trial
    d. *Durham* standard

Ans: d
Page: 593
Obj: 3
Type: A

12. A man who had delusions and hallucinations that told him to kill his parents is found not guilty by reason of insanity because, at the time of the crime, he did not know right from wrong. This insanity verdict
    a. is no longer possible in the United States.
    b. is contradictory to the American Law Institute code.
    c. illustrates the irresistible impulse idea.
    d. illustrates the M'Naghten Rule.

Ans: a
Page: 593
Obj: 3
Type: C

13. Which of the following accurately pairs the insanity rule with its description?
    a. Irresistible impulse—lack of willpower or control over behavior
    b. M'Naghten Rule—lack of willpower or control over behavior
    c. M'Naghten Rule—unable to help in one's defense
    d. Irresistible impulse—did not know right from wrong

Ans: d
Page: 593
Obj: 3
Type: C

14. The *Durham* (1954) decision suggested that insanity was
    a. an improper way for defendants to avoid responsibility.
    b. too frequently successful, particularly in violent crimes.
    c. always based on irresistible impulse.
    d. a product of mental disease or defect as defined by mental health professionals.

Ans: b
Page: 593
Obj: 3
Type: C

15. An attorney says to his client, "If we can convince the judge that when you shot your mother, you either did not know it was a criminal thing to do or could not control your behavior because you had a mental disease (other than antisocial personality disorder), you should be found not guilty by reason of insanity." What legal standard is the attorney describing?
    a. *Durham* standard
    b. American Law Institute Model Penal Code
    c. M'Naghten Rule
    d. irresistible impulse standard

Ans: c
Page: 594
Obj: 3
Type: C

16. When lawyers for Dan White, murderer of two San Francisco government officials, argued that his behavior was partially due to a diet of junk food, which legal concept was being used?
    a. Involuntary commitment
    b. Incompetence to stand trial
    c. Diminished capacity
    d. Least restrictive environment

Ans: a
Page: 594
Obj: 4
Type: F

17. The _____ case produced such outrage about the issue of insanity that it led to the U.S. Congress passing the Insanity Reform Act.
    a. Hinckley
    b. Menendez
    c. Bianchi
    d. M'Naghten

Ans: b
Page: 594
Obj: 4
Type: F

18. The insanity defense is used in _____ percent of cases and is _____ successful.
    a. about 10; almost always
    b. less than 1; rarely
    c. about 20; rarely
    d. about 2; almost always

Ans: c
Page: 595
Obj: 4
Type: C

19. The purpose of such new verdicts as "guilty, but mentally ill" and "culpable and mentally ill" is to
    a. increase the courts' awareness that mentally ill criminals are not responsible for their actions.
    b. reduce the influence of mental health professionals in trials.
    c. separate the issue of mental illness from individual responsibility.
    d. eliminate the idea of personal responsibility from the law.

Ans: b
Page: 595
Obj: 4
Type: A

20. A lawyer says to the jury, "Labeling anyone as insane makes us blame the individual and avoid looking at the social ills of society that lead to criminal acts. 'Mental illness' is a myth—just a way to take responsibility away from citizens." These remarks support
   a. the idea of "guilty, but mentally ill."
   b. Thomas Szasz's position on the insanity defense.
   c. the American Law Institute's position on the insanity defense.
   d. the M'Naghten Rule.

Ans: d
Page: 595
Obj: 5
Type: C

21. Mental state at the time of a crime is to _____ as mental state at the time before and during the trial is to _____.
   a. competency to stand trial; civil commitment
   b. dangerousness; civil commitment
   c. insanity; dangerousness
   d. insanity; competency to stand trial

Ans: a
Page: 595
Obj: 5
Type: C

22. If a person is deemed mentally incompetent to stand trial, it means that
   a. the person is not sufficiently rational to understand and assist in his or her own defense.
   b. the legal proceedings are dropped and the person is allowed to go free.
   c. the person does not have a diagnosable mental disorder.
   d. the person was not sane during the act of the crime.

Ans: d
Page: 595
Obj: 5
Type: A

23. After a defendant screams at his attorney while in court for the fifth time, the judge says, "It seems likely that your client either does not know what is going on in these proceedings or cannot rationally consult with you." The judge is questioning
   a. the attorney's desire to use civil commitment.
   b. the client's sanity.
   c. the attorney's privileged communication.
   d. the client's competency to stand trial.

Ans: b
Page: 595
Obj: 5
Type: A

24. Janice has bipolar disorder and refuses to take medication to control her manic episodes. She was arrested last night for disturbing the peace and assault. When she is brought into custody, it is apparent that she is experiencing a manic episode. She appears psychotic, and after a psychological evaluation, a psychologist files a report with the court indicating that Janice is not competent to stand trial. What will happen to Janice now?
   a. She will be given medication, and once her manic episode has been controlled, she will be released with no further court involvement.
   b. She will be confined in a prison hospital until she is deemed competent to stand trial.
   c. She will be represented during court proceedings by her legal guardian.
   d. She will be sent to a public psychiatric hospital until she is deemed competent to stand trial.

Ans: a
Page: 595
Obj: 5
Type: F

25. Because of the *Jackson v. Indiana* (1972) decision, the determination that a person is incompetent to stand trial
   a. cannot lead to an indefinite period of confinement.
   b. can be obtained without giving the defendant due process.
   c. now leads to an acquittal on all criminal charges.
   d. now leads to an automatic finding of innocent by reason of insanity.

Ans: c
Page: 597
Obj: 6
Type: C

26. Milton was found not competent to stand trial. He was admitted to a psychiatric facility where, after many months, it was determined he was unlikely to regain competency. According to the Supreme Court ruling *Jackson v. Indiana*, what will happen to Milton?
    a. He will remain in the psychiatric facility.
    b. He will be tried for the crime he was accused of.
    c. Either he will be freed or civil commitment procedures will begin.
    d. He will be found "guilty, but mentally ill" and placed in a psychiatric hospital.

Ans: b
Page: 595
Obj: 6
Type: F

27. The legal checks and balances that are guaranteed to everyone, such as the right to counsel and the right to present evidence, are called
    a. the right to treatment.
    b. due process.
    c. civil commitment.
    d. ethical standards.

Ans: c
Page: 596
Obj: 5
Type: F

28. Lorena Bobbitt was acquitted of malicious wounding for cutting off her husband's penis with a carving knife. What was the basis of her acquittal?
    a. self-defense
    b. battered wife syndrome
    c. insanity
    d. she did not commit the act

Ans: d
Page: 597
Obj: 5
Type: F

29. The prosecution asserted all of the following in an attempt to have Lorena Bobbitt found guilty of malicious wounding for cutting off her husband's penis with a carving knife except
    a. her behavior leading up to her actions appeared planned and deliberate.
    b. she had the ability to distinguish right from wrong.
    c. she acted in a premeditated manner.
    d. the allegations of spousal abuse were not relevant to the case.

Ans: a
Page: 597
Obj: 6
Type: A

30. It is used for people in acute distress who may be dangerous to themselves or others. It may be viewed as a form of protection or a loss of civil liberties before any crime has been committed. What is it?
    a. Civil commitment
    b. The insanity defense
    c. Criminal commitment
    d. Deinstitutionalization

Ans: c
Page: 598
Obj: 6
Type: A

31. Carmelita's mother has contacted an attorney to begin civil commitment proceedings for Carmelita. We can guess that the mother is
    a. highly concerned with the lifelong stigma that psychiatric hospitalization might cause her daughter.
    b. convinced that Carmelita committed a crime while insane.
    c. concerned that Carmelita is dangerous to herself or others.
    d. aware that Carmelita cannot rationally assist her attorney in a criminal case.

Ans: b
Page: 601
Obj: 6
Type: A

32. In the play *Harvey*, a man who says he sees a six-foot white rabbit is the target of people who want to admit him involuntarily to a psychiatric hospital. Why is this kind of civil commitment something to be avoided if at all possible?
    a. People who are in hospitals involuntarily are usually denied treatment.
    b. The stigma of psychiatric hospitalization leads to major disruptions in the person's life.
    c. People who are committed spend more time in the hospital than they would in prison if they were convicted of a crime.
    d. It takes away the person's due process rights.

Ans: d
Page: 598
Obj: 6
Type: A

33. A judge hears four cases involving civil commitment. Based on the criteria for civil commitment, which case is likely to be denied by the judge (the person will *not* be sent to a psychiatric facility involuntarily)?
    a. A man is so terrified of auditory hallucinations that he is likely to lose control and kill himself.
    b. A delusional woman is likely to kill her husband in the next several days.
    c. A starving psychotic man has no permanent residence and no way to stay out of subzero temperatures at night.
    d. A young married woman is seriously depressed after giving birth.

Ans: b
Page: 598
Obj: 6
Type: C

34. Civil commitment is the reason Hannah was hospitalized against her will. The criterion *most likely* to have been used in her civil commitment hearing was
    a. her parents' fear that she was about to lose emotional control.
    b. her inability to care for herself.
    c. her inability to consult rationally with her attorney.
    d. her diagnosis of antisocial personality disorder.

Ans: a
Page: 599
Obj: 6
Type: F

35. Psychologists often make errors in predicting dangerousness. What type of error is *usually* made?
    a. Dangerousness is over-predicted.
    b. Dangerousness is predicted too late to help people.
    c. Dangerousness is found more often in women than in men.
    d. Dangerousness is under-predicted.

Ans: c
Page: 599
Obj: 6
Type: C

36. Why is the prediction of dangerousness in clients important for civil commitment?
    a. Because if dangerousness exists, the person will not receive treatment
    b. Because dangerousness is central to determining whether a person was insane at the time of a crime
    c. Because dangerousness is the principal reason for committing people these days
    d. Because if dangerousness exists, commitment will be judged at a higher level of proof than otherwise

Ans: d
Page: 599
Obj: 6
Type: A

37. Dr. Chung says, "Psychologists are poor predictors of dangerousness for the same reason that meteorologists are poor at predicting when a tornado will occur." Dr. Chung means that dangerousness
    a. is unrelated to the context in which it occurs.
    b. never happens in the same place twice.
    c. is something that is affected by the weather.
    d. is a rare event.

Ans: c
Page: 599
Obj: 6
Type: A

38. A psychologist is trying to determine the dangerousness of a particular criminal. Which form of information would the psychologist *most* like to have to be accurate in making a prediction of dangerousness?
    a. The degree of family emotional support
    b. The person's personality profile
    c. The person's past history of violence
    d. The person's genetic endowment

Ans: a
Page: 601
Obj: 7
Type: F

39. Which statement about involuntary civil commitment procedures is *accurate*?
    a. A formal hearing must be held before a court.
    b. The client must be competent to stand trial.
    c. One mental health professional determines whether the person is insane.
    d. The client may not speak in his or her own defense and is denied any legal counsel.

Ans: b
Page: 601
Obj: 7
Type: F

40. In most cases involving civil commitment,
    a. psychologists must assess whether the person knew right from wrong at the time he or she was arrested.
    b. individuals are convinced to commit themselves voluntarily.
    c. there is no hearing by a judge or jury.
    d. individuals must be involuntarily committed.

Ans: d
Page: 601
Obj: 7
Type: A

41. Mustafa's family has approached the court to have him involuntarily committed. The judge, having decided that Mustafa's mental health should be examined, performs the examination herself. Then, at a formal hearing, Mustafa gets to testify. What part of this story is *inaccurate*?
    a. At a formal hearing, the person who is the target of a commitment cannot testify.
    b. Family members cannot petition for a civil commitment procedure.
    c. A judge does not have the right to order an examination of a person.
    d. A judge is not the one to perform the examination.

Ans: c
Page: 601
Obj: 7
Type: F

42. Critics of civil commitment argue that
    a. patients who are committed will eventually be thankful that they got help.
    b. patients who need treatment cannot be distinguished from those who do not.
    c. patients are being incarcerated even though no crime has been committed.
    d. patients who are treated against their will are better adjusted than those who are not.

Ans: d
Page: 601
Obj: 7
Type: C

43. An attorney says, "You should not be able to confine (punish) a person on the basis of *assuming* that the person will harm someone. And you should certainly not be able to confine the person without a jury trial. It may be called 'treatment,' but it still feels to the person like imprisonment without having committed a crime." The attorney is criticizing
    a. the deinstitutionalization movement.
    b. competency to stand trial.
    c. the right to treatment movement.
    d. civil commitment.

Ans: a
Page: 601
Obj: 7
Type: C

44. Which of the following is *not* a characteristic of civil commitments?
    a. An individual loses all civil rights during the commitment period.
    b. Longer-term involuntary hospitalization requires judicial procedure and review by legal and mental health experts.
    c. An individual may be incapable of caring for himself or herself.
    d. An individual may be an imminent danger to himself or herself or to others.

Ans: b
Page: 601
Obj: 7
Type: A

45. One attorney says, "Incarcerating a person because he or she *might* do something dangerous is for the benefit of society but clearly violates individual liberty." Another attorney says, "If a person is crazy and cannot see his or her need for treatment, we can provide the person with care so that later he or she will be healthy and grateful for the treatment even if it was involuntary." The argument is about
    a. the right to treatment.
    b. civil commitment.
    c. the ethics of confidentiality.
    d. the insanity defense.

Ans: c
Page: 602
Obj: 8
Type: F

46. The *Addington v. Texas* (1979) ruling declared that
    a. people who are involuntarily committed have no right to refuse medication that is given as treatment.
    b. irresistible impulse is no longer a valid definition of insanity.
    c. the state must provide "clear and convincing evidence" (a level of proof of 75 percent certainty) before committing people.
    d. people cannot be kept in mental institutions unless a certain quality of living environment is maintained.

Ans: a
Page: 602
Obj: 8
Type: A

47. An attorney says this to a judge in a civil commitment case: "Your honor, the Supreme Court in 1979 ruled that we cannot deny people their liberty by committing them to mental institutions involuntarily unless we have 'clear and convincing evidence' that they are mentally ill and potentially dangerous." What Supreme Court ruling is the attorney referring to?
    a. *Addington v. Texas*
    b. *Tarasoff v. Board of Regents of the University of California*
    c. *Wyatt v. Stickney*
    d. *Jackson v. Indiana*

Ans: b
Page: 602
Obj: 8
Type: F

48. *Addington v. Texas* was a Supreme Court ruling on civil commitment. It changed the standard of proof so that
    a. the judge or jury had to be 51 percent certain of the evidence to decide in favor of commitment.
    b. a lower level of certainty than in criminal cases was required.
    c. commitment could occur only if there was evidence "beyond a reasonable doubt."
    d. the judge or jury had to be 90 percent certain of the evidence to decide in favor of commitment.

Ans: a
Page: 602
Obj: 8
Type: F

49. Which of the following is *not* part of the patient bill of rights as outlined in the Mental Health Systems Act of 1980?
   a. Right to have the cost of treatment paid for by insurance or a governmental agency
   b. Right to a reasonable explanation of the care and treatment process
   c. Right to appropriate treatment in a supportive environment
   d. Right to have access to telephone, mail, visitation, and private conversations

Ans: d
Page: 602
Obj: 8
Type: A

50. Judge Franklin says, "This patient is fully able to care for herself. I recognize her need for psychological care but have decided that she should be placed in a halfway house rather than a state mental hospital." The judge's decision illustrates the principle of
   a. duty to warn.
   b. commitment based on dangerousness.
   c. right to refuse treatment.
   d. least restrictive form of treatment.

Ans: b
Page: 602
Obj: 8
Type: A

51. Max was committed to a psychiatric hospital six months ago as a result of his aggressive, combative, and physically threatening behavior. At the time of his hospitalization, his family and friends were afraid he was going to hurt someone. At the present time, however, Max is not demonstrating any physically threatening behavior. In addition, he has some minimal self-help skills and is believed to be able to function by himself with minimal supervision. What do the legal rights of mental patients suggest should be done with Max?
   a. There are no legal rights of mental patients that specifically address Max's situation.
   b. Based on the right to the least restrictive alternative, Max should be moved to a group home or halfway house.
   c. Based on the right to refuse treatment, Max should never have been hospitalized and should be released immediately.
   d. Based on the right to treatment, Max should remain in the hospital until the psychologists can predict with certainty that he is no longer a threat to himself or others.

Ans: d
Page: 602
Obj: 9
Type: C

52. Ursula's attorney argues that if she must be treated against her will, she should be treated in a halfway house rather than a hospital and be treated with cognitive psychotherapy rather than medication or electroconvulsive therapy. The attorney's arguments support the principles of
   a. right to treatment and right to refuse treatment.
   b. deinstitutionalization and mainstreaming.
   c. confidentiality and due process.
   d. least restrictive environment and least intrusive treatment.

Ans: b
Page: 602
Obj: 8
Type: A

53. An attorney says, "Patients who have been involuntarily confined for treatment have a constitutional right that is supported by cases such as *Rouse v. Cameron* and *Wyatt v. Stickney*." What right is the attorney talking about?
   a. Confidentiality
   b. Right to treatment
   c. Right to refuse treatment
   d. Due process

Ans: c
Page: 602
Obj: 8
Type: A

54. Suppose a mental patient's family sues a state hospital for failing to provide minimal treatment. What court decision would the family's lawyer probably cite?
   a. *Rogers v. Okin* (1979)
   b. *United States v. Hinckley* (1982)
   c. *Wyatt v. Stickney* (1972)
   d. *Tarasoff v. Board of Regents of the University of California* (1976)

Ans: a
Page: 602
Obj: 8
Type: F

55. Which two cases affirmed the right of mentally ill and mentally retarded people to receive treatment and reasonable care and safety in the institution in which that occurs?
   a. *O'Connor v. Donaldson* and *Youngberg v. Romeo*
   b. *Tarasoff v. Board of Regents of the University of California* and *United States v. Hinkley*
   c. *Addington v. Texas* and *Jackson v. Indiana*
   d. *Rennie v. Klein* and *Rogers v. Okin*

Ans: d
Page: 603
Obj: 8
Type: F

56. According to the 1982 ruling on right to treatment (*Youngberg v. Romeo*), who can define *therapy*?
   a. Juries or judges
   b. The family and friends of the individual patient
   c. A judge
   d. Mental health professionals

Ans: d
Page: 603
Obj: 9
Type: F

57. The *Rennie v. Klein* (1978) and *Rogers v. Okin* (1979) cases both support the
   a. principle of most restrictive environment.
   b. principle of privileged communication.
   c. concept of guilty but mentally ill.
   d. patient's right to refuse treatment.

Ans: b
Page: 603
Obj: 9
Type: A

58. Marta has been diagnosed with catatonic schizophrenia and resides in a psychiatric hospital. When Marta takes her medication, her catatonic symptoms decrease significantly. However, Marta recently has started to refuse her medication, stating that she does not like the side effects. What should staff do?
   a. Given that Marta is refusing to take her medication, revoke her right to the least restrictive alternative and place her in a locked psychiatric ward.
   b. Nothing; Marta has the right to refuse treatment.
   c. Based on her right to the least restrictive alternative, move Marta to a group home in the community.
   d. Based on the right to treatment, force Marta to take her medications.

Ans: a
Page: 603
Obj: 9
Type: A

59. An attorney is arguing before a judge that his client, involuntarily committed to a mental institution, is being forced to take medication and that medication is used only as a means of controlling patients, not treating them. He wants his client to be allowed to refuse medication. Which legal decision should the attorney use to support his position?
   a. *Rennie v. Klein*
   b. *Tarasoff v. Board of Regents of University of California*
   c. *Wyatt v. Stickney*
   d. *Durham* standard

Copyright © Houghton Mifflin Company. All rights reserved.

Ans: b
Page: 603
Obj: 9
Type: C

60. The best example of a form of therapy that would be considered in violation of the least intrusive treatment principle is
   a. rational-emotive therapy.
   b. electroconvulsive therapy.
   c. behavior therapy.
   d. psychoanalytic therapy.

Ans: c
Page: 603
Obj: 10
Type: F

61. The policy in which people with mental disorders were moved out of large mental hospitals and back into their communities beginning in the 1950s is called
   a. communalization.
   b. the right to receive treatment.
   c. deinstitutionalization.
   d. the least intrusive treatment principle.

Ans: a
Page: 603
Obj: 10
Type: C

62. Court cases that exposed mental hospitals to be no more than warehouses for the mentally ill and established the principle of integrating patients as soon as possible into the community supported the trend in mental health called
   a. deinstitutionalization.
   b. primary prevention.
   c. managed health care.
   d. civil commitment.

Ans: b
Page: 603
Obj: 10
Type: F

63. Since its inception in the 1960s, the impact of deinstitutionalization has been to
   a. reduce the need for community supports when mental patients are discharged.
   b. decrease by 50 percent the number of people in institutions.
   c. increase by 75 percent the average number of patients committed during the past 30 years.
   d. virtually eliminate the homeless mentally ill.

Ans: c
Page: 604
Obj: 10
Type: A

64. A clinical psychologist says, "I want my patients to maintain as much contact with their home communities as possible and to get their treatment on an outpatient basis using drug treatment and psychotherapy so that they can stay in the community." These comments support the principle of
   a. privileged communication.
   b. duty-to-warn.
   c. mainstreaming.
   d. right to refuse treatment.

Ans: b
Page: 604
Obj: 10
Type: A

65. A mayor is concerned about the growing number of homeless individuals in the city. Many appear to be alcoholic or suffering from schizophrenia. Which of the legal issues involving abnormal psychology is the mayor *most likely* to criticize?
   a. Principles of patient-therapist confidentiality
   b. Deinstitutionalization
   c. Due process in the criminal commitment process
   d. The right to treatment

Ans: d
Page: 604
Obj: 10
Type: F

66. Roughly one million former mental patients have been discharged from psychiatric facilities since deinstitutionalization began. It appears that the majority of them
a. no longer need treatment but remain unemployed.
b. have found ways to become employed and to overcome their mental illnesses.
c. are now in high-quality nursing homes and group residences.
d. are severely disabled and suffering from schizophrenia and alcoholism.

Ans: a
Page: 605
Obj: 10
Type: C

67. Much of the problem with deinstitutionalization appears to be the
a. lack of community preparation and resources for discharged patients.
b. ineffectiveness of medication given to discharged patients.
c. poor quality of care patients receive in the hospital.
d. frequency with which misdiagnoses are made by mental health professionals.

Ans: b
Page: 605
Obj: 10
Type: F

68. Critics of deinstitutionalization argue that
a. too much money has been spent on resources for individuals on the street.
b. discharged patients who receive neither treatment nor job opportunities become homeless.
c. discharged patients can make the transition to community living if they rely on friends and family for support.
d. not enough people with mental illness have been discharged from psychiatric hospitals.

Ans: c
Page: 605
Obj: 10
Type: C

69. The increased number of homeless people in U.S. cities is *best* linked to
a. legal changes in the definition of insanity.
b. privileged communication.
c. deinstitutionalization.
d. legal changes that allow patients to refuse treatment.

Ans: d
Page: 605
Obj: 10
Type: F

70. Research comparing the treatment outcomes of mental patients who are placed in alternative treatments with outcomes of those placed in mental institutions indicates that
a. outcomes are worse for those in alternative care.
b. those in hospitals are less likely to become homeless.
c. those in hospitals enjoy that environment more.
d. either there is no difference in outcomes or those getting alternative treatments do better.

Ans: c
Page: 606
Obj: 11
Type: A

71. A psychologist says, "I believe that the therapeutic process involves such a deep personal association between therapist and patient that it requires me to keep sensitive information secret from others. Ethically, I must put _____ first."
a. mainstreaming
b. due process
c. confidentiality
d. the patient's rights

Ans: a
Page: 606
Obj: 11
Type: F

72. _____ is an ethical standard that protects clients from disclosure of information without their consent.
a. Confidentiality
b. Privileged communication
c. Duty to warn
d. Due process

Ans: d
Page: 606
Obj: 11
Type: C

73. Keeping client information confidential is
    a. a desirable, but not essential, part of therapy.
    b. an issue with psychoanalytic therapists but not most others.
    c. assured in all circumstances, according to a United States Supreme Court ruling.
    d. an ethical, not a legal, obligation.

Ans: b
Page: 606
Obj: 11
Type: F

74. In a study of the public's view of confidentiality in the therapeutic relationship, it was found that *most* people
    a. think that therapists break confidentiality very frequently.
    b. believe that whatever is discussed is never disclosed.
    c. believe that confidentiality is against the law.
    d. do not want a therapist to keep information confidential.

Ans: b
Page: 606
Obj: 11
Type: F

75. Privileged communication is
    a. a right that is held by the therapist, not the client.
    b. a narrower legal concept than confidentiality.
    c. an ethical obligation, not a legal one.
    d. a broader ethical concept than confidentiality.

Ans: d
Page: 606
Obj: 11
Type: A

76. A therapist says to her client, "What is said in this room is kept in strict confidence unless there are legal or therapeutic reasons to reveal it. Under most circumstances, though, you have control over what gets disclosed. Unless you give me permission, I will not disclose any confidential information." The therapist is describing
    a. the therapist's right of confidentiality.
    b. the client's right to treatment.
    c. the therapist's duty to warn.
    d. the client's privileged communication.

Ans: c
Page: 606
Obj: 11
Type: F

77. Which statement about legal protection of therapists is *accurate*?
    a. The therapist-client relationship is not given the same legal protection as the attorney-client relationship.
    b. Not a single state in the United States has included the principle of client-privileged communication in its laws.
    c. The therapist-client relationship has the same legal protection as the attorney-client relationship.
    d. Psychiatric practices are regulated in only five states in the United States.

Ans: a
Page: 606
Obj: 11
Type: C

78. Monica, age twelve, gives her therapist convincing evidence that she was sexually molested by her stepfather from the time she was eight until she was eleven. According to the principle of privileged communication, the therapist
    a. must divulge this information to the proper authorities.
    b. must have a conference with the stepfather.
    c. cannot divulge this information unless Monica waives confidentiality.
    d. cannot divulge this information under any circumstances.

Ans: c
Page: 606
Obj: 11
Type: A

79. Under which of the following circumstances can a therapist divulge information about a client to a third party?
    a. If the third party is a qualified psychiatrist or psychologist
    b. If the therapist thinks such consultation is in the best interest of the client
    c. If the client is under age sixteen and the therapist thinks the client was a victim of sexual abuse
    d. If the therapist is a professor and will use the information to teach

Ans: b
Page: 606
Obj: 11
Type: A

80. Dr. Vera learns, in the midst of a therapy session, that his client has committed a series of violent rapes. Can Dr. Vera divulge this information to the police?
   a. Yes, but only if the client comes with the therapist to the police.
   b. Yes; therapists are obligated to disclose information when criminal action is involved.
   c. No; privileged communication is a right only the client can waive.
   d. No; criminal action is not an exception to confidentiality.

Ans: c
Page: 606
Obj: 12
Type: A

81. Dr. Johnson's patient Lou was distraught and mentioned several times when he referred to his mother that he was "going to kill the bitch." Dr. Johnson is required by law to
   a. notify his supervisor.
   b. do nothing.
   c. warn the potential victim.
   d. protect the potential victim.

Ans: a
Page: 606
Obj: 12
Type: A

82. Mr. P. told his therapist that he intends to shoot his ex-wife's new husband, and the therapist kept this information confidential. Lawyers are now suing the therapist because Mr. P. did shoot the new husband, as well as his ex-wife. What legal precedents will the attorneys probably use in the case?
   a. *Tarasoff* v. *Regents of the University of California*
   b. Those dealing with the right to refuse treatment
   c. *O'Connor* v. *Donaldson* and *Wyatt* v. *Stickney*
   d. Those dealing with least restrictive environment

Ans: d
Page: 606
Obj: 12
Type: F

83. The duty-to-warn principle
   a. was first discussed in Judge Frank Johnson's ruling in *Wyatt v. Stickney*.
   b. developed out of discontent over the insanity defense.
   c. suggests that there are no circumstances when privileged communication can be waived.
   d. came from the *Tarasoff* ruling.

Ans: a
Page: 606
Obj: 12
Type: C

84. "Protective privilege ends where public peril begins" summarizes
   a. the duty-to-warn principle.
   b. the concept of mainstreaming.
   c. the American Law Institute standard for the insanity defense.
   d. Thomas Szasz's position on patients' rights.

Ans: b
Page: 606
Obj: 12
Type: C

85. According to the *Tarasoff* case, a therapist who informs the police that a client intends to harm another person
   a. is unlawfully breaking the principle of privileged communication.
   b. can still be sued if he or she has failed to warn the potential victim.
   c. has done all that can be reasonably expected.
   d. has unlawfully intruded on the client's right to treatment.

Ans: d
Page: 607
Obj: 12
Type: A

86. A psychologist complains, "This ruling puts me in the role of a double agent: By law I must protect the secrets that my clients tell me, and by law I must reveal those secrets to protect society." Which legal decision is the psychologist criticizing?
    a. *Hinckley v. United States*
    b. *Durham* standard
    c. *Wyatt v. Stickney*
    d. *Tarasoff* ruling

Ans: c
Page: 608
Obj: 12
Type: C

87. Suppose a therapist's client is HIV positive and is engaging in unsafe sexual practices with his wife. The client has not told his wife of his HIV-positive status. Should the therapist warn the wife?
    a. Definitely; the *Tarasoff* decision requires it.
    b. Probably not; most of the *Tarasoff* decision has been overturned in new cases.
    c. Probably, although the *Tarasoff* decision has yet to be applied to AIDS-related issues.
    d. Definitely not; privileged communication can be waived only by the client.

Ans: d
Page: 609
Obj: 12
Type: A

88. Dr. Schmidt says, "If the court forces me to ignore confidentiality and call the police on any client I think might act violently, all therapeutic relationships will be lost, and the chances of violence will actually go up!" Dr. Schmidt's statement represents
    a. conflict over the requirements of the *Wyatt v. Stickney* decision.
    b. an objection to the privileged-communication principle.
    c. a psychoanalytic view of dangerousness.
    d. a common objection to the *Tarasoff* decision.

Ans: c
Page: 609
Obj: 12
Type: F

89. Critics of the duty-to-warn principle argue that
    a. unless the prediction of dangerousness improves, few truly criminal individuals will be arrested by police.
    b. it will lead to overcrowding in mental hospitals.
    c. it will defeat the principle of privileged communication.
    d. without adequate community resources, too many mental patients will become homeless persons.

Ans: b
Page: 609
Obj: 12
Type: C

90. Guidelines for psychologists concerning the duty-to-warn principle include which of the following?
    a. "Warn the potential victim every time a client discusses potential violence."
    b. "Inform the client of the limits of confidentiality and the actions the therapist must take to protect a third party."
    c. "Allow the client to make his or her own choices concerning the use of violence to solve problems."
    d. "Tell clients at the beginning of therapy that confidentiality has no limits."

Ans: c
Page: 609
Obj: 12
Type: A

91. A therapist is concerned that if, at the beginning of counseling, she tells clients that there are limits to confidentiality, clients will be unwilling to disclose the secrets of their lives. Research seems to
    a. show that limits on confidentiality increase disclosure.
    b. indicate that only men are influenced by limits on confidentiality.
    c. show that limits on confidentiality have little impact on disclosure.
    d. support this concern.

338   *Chapter 18*

Ans: a
Page: 609
Obj: 13
Type: A

92. Lillian is considering going to a psychotherapist but has a fear that a male therapist might engage in sexual behavior with her. She reads the ethical principles of the national psychiatry, psychology, and social work organizations. She finds that
a. all professional organizations condemn and prohibit sexual behavior between therapist and client.
b. none of the organizations directly condemns or prohibits sexual behavior between therapist and client.
c. social work condemns sexual behavior between therapist and client, but psychiatry and psychology have taken no position on this issue.
d. psychiatry and psychology condemn sexual behavior between therapist and client, but social work has taken no position on this issue.

Ans: d
Page: 609
Obj: 13
Type: F

93. Which statement about sexuality and therapists is *accurate*?
a. Because of their training, it is rare for psychologists to have sexual fantasies about their clients.
b. A majority of therapists have sexual fantasies about clients, but the number of complaints filed with state licensing boards has gone down recently.
c. Roughly half of therapists have, at one time or another, lost control of their sexual feelings and acted unprofessionally.
d. While sexual fantasies about clients are not uncommon, the vast majority of psychologists control their feelings.

Ans: b
Page: 609
Obj: 13
Type: F

94. A survey of 1,000 psychologists showed that
a. sex between therapists and their clients was spontaneous, and they never repeated the practice.
b. more male therapists than female therapists reported having had sex with their clients.
c. more female therapists than male therapists reported having had sex with their clients.
d. most cases of sexual intimacy were initiated by the client.

Ans: a
Page: 910
Obj: 13
Type: A

95. Patty and her therapist developed a sexual relationship. According to the research, we can expect that
a. Patty will respond with symptoms similar to those of people who have been raped or abused.
b. the therapist will be sued for failing to comply with the *Tarasoff* ruling.
c. Patty benefited from the relationship, especially if she initiated the sexual contact.
d. the therapist became more effective after the sexual relationship developed.

Ans: c
Page: 610
Obj: 13
Type: F

96. Which statement *accurately* describes the situation for the ethical oversight of psychotherapists?
a. There is currently no procedure for filing complaints against therapists.
b. Clients are expressly forbidden from suing therapists for malpractice if they have engaged in sexual intimacy.
c. Clients always have the legal recourse of suing their therapists for malpractice.
d. In only six states is there a way for clients to file complaints against therapists.

Ans: a
Page: 610
Obj:
Type: C

97. It is believed by many mental health professionals that current concepts of mental health are
    a. culture bound.
    b. insufficient.
    c. focused too heavily on minority issues.
    d. focused too heavily on abnormality instead of normality.

Ans: d
Page: 610
Obj:
Type: C

98. Mental health professionals have expressed concern that all of the following problems are incident to theories of therapy that are based on values specific to a middle-class, White, highly individualistic population *except*
    a. misdiagnosis of ethnic-minority clients.
    b. inappropriate treatment of ethnic-minority clients.
    c. services that are antagonistic or inappropriate to the life of ethnic-minority clients.
    d. overuse of mental health services and facilities by ethnic-minority clients

Ans: c
Page: 611
Obj: 14
Type: A

99. A student asks her professor whether the American Psychological Association (APA) has ever taken a stand on the ethics of being culturally competent. The professor responds that
    a. the APA refused to include such guidelines in its association codes.
    b. the APA wrote such guidelines into its original charter more than one hundred years ago.
    c. the APA has developed sets of guidelines for dealing with ethnic, linguistic, and culturally diverse populations (1993) and for psychotherapy with lesbian, gay, and bisexual clients (2000).
    d. the APA has planned to include such guidelines in its code of conduct but due to controversy has never actually done so.

Ans: b
Page: 611
Obj: 14
Type: C

100. Dr. Warren is a European American psychotherapist who has moved her practice to a region of the country in which there are many Latin American clients. From an ethical perspective, she has a moral responsibility to
    a. alter the social and cultural views of her Latin American clients so that they are more in harmony with the general American culture.
    b. develop intervention strategies that take into account the cultural and environmental influences of her Latin American clients.
    c. offer treatment only to European American clients.
    d. provide the same style of treatment to Latin American clients as she does to others.

ESSAY QUESTIONS

1. Review the history of legal precedents on the insanity defense. Describe the current standing of this defense.

2. The McLeods want their adult son, Brewster, to be involuntarily treated in a mental facility. Describe the criteria and procedures for civil commitment that they face. What legal protections exist against the abuse of Brewster's rights?

3. Name and describe two rights of mental patients.

SAMPLE ANSWERS

1. Criminal law is based on the assumption that criminal behavior is freely chosen and the responsibility of the person who commits it. If, because of mental illness or mental retardation, a person is not able to control his or her behavior or appreciate that what he or she is doing is wrong, that person should not be held as responsible as someone who has such control and understanding. One of the first cases to make this distinction was in 1843, when Daniel M'Naghten attempted to kill the British prime minister. Because he was quite delusional, M'Naghten was found not guilty by reason of insanity. At the time of the crime, he did not know right from wrong. This is a strictly cognitive standard for deciding insanity. A second major standard that developed was the irresistible impulse test. This says that defendants are not responsible if they cannot control their behavior.

   In 1954, Judge David Bazelon ruled in *Durham v. United States* that defendants are not responsible if their behavior is the product of a mental disease or defect. This so-called products test or *Durham* standard put considerable influence in the hands of mental health professionals, who, as experts, could testify as to whether a mental illness existed and whether it produced the criminal behavior. Eventually, Bazelon himself withdrew his support for this position.

   In 1962, the American Law Institute (ALI) produced guidelines to help jurors judge insanity. This code says that if, due to mental disease or defect, a person lacks substantial capacity either to appreciate the criminality of conduct or to conform conduct to the requirements of the law, the person is not responsible. Antisocial personality disorder was specifically excluded from the mental diseases or defects that might apply. The ALI code supported both the M'Naghten and irresistible impulse tests. In 1982, John Hinckley was found not guilty by reason of insanity when he was tried for attempting to assassinate President Ronald Reagan. The outrage that followed this verdict led to the Insanity Reform Act of 1984, which bases insanity totally on the M'Naghten cognitive standard. Still, some states have adopted alternative pleas, most of which involve a merging of guilt and disorder such as "guilty, but mentally ill." Despite attempts at reform, the insanity tests vary widely, and the use of the insanity plea remains controversial.

2. The McLeods are trying to have their son involuntarily confined for treatment. This is called civil commitment. Although states vary in the criteria they use to commit individuals, there are general standards. In addition to being mentally ill, Brewster must be found to be (a) presenting an imminent danger to himself or others (suicide or homicide), (b) unable to provide for himself sufficient food, clothing, and shelter to live without danger, (c) unable to make responsible decisions about treatment so that severe deterioration is likely, or (d) in such an unmanageable state of panic that he will lose all control. It is important to note that all of these criteria involve judgments and, in many cases, predictions must be made about future behavior including dangerousness to self and others.

   The law recognizes that involuntary hospitalization means depriving a person of his or her liberty despite the fact that no crime has been committed. The person's due process rights are protected in several ways. First, commitment can occur only through a court when the judge believes there is reasonable cause for such action. In Brewster's case, the judge would appoint two mental health professionals with no connection to each other so that Brewster could be evaluated with as little bias as possible. After Brewster was examined twice, a formal hearing would be held before the judge, at which point testimony would be given. Brewster would have a lawyer to represent him and would be allowed to speak for himself. If the judge determined that Brewster needed treatment, he or she would have to be 75 percent sure that Brewster was mentally ill and dangerous, according to the *Addington v. Texas* decision. *Addington* noted that while this was lower than the 90 percent certainty of "beyond a reasonable doubt" used in criminal cases, it was a higher standard of proof than that advocated by most mental health organizations. Further, the judge would either specify the time Brewster would be in treatment (usually less than one year) or declare that there be periodic review and assessment of his need to be in treatment.

3.   (Answers will vary)

a.   Mental patients have the *right to treatment*. This right basically ensures that patients cannot be confined without receiving active treatment in a humane environment (i.e., they cannot simply be sheltered or housed). In addition, persons cannot be confined who are not dangerous to themselves or to others or who are capable of surviving on their own or with the help of willing friends or family.

b.   Mental patients have the right to the *least restrictive alternative*. The law requires that involuntarily committed patients should be confined in environments that are the least restrictive alternative (i.e., provides the greatest freedom consistent with their conditions in terms of personal security and the safety of others). Thus, some individuals might be able to live in group homes or board-and-care facilities in the community, where they have supervision but also some freedom, whereas only patients who would be considered to be a threat to themselves or to others would be confined in more restrictive facilities such as mental hospitals. Within the hospitals, some patients might require locked wards or restraints only when necessary to reduce harm to themselves or to others.